The Modern Polish Mind

The Modern Polish Mind

An Anthology

EDITED BY

MARIA KUNCEWICZ

Little, Brown and Company · Boston · Toronto

LIBRARY OF CONGRESS CATALOG CARD NO. 62-10531

FIRST EDITION

The editor acknowledges with thanks permission from Roy Publishers, Inc., and the author for "The Crystal Stream" from ASCENT TO HEAVEN, by Adolf Rudnicki.

Published simultaneously in Canada
by Little, Brown & Company (Canada) Limited

PRINTED IN THE UNITED STATES OF AMERICA

CONTENTS

II. *HOW THEY SEE LIFE*

III. *WHAT THEY BELIEVE*

IV. *THEIR HUMOR*

The Modern Polish Mind

Introduction

THE CURRENT DECADE is celebrated by Poles as the end of the first millennium of Poland's recorded history. In the United States, where about seven million citizens claim Polish descent, and scores of public places bear the names of Pulaski and Kosciusko, two fighters for American independence, the historic fact may have its sentimental connotations, but interest in Poland is mainly centered on its political aspects.

West-oriented, Catholic Poland, a Slavic country, with its population of thirty million, increasing at the rate of half a million each year, represents more than its numbers in the political setup of modern Europe; it serves as meeting ground for the two great forces of our time, Western democracy and Eastern communism. Therefore, what a contemporary Pole thinks, how he feels about life, exposed as he is to German nationalist vindications on one side and the Soviet might on the other, contributes valuable material to mankind's experience. Indeed, it might be said that after World War II, the Yalta Agreement between the Western allies and the Soviet Union had the unexpected result of transforming Poland into a laboratory retort where the most incompatible elements of human destiny are melting into new forms of coexistence.

The living cells in that uncanny crucible — brains, hearts, red and white blood corpuscles — still simmer, producing reactions and mixtures, sputtering anger, exuding hope, in preparation for the synthesis to come. This, in Poland, is not a time for achievement; it is a time for rebuilding and experimenting. Therefore, when surveying recent Polish writing, we should treat it as a panorama of life rather than a show of literary excellence. Life, however, seems to be served best by good writers, and so our choice for this anthology led, on the whole, to an adequate level of professional skill and, in a few instances, to an artistic vision of universal purport.

But let us consider first the role of the writer in Poland, a role so different from that of poets and literati in free countries with normal standards.

After more than eight hundred years of independence as a state, Poland, at one time the largest country in Europe (I have recently observed this on a map in the Philip II apartments in the Spanish Escorial), lost her sovereignty at the end of the eighteenth century. She was subjugated and partitioned by the powerful alliance of her neighbors — Prussia, Russia and Austria. Except for short intervals, for about one and a quarter centuries she possessed no parliament of her own, no national public services or schools, the Austrian Zone being the exception as far as education was concerned. Literature alone kept the dismembered nation together in its unity of language and tradition. During this period, labeled romantic in European civilization, Poles dutifully fought on all battlefields, Savannah included, where human freedoms were at stake, while such poets as A. Mickiewicz, J. Slowacki, Z. Krasinski and C. K. Norwid served as exponents of the Polish cause to the West. In exchange, Western romanticism offered Poland a few songs, some poems, some personal friendships and the honorary title of a martyr nation.

That massive invasion by poetry of the field of international politics, although it did not greatly affect international politics, mobilized and electrified the originally somewhat rustic spirit of the Polish nation; it left its literature flourishing. As Jan Parandowski * says in his brilliant essay "The Word":

> The nineteenth century not only gave Poland her first unquestionable geniuses (the romantic poets), but it also created the drama, the novel, the essay . . . it developed lyric poetry on a scale unknown in earlier centuries; it widened the sphere of sensitivity, gave daring to thought which had been earthbound too long; finally, it enlivened the language by adding to the vocabulary and endowing the syntax with new lightness and verve.

The glorious medal, however, had as usual a not-so-attractive other side. The immense prestige won for literature by the romantic poets who had risen to messianic heights of prophecy and leadership fell like a superhuman burden on the shoulders of writers whose aims ought to have been more modest and personal. One can imagine how

* Jan Parandowski, president of the Polish P.E.N. Club Centre, is a distinguished essayist and novelist. His volume of essays *The Sundial,* from which the quotation derives, appeared in 1962 in the UNESCO collection of contemporary European writers. Mr. Parandowski lives in Warsaw.

crushing the overload was for authors of a purely artistic temperament. And so, when independent Poland was restored in 1918, she found the mood of her letters greatly changed.

Tired of their long public service in building up patriotism, most Polish writers plunged headfirst into artistic freedom. And in the twenties and thirties, as a socially minded *littérature engagée* was emerging out of the individualistic excesses of the "beautiful epoch" in the West, Poland's poets and prose writers tried hard to disengage themselves from political chores and revert to the long-neglected psychological exploration of life's intimacies.

Since this is an introduction to — and not a work on — Poland's literature, I shall not dwell on its dynamic interwar period of struggle for "normality." Here, we are interested in the recent contribution to the humanities; this also explains our silence on the early stages of Polish writing. We can only hope that this anthology will serve in America as an incentive for another collection with a historical approach to the problem.

The by no means simple and effective process of liberating art from its patriotic fetters was still in full swing when Hitler's armies invaded Poland in 1939, her government went into exile, and a reign of unprecedented terror began. Again Polish literature was forced underground into a Vulcan's forge of arms. In 1945, when it once more saw daylight, it spoke in a subdued voice. Horror and frustration were not yet ripe for words; they bore the bitter fruit — with few exceptions — only years later, after the Polish writers had scanned the landscape of desolation where their people were to live now on the victorious side of the world. A country with six million dead; a capital city leveled after one siege, in 1939, and one uprising, in 1944; the wasted effort of regrouping and throwing national divisions into battles on foreign fields, and whole armies of Polish veterans scattered over the Continent and the British Isles; the eastern territories lost to Russia, their uprooted populations shifted to newly acquired yet devastated areas in the West; broken treaties, forgotten alliances — such was the reality which Polish literature had to absorb after the Second World War was over.

In the meantime the Soviet armies had driven the Germans out of the country, and in the ambiguous light of that liberation a regime was established from which the few initial democratic features, such as are known in the West, soon disappeared under the pressure of the Communist colossus. And so another chapter of Polish history was closed.

Slowly, the Stalinist night of "errors and distortions" set in over Poland. Some poets it numbed into silence, but to many it brought dreams which were not at once recognized as nightmares. After five years of Nazi occupation, the abuses of the new officials seemed more humane than crime instituted and codified as supreme law by a "master race." We can trace this sentiment to utterances of those Polish authors who do not disclaim responsibility for the advent of communism in their country. In defense of the young Communists' Granada Theater in Warsaw, Kazimierz Brandys says: "No one wanted to be cut off from the truth of his time. We loved the dark and complex twentieth century. We only asked, 'Was the sacrifice demanded of us truly in the spirit of the century?' " But, although he also remarked that the party pundits were "hairdressers trying to give reality a permanent wave," Stalinist orthodoxy was dead among Polish intellectuals even before Stalin died.

At last, in 1956, a new national upheaval put an end to the police regime and, greatly helped by young Marxist brains around the weekly *Po Prostu* (*Plain Speaking*), Polish writing attained relative freedom. Its impact was immediately felt in other countries under Communist domination, including Russia, where in spite of the historic feud, Polish culture has always enjoyed the prestige of a Western importation, attractive to the intellectual elite. And the West wondered at the ferment within the Marxist camp.

In 1958, *Po Prostu* was discontinued. "Revisionism" became a bad word in the Communist good books. Yet Polish writers continue to puzzle the world with their personal opinions and the many artistic idioms in which they express themselves. To what can such an exception to the iron rule of Communist conformity be ascribed? To my mind, the reasons are the following: First of all, Poland is, in eastern Europe, second in importance only to Russia, and a bone of contention at the crossroads of civilization. Secondly, the interwar period was too short a time for the artistic instinct of Polish authors to have spent itself independently of politics. Thirdly, communism was imposed on Poland by a hereditary foe, Russia. To most writers the call to duty, in this case, did not sound like a summons to national service. Fourth, writing and reading and understanding between the lines are skills which were acquired by Polish writers and readers under three different censorships in the past, and therefore they are masters at it. Last, but not least, communism itself is undergoing changes. What was inadmissible in print several years ago, and is still frowned at by diehards in Moscow, Tirana or Peiping, is being openly debated by ever wider circles of Marxists throughout the world.

In this anthology we have endeavored to show, without any bias, how the Polish mind works under the pressure of communism as opposed to national tradition. The number one force in that tradition is the Catholic religion. Poland entered Christian civilization in 966, through the Roman door. Soon after, Russia pledged its allegiance to the Greek Orthodox pontiff in Byzantium. The Polish alphabet is Latin; the Russian alphabet is modeled on Greek characters. This made the Slavic world resemble a monster with two heads, one looking for light to the West, the other to the East. Today the nature of the duality has changed. The Byzantine drive for worldly power was absorbed into the atheistic doctrine of communism, while the Roman church relinquished its ambition to overrule the state. But faith in ideas transcending personal interest remains the mainspring of progress, and materialistic beliefs tend to assume religious attitudes. Thus, the two religions thrown together in the Polish crucible are Catholicism, the form of Christianity prevalent in the region, and communism of the Russian brand. The value of the experiment may be queried by those who do not see the relevance of religion in the West's struggle for democracy. Yet how can Western democracy win the ideological war without adhering to some concept of life capable of instilling religious zest?

The modern Polish mind, exposed to the two influences, does not react in a spontaneous, traditional way. It does not, because the elements of tradition have lost their old meaning. Although Western-inclined, Poles cannot help considering that fascism and Hitlerism came to them from the West — or that the Western allies traded Poland's freedom for a temporary relief in the East. On the other hand, the present anti-German course of Soviet policies suits Poland's interests. In consequence, a new antiromantic, antiheroic attitude is taking shape, termed "neopositivism," a realistic approach to facts, a reluctance to unleash popular sentiment. The atmosphere in People's Poland is equivocal, saturated with danger. Polish politics, which had been sublimely at ease in the time of a patriotism springing from the heart, are now becoming a highly specialized profession. If they want to remain fine, the fine arts must step aside, hence creating a chance that Polish literature had sought for centuries: freedom from obligation. But here two questions arise: how far will the Communist rulers allow artists and thinkers to go up the uncommitted way, and can fine arts really thrive on a permanent separation from public life?

We cannot foresee events; we can only try to establish trends. The trends seem evident: there are writers who "love the dark and complex twentieth century," but do not want to "miss the truth of their era." Some among them are convinced Communists. Then we see a group, mostly in the younger age bracket, whom one would be tempted to call existentialist, if this term were not used so loosely. In its Polish version existentialism offers a blend of nihilism and vitality, a heady concoction with, occasionally, a poetic or a sardonic flavor. The third trend, with a broad base in the masses, is headed for Catholic revival.

It would, perhaps, be honest to say that communism in Poland is an affair in the making; it affects both the reluctant nation and the eager doctrine. Poles are anti-Communist by nature. But nature wants life. And life wants food and air. Since 1945, communism has been the bailiff on Poland's cultural estate; it acts through a handful of political professionals and a few genuine zealots. However, in the climate of uncertainty prevailing now in Europe, the attraction of a well-organized, logical and ruthless doctrine with a humanistic façade and many effective administrative and economic devices in the offing is great. And so much depends on what new and nourishing ingredients the wind from the West will bring into the Polish atmosphere. Two things are certain: Polish communism has a strong tendency to stray from its Russian model; and Polish Catholicism is undergoing a change. Painfully, laboriously, it turns from national custom to philosophy and internationalism.

Since the mood of the majority of Poland's writers is pragmatic, it seems only fair to prognosticate that the Polish experiment in the realm of letters proceeds along constructive lines. I shall not point out names in any of the suggested categories, but leave the reader free to judge for himself. Instead, I should like to stress some permanent features of the Polish artistic genius: sensuality, a love of nature verging on pantheism; a keen eye for material detail coupled with the very Slavic propensity for the abstract; above all, a rapt attachment to historic tradition. Truly, nothing surprises a foreigner more than the sight of palaces and churches being rebuilt at an enormous cost by that People's Republic, anxious to revive the glories of the past even before it provides its citizens with decent living quarters. The same thirst for unbroken identity manifests itself in the popularity of all kinds of publications referring to old times; those concerning Warsaw, that phoenix rising from the ashes, are the favorite ones.

Reverence for native tradition, however, is coupled in Poland with a great alacrity in assimilating foreign cultural values. This can be observed not only in the immediate impact of the latest international literary trends, schools of thought and personalities on the young writers, but also in the numerous and resounding echoes from abroad in the many magazines devoted to fine arts. A similar receptivity exists for importations from abroad in the theater, music ("The Warsaw Autumn" is an international festival of modern music), and art (Polish painters excel in abstract art); and translations — mostly from Western literature — in tremendous number are to be found on the lists of the publishing houses.

This survey of the Polish mind may by now sound confusing. East and West, communism and Catholicism, existentialism and neo-positivism, patriotism and internationalism. How many more opposites can one throw into one beaker? But Americans, often without realizing it, also live in a confused world. Oceans, outer space and affluence have ceased to serve as shields against the physical and spiritual complexity of an expanding universe. To survive, we have to travel, and books are an inexpensive means of traveling in foreign lands. But as one who tries to acquaint himself with an alien reality soon discovers, nothing exceeds the potentialities of his own individual and national existence.

We have not included poetry and drama in this collection for reasons of practicality and respect: a poet is more easily betrayed by a translator than a prose writer, and playwrights usually prefer a stage for presentation rather than a book. And also for reasons of practicality, we could not touch on such renowned areas of Polish creative activity as music, sociology, semantics or mathematics.

Finally, one more omission: the *émigré* literature. Although very much a part of Poland's modern mind, this important branch of its literature, as represented by some brilliant writers on several continents, grew and came to fruition under skies different from those at home. It cannot, therefore, exemplify to the full the mood and experience of the nation.

To make that mood and that experience even more explicit, we have interspersed fiction and essays with journalism. Since such elements as past and present, objectivity, faith, and humor are obviously difficult to isolate in a writer's work, the way in which the material was ordered may seem arbitrary. Far from being an attempt at reducing the author's capacity to a single element, it was adopted as a means of directing the reader to areas of his particular interest.

As this book goes into print, my only remaining commission is to thank those who made the anthology possible: writers, translators, publishers, editors and friends. I should especially like to single out Sam Blumenfeld, Pawel Mayewski, Alan Williams, Dr. Alfred Berlstein, Ruth Aley in New York, Konstanty Jelenski in Paris, Jerzy Turowicz in Krakow, Gustaw Gottesman and Ludwik Kasinski in Warsaw, and Maria Danielewicz in London, whose help, either in clarifying my ideas or collecting the material and organizing the multifarious work, I found most valuable. As a detail of bibliographical interest, I might add that Little, Brown and Company introduced one of Poland's Nobel Prize-winning writers, Henryk Sienkiewicz, to the American public in 1896.

Many distinguished authors were left out of our project, owing to limitations in time and approach; some others were overlooked by chance, that malicious companion of all human endeavor. For this I apologize.

MARIA KUNCEWICZ

I

What Polish Writers Remember

Memories of Warsaw

BY ANTONI SLONIMSKI

ANTONI SLONIMSKI, born in 1895 in Warsaw, is a poet, critic, playwright, novelist, satirist and journalist. In the period between the two world wars, he was one of the leaders of the Skamander group, a brilliant assembly of poets, and has some twelve volumes of poetry to his credit. His plays – Shavian in wit and irony – are *The Warsaw Negro* (1928); *The Homeless Physician* (1931); *The Family* (1934). Slonimski's weekly chronicle in the prewar Warsaw magazine *Literary News* has been for nearly twenty years an outpost of bold thinking on public morals, politics and literature. A pacifist, an ardent admirer of H. G. Wells, and a prominent man of Jewish origin, in 1939 he fled before Hitler, first to Paris, then to London, where he spent the war years editing the monthly *Nowa Polska*. An Anglophile of long standing, he made many friends among English writers. His poem "Air Raid Warning for the City of Warsaw" (1940) became a classic to the Polish forces both at home and abroad. In 1946 he returned to Warsaw. In 1956, during the October crisis, he showed great moral courage as president of the Polish Writers' Union. The sections which follow are from *Warsaw Memories* (1949). He is living in Warsaw.

I

WHEN I THINK of the Warsaw of my youth, I am amazed that this comparatively small city had so many characters and eccentrics.

The first genuine eccentric I came across in my childhood was the poet Antoni Lange, a friend of my father's, a well-known translator from the Sanskrit and a less-known author of numerous papers, schemes and inventions. Each time he came to see my father, he had a brand-new and brilliant scheme for making a large fortune. He once sent a long memorandum to the Russian War Ministry, explaining the necessity of supplying the Russian Army with one million chairs. The memorandum made it quite clear that such a big army should not be a standing one. The stools suggested by the author, with drawings illustrating his idea, were like shooting sticks. Despite its obvious absurdity, the memorandum was given serious consideration at the Petersburg War Ministry by officials, or rather officialdom, for the simple reason that such big supplies also meant big bribes.

Lange invented his own system of winning at roulette. For that purpose he made a couple of reconnaissance trips to Monte Carlo. The trips ended in frantic telegrams to my father or some other friend, in which the hapless inventor begged for money. When he first went from Paris to Monte Carlo, Lange was in luck and won a considerable sum, large enough to start a real gambling career. He was a complete innocent at roulette and began his play by putting some money on number one. Number one won. He pushed his winnings on to number two, and number two won. He proceeded logically to number three and won again. When he was playing number four — number twenty-seven won. Lange raised a hue and cry and demanded his money on the obvious claim that it was number four's turn to win. His brilliant winning system was that one had simply to put money on consecutive numbers. But what it meant to be a real gambler I understood only later when I heard Fiszer's story. Franciszek Fiszer was a friend of my father's, too, and in later years also a friend of mine. He used to tell the following anecdote. A certain rich landowner used to play cards at the railway buffet whenever he had to wait for a train. One day he had to wait for several hours but had nobody to play with. He asked the barman to suggest somebody. The barman said that he could provide two regular cardsharps. "I'm not playing with cheats," stormed the squire. Having wasted his time for another half hour he went up to the waiter and said, "Send in those crooks; I'll play with them, but for cash." The barman came back after a while saying that the crooks were broke, because they had been cheated by some bigger Warsaw cheats. "With penniless crooks, nothing doing," panted the squire. After another half hour his morale was completely broken. He went up to the barman and said, "Send them in; I'll lend them some cash."

Fiszer occupies a special place among Warsaw characters. He was not only an eccentric but one of the wittiest men alive. A certain writer of mediocre talent said once to him, "Don't you think, Franciszek, that I have Dante's nose?" Without a moment's hesitation, Fiszer howled back, "Then why don't you write with it?"

I used to love Fiszer's story about a party given in honor of the

Czar, who was visiting Poland. "There were forty-eight kinds of soup brought from Paris in special barrels," Fiszer would say. "Two hundred and fifty kinds of meat dishes. The feast went on for three days and three nights. When we left the Royal Castle after this gorgeous party, we were attacked in the courtyard by a squadron of Circassians, who beat us with the flat of their sabers." "Whatever did they do this for?" I asked, taken aback. "Why, to beat the conceit out of us, of course," Fiszer replied indignantly.

To Fiszer, Warsaw was not only the most beautiful but also the only city worth considering in Europe. Somebody was raving once about Paris, and Fiszer interrupted him angrily. "Horrible city. Dirty, dark, stinking sewers. Not even gaslight in every street." "How can you say such things," came the protest. "When were you last in Paris?" "Immediately after the siege,* of course," said Fiszer with great pride.

Speaking of Warsaw characters, it is impossible to omit the distinguished actor Wladyslaw Grabowski. He once played Sir Andrew Aguecheek in *Twelfth Night*. Under the influence of too much spirits, instead of speaking his lines, he repeatedly announced, "Now it's me." He went on doing this all through the act. The actors managed somehow, and the audience sat patiently till intermission. But the performance had to be stopped and there was a scandal. Grabowski was sacked. Some time after this incident, he came up to my table in a restaurant where I was sitting and delivered the following oration: "My soul is *tabula rasa*, and Volga's in my eyes," meaning that they were full of tears. "I've lost faith in man. If a drowning person came to grovel at my feet begging a stamp, I'd refuse!" The picture of a drowning person groveling at somebody's feet and begging for postage was so ridiculous that I asked Grabowski why this drowning person should want a stamp. "To write a letter about his accident" was his earnest reply.

Another character who had a most peculiar way of expressing his thoughts was the painter Leonhard. His was not the Mister Jingle type of speech used by Grabowski; his peculiarity was in his extraordinary and original syntax. He always began at the end of a sentence. For example: "There won't be any. Hands or feet. Extinction. Civilization. In a thousand years. Only brain. The philosopher Wysocki thinks so. The one with the feather in his hat, because there are

---

* In 1870.

two." Leonhard was married to a banker's daughter. Fiszer said of him once, "Do you know the difference between Leonardo da Vinci and Leonhard? Leonardo painted 'The Lord's Supper,' and Leonhard eats it."

There were many inimitable characters among Warsaw painters. Witkacy alone calls for a special study. I used to be a friend of this extremely interesting writer, painter and philosopher. At one time, I was even third on his list of friends. Witkacy literally had such a list and would shift his friends up and down, notifying them each time he changed their positions. After I had criticized his play *The Pragmatists* he sent me the following card: "We hereby notify you that you have been shifted on our list of friends from number three to number forty-eight — beneath the painter Chwistek." This place was on the very outskirts of Witkacy's friendship.

The gallery of Warsaw originals was limited almost entirely to the intelligentsia and middle classes. Our aristocracy, cosmopolitan in the worst sense of the word, added nothing to the specific color of Warsaw. The underworld, especially Warsaw burglars, were in many respects superior to the aristocracy. They could not, of course, compete with the magnates in wrongdoing, but they made up for this in originality and lent a special kind of glory to the capital. When a burglary was discovered at the Odessa branch of Russia's National Bank, having been accomplished by tunneling in, the board of the bank issued a special bulletin stating categorically that the job was done by Warsaw burglars and not by local ones. This was a serious argument, and public opinion was convinced that the board could not be blamed. The inferiority of the bank authorities to Warsaw burglars was obvious to everyone.

The number of originals and the richness of human types in the Warsaw of my youth were the result of an easier life and of the comparative leisure of the middle classes.

2

MUCH AS I liked to travel — and I have done quite a lot of traveling in my life — it was not the journey but the homecoming that counted. I always came back hungry and thirsty for Warsaw. Until the tragic parting.

On September 5, 1939, my wife and I left Warsaw. Our destination was a small township on the other bank of the Vistula, where we intended to tide over the first phase of the war. Our reasoning was simple.

The German tanks — as everyone knew — were made of cardboard and wouldn't be able to cross the Vistula, and would fall apart if they tried. At Kazimierz, my wife took a room and paid one hundred zlotys' rent in advance. As our information about German tanks was not quite accurate and the Germans crossed the Vistula that very day, we had to leave Kazimierz at once. At Krzemieniec, my wife took a room and paid only fifty zlotys in advance. Half an hour after this transaction we were on our way farther east. At Zaleszczyki, on the Romanian frontier, we had no time to take a room at all.

At this stage, our adventures did not differ much from the flights and pursuits in Sienkiewicz's novels describing seventeenth-century wars. On the face of things, this, too, was a war out of books for children — a war of small events, jolly, friendly skirmishes fought with completely unfounded optimism, in which the soldiers never lost their good appetites. A wave of air raids followed in our wake. They were not serious air raids compared with the destruction wrought by later ones, but the effect of two or three bombs dropped by German planes on some small, peaceful town was like a thunderbolt.

On arrival at any of the small towns we passed, we would inevitably find the same picture of torpid provincial life, with all the restaurants and shops doing normal business. Then in a very short time, as in some speeded-up motion picture, everything would be in chaos. Frightened horses would be neighing pitifully; barbers in their white smocks would almost be floating in the air, as if they'd come down off some Chagall canvas. At such moments, the poet Stanislaw Balinski would start dividing his family heirlooms among us. Then all of a sudden good news would come from the front, rumors of victories by some general or other, and we would again be in good spirits. We commemorated one such victory by drinking a bottle of Napoleon brandy. But gradually I began to resist entering fool's paradise and took a rather pessimistic view of the military situation when I caught sight of the muddle in which our troops retreated, and the utter lack of organization and undisguised panic of the civil authorities. At one of the frontier villages, the local *starosta* (an official next to the *voievoda* in the country's administration) ordered us to turn back, because of some obscure law that said, "In time of war, civilians are not allowed to approach the frontier." This, translated into plain language, meant that in time of war only troops had a right to flee the country — which was not very far from the actual state of affairs. After many ups and downs, we finally arrived at Zaleszczyki, and a few hours before the Soviet troops crossed the famous bridge leading to Romania.

I was leaving Poland with a heavy heart but also with a firm belief in our speedy return to Warsaw. England, France and America were certain to put the Germans in their place. The thing was to get to the Allied forces and to put oneself beyond the reach of the Nazis.

It was by no means a small thing to get from Romania to France. One had to pass through Italy, and in Italy the Gestapo were given a free hand, while the Italian police were said to have a list of anti-Fascist writers and journalists and had in fact arrested some. As my anti-Fascist stand had once been the cause of a diplomatic *démarche,* I had reason to suppose that I might be on that list. During Minister Dino Grandi's visit to Poland, I wrote that his name was no name but a profession (*Granda,* in Polish slang, means something like a dirty trick). In answer to this, the Italian Embassy made a diplomatic protest to our Ministry of Foreign Affairs. When on the Italian-Yugoslav frontier the police came into our compartment and began to check documents, I had to use all my self-command not to show my anxiety. The policemen began to talk excitedly. It turned out that they were excited about my companion, Count Sobanski. He was fair with a reddish complexion and was taken for a Jew. I succeeded, without much difficulty, in convincing the police that this aristocrat and papal count was no Jew. I say "without much difficulty" because, on the whole, the Italians closed their eyes on documents of Polish refugees.

Then came the long-awaited moment. After a series of tiresome train stops and document checks, we crossed the French frontier. At last we had reached an Allied nation that was fighting the Germans. Safe at last! Between us and the enemy there was the Maginot line. We had faith in it as we had in many foolish things, as we had faith in the story about the cardboard German tanks or the expected Allied air force help for besieged Warsaw. The Maginot was more of an Imaginot line and yet another item in the catalogue of our illusions.

On our first day in Paris, we met Artur Rubinstein on the street. Artur and his wife were old friends of ours. As usual, he was very sweet to us. He took us to a splendid restaurant, gave us lunch and some money. The truth was that we had been living from hand to mouth and so could do now with something for both mouth and hand.

As we thought we were leaving Warsaw for a very short time we had taken just a little money and one suitcase, intending to return as soon as the German Army dispersed — that is, in a couple of weeks at the most.

In all our peregrinations through Poland — whether by car, cart or on foot — we were blessed all the time by sound sleep and excellent digestion. As if some atavistic force, latent in normal and peaceful times, became active in us when danger was imminent. In Paris, where I was safe — or thought I was — I spent my first sleepless night for weeks, lying in a comfortable hotel bed. As soon as I could relax, I was in the grip of restless thought, which poisoned my sleep and brought memories from the recent past. I was tortured by anxiety over what the future might be like for my wife and myself and for friends and relatives left behind in Poland.

The disasters of the first war months were something we could bear. In France, Warsaw was still near, and nothing could shake our faith in our ultimate victory. Only occasionally would that faith be shaken by some apparently insignificant fact. For instance, when I was going somewhere with a friend in a taxi and the driver turned to us and said:

"I shouldn't wait, if I were you. Get a taxi straight away, while you're still in funds. The longer you wait, the worse it's going to be."

The Paris driver was a White Russian and gave us this bit of advice without malice; you might say a wise elder brother warning us against the carelessness of youth. We did, however, manage to get back to Warsaw after the war without the help of that *émigré* taxi. Yet the worst was still ahead of us. How unexpected was that dark night at Bordeaux, when a tiny Polish ship, without a single lifeboat, without a convoy took us to our last place of refuge, to the country which went on fighting Germany all by herself — to England.

Institutions of a long-standing tradition appear to us eternal. When I saw the first German planes over Warsaw, when from my gay and peaceful window I detected in the white summer cloudlets the first bacilli of the war epidemic, I never thought that they might indicate the beginning of an almost fatal disease. It never occurred to me that the order and conventions of my life — as I had lived it until that moment — were falling to pieces, that I was, in fact, entering a new and terrible reality, that those planes were writing in the skies the death sentence of millions of people, that they announced the annihilation of Warsaw.

Despite their uncertainty and bitterness, despite their painful disappointments and struggles, the twenty years of the interwar period had a lasting quality for me and were as much my own as my very body. I saw their blemishes, their sicknesses, as I might call them, and I did my best to provide a cure, but the thought of their death never really reached the deeper levels of my consciousness.

When on a misty summer morning — after the fall of France — we reached the shores of England, I was richer for one more bitter experience and I looked upon the flat, defenseless coast of Cornwall with diffidence but also with a newborn calm and relief. My wife and close friends were here with me, and I was about to enter a country for which I had much sympathy and admiration. The danger was still grave, but I felt I could stand up to it now with human dignity, freed from the debasing agony of the hunted animal that never left me during my last few days in France.

Particularly nightmarish was my last night on the old continent. The tiny Polish boat *Chorzow* was to sail before dawn with inadequate food supplies for her passengers. Late that afternoon, I went to town to get some bread, wine and fruit. The city turned out to be much farther from the wharf than I expected. Most of the shops were closed. Those that were open had long queues in front of them. I was so worried that I could hardly wait for my turn and wanted to rush back. But with the obstinacy of a gambler who stakes his last penny, I went on queuing, though a feeling of disaster overtook me. When at last I did leave the shop, it was quite dark. Sirens sounded the alert, and there was no question of getting a taxi. I started almost to run, sweating, stumbling in the dark and forcing my way through a maze of unknown streets. I stupidly trusted my memory and didn't even know the name of the wharf where our boat lay. How was I now to find a small Polish boat in the pitch-darkness of a blackout and in a port which stretched for tens of kilometers? That boat was now the most desirable spot on earth and the only place of safety for me.

I knew in what despair my wife, Janka, would be; I knew the boat might sail any moment, and I was lost in ever new — or perhaps the same — streets, littered with packing cases and ropes. It was getting very late. Through the narrow gap in the blackout of some window there shone a faint light. My hands felt for a door, and I pushed it. It wasn't locked. I entered an empty pub where the half-clad *patron* was busy washing up. I told him of my troubles and fortified my demand for help with a one-hundred-franc bill. The *patron* refused to take the money. He dried his hands quietly, took me by the arm and led me outside. We were a few steps away from some wall with a gate in it, which the Frenchman found as easily as if he had done this many times. Behind that gate I was able to discern the outlines of a boat. I called out my wife's name. I shouted, "Is this the *Chorzow?*" Somebody answered in Polish. I shook hands with the kind Frenchman and went up the narrow gangway. The engines of the ship were already rattling under full steam. The lower deck was crowded, and the lights hurt my eyes. I was still holding two bottles of wine and a bag with bread and grapes. On that night, when the French state fell and with it almost all our hopes, my wife — whose face was stained with tears — and I ate those grapes with a feeling of complete happiness and blissful peace.

— *translated by* Cecylia Wojewoda

(Two sections from *Wspomnienia Warszawskie.* Published by "Czytelnik," Warsaw, 1957.)

The Watch

by Wiktor Woroszylski

Wiktor Woroszylski was born in 1927 in Grodno, now part of Lithuania, and is the son of a physician. After the eastern Polish territories became part of the Soviet Union, the whole family was evacuated to Lodz, in central Poland. In the same year, 1945, Wiktor Woroszylski completed his high school studies, published his first poem, joined the Communist party and began work as a journalist. Later on, he studied medicine and the humanities. His first book of poems, *There is No Death,* appeared in 1949. From 1952 to 1956 he was a student in Moscow, where he received a master's degree in philosophy. During these years he traveled extensively in the Ukraine, Byelorussia, the Baltic countries, the Caucasus, middle Asia and Siberia. Back in Poland, he contributed regularly to the periodical *Nowa Kultura* and the young intellectuals' weekly *Po Prostu.* During the Hungarian Uprising, he was an on-the-spot correspondent in Budapest for *Nowa Kultura*. His *Hungarian Diary* was serialized in France. He has also published a few volumes of verse, and in 1958, a selection of short stories, *The Cruel Star,* of which "The Watch" is one. Since 1958, he has not been associated with any political group or publication. He lives in Warsaw.

I WOULDN'T SAY that Mother and Father really disliked Roman, or that they took a dim view of our marriage. On the contrary, they were rather impressed by their educated, well-bred son-in-law, and Father gladly discussed international politics with him.

One thing, however, my parents could never forgive Roman: his failure to share their reverence for "things." A material possession, in our household, meant everything; it was the measure of attained wealth and social standing, the repository of ambitions and dreams, the symbol of a happy family life, the goal and the crowning glory of all efforts. A possession was a moral ideal, character was judged by the quality of a person's possessions, and his attitude toward possessions determined whether or not he could be trusted. We lived simply. Father had no expensive vices; he didn't smoke or drink. But after almost every payday a new object appeared in our room: a silver sugar bowl, a pillow, a lamp. On the thirty-fifth anniversary of his employment at the factory, the workers' committee gave Father a phonograph — and Father was proud to have been worthy of such a splendid gift.

Roman never ridiculed this passion of my parents — he considered it understandable and natural — but he was just a little too quick in taking for granted each new acquisition, or, once in a while, he would absent-mindedly bump into some of the objects arranged around the room. What's more, he sometimes spent money on flowers or theater tickets, and when Mother and Father would begin enumerating all the "lasting" things he could have bought instead, he just shrugged his shoulders.

When, during the First World War, Roman was called up, Father gave him his old watch — a very good watch, foreign-made. Roman thanked him, put the watch in his pocket, and said nothing more about it. But a few weeks later Father spoke up at dinner:

"Mark my words, he's bound to lose it somewhere in the trenches."

More time went by, and then again Father remarked:

"A sloppy fellow, that hubby of yours. I'd bet my boots someone swiped his watch without him knowing a thing about it."

After this, there were long daily discussions — that one didn't really need a watch at the front, and that a reasonable man would have left it at home. And besides, there were watches and watches; one should realize this, but, regrettably, some people didn't seem to. And, surely, there must be something behind the fact that Roman never mentioned in his letters whether the watch was running well, whether perhaps it needed fixing, or even whether he still had it.

A year later Roman came home on leave. When asked about the watch, he took it out of his pocket and put it on the table.

"You know," said my father, "we're adults, all of us; we understand what war is. Should, God forbid, anything happen to you . . . ."

"Dad!" I exclaimed.

"Father is right," said Roman indifferently. "I'll leave the watch at home."

"You see!" cried Father, delighted. "Roman is more sensible than you."

Roman went back to the front, and a month later we were notified that he had been killed in action.

I haven't spoken to Mother and Father since. I didn't move out of the house, for I had no place to go, but I ate alone and hated to touch any of their things. Mother cried all the time, and Father, seeing this, would leave the house at once. It was then that he started drinking. The habit developed rapidly, and after a while things began to disappear from the house. Father held on to the watch for a long time — he didn't sell it until after the phonograph, the pillows, and the silver sugar bowl were gone.

— *translated by* BARBARA VEDDER

(From *Okrutna Gwiazda,* short stories. Published by "Czytelnik," Warsaw, 1958.)

Death of Grandmother Zabielska

BY ZOFIA STAROWIEYSKA MORSTIN

ZOFIA STAROWIEYSKA MORSTIN was born on an estate in southern Poland in 1895, the daughter of landowning members of the gentry. Educated in Poland and abroad, before the war she was on the staff of the conservative Krakow daily *Czas* and also wrote several books. The first to attract the attention of the critics was a psychological novel about a child. During the German Occupation she completed a volume of essays on Italian Renaissance poets and artists. This was published after the war under the title *The Cabal of History*. In the fifties two other books appeared: *Facts and Words* (meditations on the Gospel) and *Our Home* (memoirs), from which the following excerpt is taken. Madame Morstin, who is a Catholic liberal of long standing, is now a book reviewer and columnist on *Tygodnik Powszechny* and a member of its editorial board.

THE DEATH of Grandmother Zabielska was the first one experienced by the children. Both their grandfathers had died long before. None of the children remembered them. She was the first person whom they knew, whom they lived with, to leave this familiar life. For that reason her end became for them a kind of model death. It also explains how the seventy-second year, the age at which she died, came to mark for them the close of human life, just as the red line on a thermometer points to the normal temperature. They always believed that whoever died before that age died too young, while every additional year was a gift.

In the same way, through her death, their attitude towards that special moment of life was determined—and determined properly; although sad, the fact was simple and natural. There was nothing dramatic about it. It was, like Grandmother's life, well balanced, Christian, conducted intelligently and generously.

As soon as her condition was diagnosed as pneumonia, her bed was moved from the northern bedroom to the sunny living room. Treatment with oxygen was then unknown, and the disease was not accompanied, as it is now, by the threatening hiss of the oxygen tank. As much fresh air as possible was supplied for the congested lungs, but of course only natural sources were available. Here, in the red living room, air was plentiful. Also, there was enough space for an altar, in front of which Father Wojciech, one of Grandmother's sons, said Mass every morning so she could share in the service and receive Holy Communion.

The sick woman, like everyone around her, fully realized that the end was near, for at that time there was no recovery from pneumonia for an old person. Grandmother Zabielska was not in the habit of deceiving herself; even this awesome fact she met as reasonably as she had always met all unavoidable events.

She did not complain, nor was she ever restive. On the contrary, she was gracious and grateful for the gentle care with which Emilia, her daughter-in-law, nursed her so efficiently. Nobody could please the sick woman as well as she did, for Pani Emilia, though she had no natural leanings toward good Samaritanism, wanted to do everything well for those she loved.

Meanwhile, Grandmother Zabielska set about preparing for death in her orderly way. As Wojciech did not leave his mother's side, he would be on hand at the appropriate moment to administer the last rites. In the Zabielski family it was not the custom when someone was dying to tell that person a white lie about recovering, but for Emilia's people, who loved talk, ornaments and gentle ironies, these straightforward manners seemed brutal. They used to say that the Zabielskis died like peasants.

The sacrament of Extreme Unction was received by the patient in all the severity of truth. The business of the will was clear and decided ahead of time; it needed no explanation. The last instructions by Grandmother Zabielska, however, concerned matters so trivial that everyone was astonished that they were recalled at such a moment. But she, always tidy to the point of perfection, did not believe that small things should be forgotten on the doorstep of eternity. And so one day she called the eighteen-year-old sister of her daughter-in-law, and rather harshly ordered her to put the last stitches on the embroidery of a gray tablecloth. She herself would not have time, and she hated to leave a piece of work unfinished.

"But make sure that all the cross-stitches go in the same direction," she said.

And when Basia began to reply that she could finish it herself upon recovering, Grandmother Zabielska interrupted. "I know what I'm talking about; you will finish the tablecloth. But you are messy and always mix up the stitches, and this time I want you to work carefully."

Basia kept her promise. Those were the only straight stitches she ever made.

A frequent guest at the sickbed was Emilia's mother, Pani Liza. The two old friends talked about the approaching parting. Pani Liza was very sorry to see her companion go, and with all her warm heart she tried to anticipate and understand the dejection and sorrow of her relative. The tearing-off process of death frightened her because—although reaching longingly for God—she had her roots deeply in life. Letting her thoughts out, she would say, more frankly than diplomatically, "How hard it must be to leave this world! To leave everything and everyone."

"Oh, no," the answer came. "When the dessert is to be passed, we don't want to go back to the soup."

But Pani Liza was not convinced that one could leave this world without regret. Not only was she more passionately attached to life, but also—being more pious—she was continuously stirred by feelings of doubt and guilt, never sure whether she had not committed a grave sin. That was why she could not understand her friend's composure. (Her own death, when it came, was very different: although she died in a nun's habit, and in a state of grace, her end was full of anguish, dreadful fears and heart-rending sorrow. And perhaps in forewarning of these tortures she did not hesitate to say things which, presumably, would upset her friend.)

"It is so horrifying," she would say, "to know that soon one will face God's Judgment."

This prospect did not disturb Grandmother Zabielska either.

"But why?" she said soberly and reasonably. "When we knew that something was bad, we simply tried not to do it."

People are apt to judge themselves tolerantly; nevertheless in decisive moments panic seizes them. Then from the peaks of self-confidence, they fall into the depths of doubt. Not so Grandmother Zabielska; she never lost her balance. What she thought of herself no one knew, for she never talked about herself. Her one bit of self-praise in that last hour was a modest one. She simply stated that she did no wrong, or rather, tried to do no wrong. She was sure of it. Her moral standard was minimal: to avoid wrong. It was realized in full.

She imposed this peace-in-death on everyone around her. Everyone was sad — no one despaired.

Once a day the children were called to Grandmother's bedside. They would stand there a while, silent, suddenly hushed, and then they would go back to their rooms. Mrs. Zabielska looked at the children seriously — strictly, they thought. But this was entirely on the surface. She loved them very much and was proud of them. She was proud of their robust health, their tallness, their gaiety and brightness.

One afternoon Pani Emilia entered the nursery where they sat at the low table having their afternoon snack, and told them that Helenka and Maciej were to come with her, because their grandmother was dying. She waited, leaning down on the little table. From her neck hung a long, heavy chain the end of which, together with the watch, was tucked under the belt. Tears rolled down her face. The children got up quietly and went with her down to the living room, where everyone — family and servants — was kneeling in a circle around the bed, reciting the litany for the dying. The children knelt and prayed with the others — for the first time participating in the grave matter of death.

No shadow of terror fell on their lives. This "good death" they remembered many, many years later, when — quite grown-up — they followed the coffin of Grandmother Zabielska's son, Uncle Kazimierz. Around them the Second World War was blazing and the terror of the German occupation raged. It was a time rife with death — dreadful, cruel and unnatural. But Uncle Kazimierz escaped this fate. He died at a ripe old age in his own home, among his children and grandchildren. He died a sudden death, but not unexpected. His coffin was carried by his neighbors out of the place in which he had spent his life. According to ancient custom, the casket was lowered three times on every threshold: the dead man had to say good-bye to his house.

Later on that sunny summer day, among the murmur of trees and flutter of flags, with ringing bells and wailing funeral chants, he was taken to the cemetery by his family, neighbors and friends. And everyone felt, in spite of their sorrow at bidding farewell to this good and cheerful man, that they were taking part in something proper — not frightening at all. This was how a man should die, in his house, among his own people — by God's, not man's hand.

— *translated by* WANDA JAECKEL

(From *Dom*. Published by "Wydawnictwo Literackie," Krakow, 1959.)

A Speck of Dirt

BY KORNEL FILIPOWICZ

KORNEL FILIPOWICZ was born in 1913 in Tarnopol. He studied biology at Krakow University. In his student days his short stories were published in Polish magazines, but his first book, *The Impassive Landscape*, did not appear until 1947. He saw active service in the Polish September campaign in 1939 and spent a few years in German concentration camps in Gross Rosen and Oranienburg. Since 1947 he has published five novels and four volumes of short stories. His most important works, including his first novel, are *The Profiles of My Friends, Darkness and Light* and a collection of deeply moving stories about children, *The White Bird*, published in 1960. Mr. Filipowicz lives in Krakow.

WE WERE HELD in a long and narrow cell closed at one end by a barred window, at the other by a massive door. The window was blocked on the outside by an iron shutter; over the top of it we could see the merest scrap of sky, and below it, through the chink between the window sill and the edge of the shutter, a section of the courtyard. The chink was half a centimeter wide, but through it one could observe a three-meter strip of the prison yard sprinkled with gravel and crushed slag. The door was set in a deep frame, its wood artificially grained with varnish; the lock and the door fixtures were old-fashioned and stout — it was more like a door to a crypt. In the middle of the door a round spy hole had been cut. Through it, when occasionally the guard forgot to slip the cover back, we stared at the opposite gray wall of the corridor.

Everything that affected our life in this place was arranged through the door. We used the window only to look out. Sitting in a group under the wall, we watched the oblong of sky: bright and fresh in the morning, darkening as night came on. Each morning through the window we could hear the twittering of sparrows, each evening the warble of swallows flying around the prison. Sometimes, when there was rain in the air outside, the very noisy grind of trams reached us from afar. We heard the sound of automobiles close at hand. Occasionally, a shot was fired.

The sixteen prisoners crowded into this small, narrow space were a mixed lot; they included scientists, house painters, restaurant keepers, students, professional soldiers; also there were a cobbler and a person of no profession who had played the guitar before being imprisoned, and who had a parrotlike gift for languages. Only here, in prison, did this man achieve prestige: he was the "senior in the cell." The youngest of us was seventeen, the oldest close to seventy. Among us were fair-haired and dark, bald and gray; many were probably what the world calls bad characters; from what they said it appeared that they had been devils with the women they had met in their days of freedom, and that they had no exaggerated scruples in regard to business matters. We were also of widely differing political convictions; but, as a man who before the war had been a lecturer at a university used to say, we were united by a common bond: we loved our native land, each in his own way, and we hated those who had deprived us of our liberty. The same man also once said that everyone, whether he was tall or short, bandit or postal clerk, has something which he loves more than his own life. That was rather highfalutin talk, for we others never mentioned such things or even thought of them. It sufficed that all sixteen of us were so-called political prisoners. We had run afoul of the Germans in various, mutually contradictory ways — so contradictory in certain cases that before we found ourselves here in prison we had tried very hard to make a mess of one another's lives. Yet in the end we had all come together here, where our fate depended on what our common enemy felt like doing with us. Certain of us maintained that our future was in the hands of God. But whatever the truth, we were locked in and were surrounded by stout walls.

At six o'clock every morning the cell senior sounded reveille through his fist. Many had already been awake for an hour or two; we lay with closed eyes, thinking. The cell senior said the room stank like a latrine, and he opened the window. A stream of cold air smelling of locomotive steam blew in from outside. We washed, pouring water over our hands; we shaved; we swept the floor. Some knelt on the pallets and prayed. The building was filled with clatters and rustles, which penetrated through the walls and reminded us that everywhere, around us, above us, and below us, other prisoners were occupied in the same activities. Outside in the corridor keys jangled; we could hear muffled voices and the shuffle of boots. At that moment the corridor seemed to be open directly to the town and liberty. A key rattled violently in the lock, we hurriedly assembled with billycans in our hands, and a great mobile and nimble caldron swiftly poured out a portion of coffee for each of us. While this was happening, if one was lucky enough to stand in the right spot, through the barred window of the corridor apple and pear trees in bloom could be seen, and the fresh hues of the flower beds between the little houses of the suburb. Columns of blue smoke rose from the chimneys; automobiles drove along the highroad, passing carts and cyclists. The aluminum caldron withdrew, the stout door shut, and the key made two noisy turns in the oiled lock.

An hour or two after breakfast there was a regular procedure of which we were the subjects. An iron gate grated as it opened, and small black Opels, great tarpaulin-covered Heinkels and Bussings drove into the yard. Through the chink below the window shutter we saw the Gestapo men getting out of the automobiles, attaché cases under their arms. The drivers smoked cigarettes, strolled about the yard, looked around them or sat on a bench, closed their eyes and turned their faces up to the keen spring sun. All kinds of sounds filled the corridor. After the clatter of a key in the lock, the guard called out the names of prisoners. The automobiles carried us off for examination, off to a camp, or out of the town to a deserted spot intersected with clay trenches. Those who returned to the cell after being examined had to be cared for: their underclothes were caked with blood and excrement, and they had to be undressed, washed, and bandaged. They swore and laughed as we treated them, or fainted again and again. We talked about the Gestapo men who examined us, for we knew them very well; we were interested in their moods and in what they talked about among themselves. We never talked about death.

Twice a week Krysia, escorted from the women's side by a guard, made a round of the cells. She brought us clean folded underwear; we saw her through the open door as she bent over the basket, took out a parcel, unfolded it in front of the guard and passed it over to the cell senior. The guard stared indifferently at her. She had black hair and was short, with a pale face and delicate hands always meticulously clean. Then the door was shut, and the cell senior, the only man we had empowered to do so, searched thoroughly through the seams in the shirts, the spots where secret messages were concealed. Only he was permitted to pass around the contents of a message; only he had the right to convey it by the agreed means to the next cell. The information gleaned from the messages consisted of ancient communiqués from the Eastern and Western fronts, or more recent news of the latest developments in the town; sometimes it included a list of persons whom the Germans had sentenced to death. As this might concern us personally, we thought it best that the cell senior should be the first to know of it; and if he, the guitarist, considered it advisable he could refrain from making it public.

At one o'clock a fresh stream of noises flowed through the massive iron door, as if the corridor were open at both ends to the street, and a wind blowing along it. The door was unlocked, and the aluminum caldron gave us soup. We ate the soup, squatting on our heels under the wall. Then we washed the billycans, swept the floor once more, and the day slowly began to decline toward evening. Some of us went for a walk. We marched in pairs from the window to the door and back again, making turns like bears in a cage. By this means we could cover quite a few miles, talking in undertones all the while, or, if we preferred, saying nothing and thinking. Beyond the window the day slowly faded. Then it suddenly grew cold in the cell, and we ceased to see one another's faces. But outside the window, above the iron shutter, a long scrap of clear sky was plainly visible for a long time.

It was Friday, Krysia's day for visiting us. The next day, Saturday, was as usual to be devoted to putting the cell in order in readiness for Sunday, which was a day of peace, because those who were in charge of us did not work on Sundays and holidays. Another week had passed; during that time two men had been lost from our cell, carried off to a concentration camp. Two others lay on a pallet in one corner: one had had both arms twisted till they were dislocated; the other had had his buttocks minced like a cutlet and his kidneys pulverized. They lay in the dark corner, gazing at us with eyes glittering feverishly; sometimes they called to us, asking to be turned over or to be given a drink of water.

At twelve o'clock the sound of the key rattled through the cell, the door was opened suddenly, and we saw Krysia in the corridor. She was bending over the basket, rummaging through the parcels of underwear, looking for the number of the cell. She had an absurdly full upper lip; her black, gleaming hair peeped from under her scarf. The guard in charge of the floor, a stout German with an artificial jaw, stood with one hand empty and the other holding the keys threaded on a large iron ring. He turned his head and stared, open-mouthed, through the corridor window at the little houses and flowering apple trees. He nodded without bothering to look at the parcel. Krysia handed it to our cell senior and smiled, distending her upper lip, then stooped and dragged the basket toward the next cell. The guard closed the door and turned the key twice in the lock. The cell senior squatted down by the door, on a spot which could not be observed through the spy hole, and looked through the underwear. We pretended we were not greatly interested; we were occupied with watching the prison yard.

The cell senior unfolded a narrow twist of paper, held it close to his eyes for a moment, then folded it and put it in his pocket. He had quite a cheerful face, but then he was a pleasant fellow anyway. He came over to the window with his hands in his pockets and remarked, "Things are going fine, boys. The Russians have occupied Wielkie Luki, Viazma and Rzhev. Complete destruction of two German armies. And a smash for them in Africa: Rommel's been called back to report."

"But what's the news of the town?" the man with the damaged kidneys asked.

The cell senior turned to him. "No change. The bugs are packing their cases and smearing their feet with grease. . . ."

The joke, heard so many times before, still raised a laugh. Both our comrades lying on the pallet in the corner laughed too.

But we soon learned that there was more to the message, though the additional information was not made known generally. The cell senior told it to one of us during the afternoon walk, and this man found an opportunity to pass it on to a third, and he in turn to the next. Thus, by the evening we all knew it, except just one: the one concerned. Some days earlier the Underground organization had made an attack on the German chief of police. Posters had been put up yesterday in the city, with a list of Poles sentenced to death. Among the first ten names, printed in heavy type as usual, was that of a man in our cell.

His name was Osmudzki; he was about thirty, with dark hair, cut short, and was tall, with a slight stoop; he was self-centered, as sportsmen often are. He wore a well-cut but worn gray suit of good quality. Apparently he had been trained as a chemist or physicist; by conviction he was a syndicalist; we didn't quite know what that meant, yet it didn't surprise anybody. He was an even-tempered sort of fellow. He had been put in our cell some two weeks before, had been twice examined, on two successive days, then had lain for several days in one corner of the cell. But he had quickly recovered and now was one of us; he behaved just like everyone else: he got up, he shaved, ate, washed his billycan and lay down to sleep. There was nothing to distinguish him from the rest of us. He began to have a strange, separate existence only when we learned that before long he would be dead.

That day dragged on and on into infinity. Osmudzki was among us; he walked about the cell, talked, shifted his arms and legs. We tried to be natural, tried not to let him see that we were interested in him, or, God forbid, let him feel that we were concealing something from him. We wanted to be quite ordinary, just the same as every other day, just as we had been ever since he joined us. But were our gestures and words, despite what we wanted, not too exaggeratedly restrained or excessively free? The devil only knows! For our part we couldn't feel at all sure. We had some difficult hours before us. We saw him everywhere, even when we weren't looking at him. We saw his shoes tramping over the floor, the sleeves of his old gray jacket, his neck supporting his head; we heard his voice as he talked of trivial matters.

At last night came, and we stopped seeing him. We lay down on the floor, one beside another. We chatted a little; then several of us hummed and sang in undertones: "All our everyday deeds accept in mercy, righteous God." Before we dropped off to sleep we heard an older prisoner, a restaurant owner by trade, who was lying next to Osmudzki, ask him, "What are you twisting and turning like that for, damn it?"

"I've got a pain in my stomach," Osmudzki answered.

"So have I. It's their filthy soup, blast them. Get some water, and I'll have a drink too."

The restaurant owner played his part well. He was an old, bad-tempered and impatient chap. Osmudzki got up. We heard the sound of the mug knocking against the water bucket. A moment or two later all was quiet in the cell.

The next day, Saturday morning, the cell senior set us to work the moment we got up: he had four of us scrubbing the floor, two cleaning the window, two to the slop bucket. When Osmudzki had shaved, he told him to wrap a rag around the broom and collect the spider webs from the walls and ceiling. We got cracking. Through the open window a cascade of cold, fresh wind poured into the cell. Above the window shutters we could see a scrap of clear blue sky. The sparrows were twittering furiously. Soon after breakfast, two small automobiles drove into the yard, followed by the local runabout, and a moment or two later, by a truck with a tarpaulin cover. The cell senior ordered the floor by the door to be washed a second time; he considered we hadn't done it thoroughly enough. And he urged Osmudzki to greater efforts in his collecting of spider webs. He himself stood in the middle of the cell with his head thrown back, staring at the ceiling, showing no interest in what was happening in the yard. He watched the broom moving along on its long handle, and encouraged Osmudzki. "Ah, just there, by that patch," he said. "And look over there. They're hanging like scarecrows. Good! Now here."

We scrubbed the floor by the door, we washed the bucket, we chased the dust. Everyone was busy. Only the two sick comrades, the one with damaged kidneys and the one with dislocated arms, lay on the pallet and watched us. From the corridor came the bang of the door which cut off our floor from the rest of the building; then we heard footsteps and felt a draft of air. The steps came along the corridor; they passed our cell. At the end of the corridor there was the clatter of a key in the lock. Osmudzki suddenly dropped the broom and stood a moment perfectly still.

"What's the matter?" the cell senior asked him.

"I've got something in my eye," he said.

"Close your eye tight, draw a deep breath through your nose and spit," the restaurant owner advised him.

We all stopped work and stared at Osmudzki. He rubbed his eye with his fingers, and looked as if he were crying. His normally tranquil face was twisted and ugly. The footsteps outside in the corridor approached again; they rang as though the boots were marching over glass. Somewhere close to ours a cell was opened, and a name was called.

Osmudzki tried to open his eye, but it hurt, and he twisted his lips. "It's burning . . ." he said.

"That's the lime."

"Someone wet a handkerchief in water."

"Anything but water!"

"Who's got a clean handkerchief? Let me look. Don't be afraid." The cell senior rolled the corner of a handkerchief into a tiny twist, raised Osmudzki's eyelid and gently tried to wipe the dust out of his eye. We all stood watching them. The footsteps in the corridor again went by our cell. But a moment later a key grated in our lock unexpectedly, as if the individual who had put it in the lock had been standing outside the door for a long time. The guard in charge of our floor opened the door and called, "Osmudzki."

"Here."

The guard stood and stared. In one hand he was holding the keys bunched on a ring. A group of men were crowding in the corridor not far off. We could hear their presence. They scraped their boots and rubbed against the wall.

"What's going on in here? Now, Osmudzki, get a move on."

"Something's got into his eye, sir," the cell senior said, working away with the corner of the handkerchief. "That's got it," he said calmly, and showed Osmudzki the handkerchief with the tiny speck which had been causing him pain. Osmudzki blinked and smiled. His face smoothed out, was once more serene and handsome; it seemed even handsomer than before.

"Come out," the guard said in quite a pleasant tone.

"Thank you," Osmudzki said to the cell senior, and strode out swiftly. We stared after him. The guard turned the key in the lock twice, very noisily. When the footsteps died away along the corridor, we rushed to the window. The sun lit up the prison yard clearly. Through the long, narrow chink we could see the back of the truck quite distinctly. Its tailboard was let down, and a small bench was set against the board. All around the truck we could see the ground sprinkled with gravel and crushed slag. The driver walked around the truck with his hands in his pockets, stopped and tested the tires by kicking them. Then he lit a cigarette and returned to the driver's seat. A long time passed before we saw the first of the condemned men. They came out in twos, tied together with white rope by their arms.

Cooperatively they climbed onto the little bench, clambered into the truck, and vanished inside it. Osmudzki was one of the third pair, tied to a man shorter than himself, he walked with a slight stoop. These two also climbed readily onto the bench and got into the truck. Ten prisoners altogether climbed in, then four SS men in highly polished boots, with machine pistols hanging across their chests. They fastened up the tailboard by its hooks and lowered the tarpaulin. The truck described a half circle over the gravel and drove out of the gate.

— *translated by* HARRY STEVENS

(From *Ciemnosc i Swiatlo*. Published by "Wydawnictwo Literackie," Krakow, 1959.)

The Tramp

BY JAN JOZEF SZCZEPANSKI

JAN JOZEF SZCZEPANSKI was born in Warsaw in 1920, the son of a former Polish consul general in Chicago. A man of many interests, he is a short story writer, novelist, film critic, traveler and Alpine climber, and at the universities of Warsaw and Wroclaw he studied Sanskrit and Hindu. He took part in the September campaign in 1939 and was in the Home Army's* units during the Occupation. Since 1953 he has contributed film criticism to *Tygodnik Powszechny,* the Catholic weekly, and he also writes film scenarios. His books are *Odysseus' Pants* (1954), a novel; *Boots* (1956), short stories about the Underground Army forest units (one follows); *Polish Autumn* (1957), an account of the September campaign; *Duel* (1957), a novel plotted around an imaginary dictatorship in a South American country; *The White Bears' Gulf* (1960), a travel-adventure book about the Arctic. In 1959 he received the Hemingway Award, a prize set up by the late author to be paid annually from his Polish royalties to a Polish writer of prose. Szczepanski is presently living in Krakow.

* The Home Army was the underground military force which pledged allegiance to the wartime legal Polish Government in London, while the People's Army with its partisan units was a Communist formation.

SERGEANT GLOSNY'S steps sounded energetic and efficient; he was wearing a red and white arm band. Stopping at attention in front of the lieutenant, he barked out the military formula and announced that Szarak had come from the village on important business.

Through the window they could hear Szarak's muddy boots stomping up and down outside the forest barracks of the partisan unit.

"Bring him in," said the lieutenant.

Szarak carefully placed his green sweaty cap on the wooden bench, unbuttoned his faded jacket, and shook hands with all present. Then he seated himself on the nearest cot, stretching out his stiff leg. He blew on his hands and proceeded to rub them until the knuckles cracked.

"Nice and warm in here," he said. "This morning we had a bit of frost. A hard winter's on the way, it looks like."

From the inside pocket of his jacket he pulled out a metal tobacco box, and passed it around. On the top was a small packet of fine cigarette paper. They rolled their cigarettes with satisfaction.

"Where did you get the fancy paper, Mr. Szarak?"

"The Forestry Office distributed it. There's still some left in the warehouse."

"Lieutenant, sir, how about giving that warehouse a good going over?" Hieronim called gaily.

"No, not now," Szarak said. "Yesterday they brought a new battalion of German SS into town. I'll figure out a way to dig up a couple of cartons for you."

"Are they preparing for something?" asked the lieutenant.

"So it seems. They're sniffing around the woods. That's what I came to talk about."

"Well? Speak up then."

"Did Skrzetuski report to you about the tramp, Lieutenant?"

"Yes, he mentioned it. I thought he was imagining things."

Szarak shook his head.

"A fishy character. For three days now he's been snooping around here. Yesterday I spotted him on the embankment, near the clearing. When he saw me, he tried to pretend he was picking mushrooms. At this time of year!"

"Eh, he's probably some half-wit . . ."

"Ho ho! He's got his wits about him, all right. Yes sir. He's on the scent of what goes on around here. Whenever your men go to the village, there he is, waiting near the little church. Never one minute late. You'll see for yourself today . . ."

Glosny sprang from his seat and banged the table with an open palm. "Sir, I have an idea! I could sure put 'im through a test, the old rat!" His wilted face lighted up. "The boys and I are going to the village after dinner. We'll dress up in the German uniforms we have in the shed — and then we'll see what he'll do."

Szarak kicked the floor loudly with his good leg. "He's got something, by God!"

"Nothing like using your head," agreed Hieronim heartily. "Yes sir, it's a great idea! Glosny can make like a Kraut, easy, the others'll keep their mouths shut, just *jawohl* and *befehl*, or whatever."

"Yes, it could work," said the lieutenant. "Only you'll have to warn the village about these 'Germans,' Mr. Szarak, or else there might be trouble."

"Sure thing. You've nothing to worry about, Lieutenant."

"And you with your men, Glosny, will report to me before leaving. I want to look you over."

Szarak stood up with effort. Leaning heavily on a cane, he put out his hand to say good-bye.

"Maybe he's gone already," worried the lieutenant. "If he really is spying, we'll be in a fix."

Szarak let out a few guffaws through his bushy mustache and smiled cunningly. "I can see you don't know me very well. Any stranger can enter the village, but to leave, he needs my permission!" He put on his cap with a resolute gesture and pulled it down over his eyes like the visor of a helmet; his dark, furrowed face took on a look of soldierly severity.

When he and Glosny were gone, the lieutenant got up and tightened his belt. "I'll go and see how dinner's coming along."

They were stomping and shuffling their feet in excitement, unable to stand still. Even Glosny's face showed some color under the heavy green helmet. Everybody was speaking at once, but Skrzetuski's basso drowned out all the other voices.

"You should've seen the lousy tramp, Lieutenant! He'd have skinned me alive without batting an eye. And that silly look on his face when he saw he'd been taken for a ride!"

Amid bursts of laughter Glosny was trying to relate his story: "Sure enough, just as we come near the Bentkowski place, he crawls out from behind the fence and right away walks up to me."

"That's right, by God!" Nadzieja supported him. "And how he grinned, that son of a bitch. Like he was coming to greet his bride."

"Right away he walks up to me, sir. An ugly devil, covered with rags, hairy like a monkey. . . . And he glares at me with those little slit eyes of his and says, *'Herr Leutnant, Banditen.'* So I ask him questions in German, but he can't understand; just *'Banditen, Banditen,'* and he points his finger at the Bentkowski place. So I yell to the boys, *'Vorsicht, deckt euch,'* and make them go hide in the ditch; and me, I pull out my shooter; and then I try in Polish with the old guy, but as if I can't speak it right. Right away he pipes up, 'Sure, they'll be comin' around this way real soon. Dressed up like civilians,' he says. 'You just wait here, and you'll nab 'em for sure.' And so I ask him, would he know whereabouts they live, and he says, 'Yes,' he knows, 'in them big holes,' he says, 'in the woods, past the swamp,' but he's afraid to take us there."

"The stinking bum!" exclaimed Hieronim with amazement. "And you thought, Lieutenant, he was nothing but a half-wit."

"To top it all, he wanted us to give him something in return," put in Nadzieja.

"Wait. Then I says to him that we're not scared, that any minute there'll be more soldiers coming along, so he ought to go ahead and lead us, and he asks me, 'What's in it for me?' I promised he'd be paid five hundred zlotys at headquarters in Wloszow, but he starts haggling with me, saying it's not enough — for something like that he should get at least a thousand. He even asked for a receipt."

"We would've given him one, but none of the boys had any paper."

"Wait. So then, sir, I give him the once-over, but I see he won't go anyway, so I pull out my watch, and I says to him, 'Here's a prize from me, if you lead us right.' His eyes lit up like stars."

"He even asked us to put it to his ear, so he could see if it's running," put in Nadzieja.

"And he made sure he'd get my sheepskin coat," added Skrzetuski.

"That's right; he seemed to think he wasn't getting enough, so he says that one of the bandits has a real nice sheepskin coat, and shoes, too — he could use a pair for the winter. So I told him he could take anything he wanted from the bandits. Then he agreed and started to lead us. And how! Straight over the clearing; not once did he get off the track. He brought us as far as the little alder grove on the edge of the swamp, and then, 'Halt.' That's as far as he'll go, he says, because just over the ditch, in the bushes, the bandits have their guards on watch, he says. He knew everything, the old fox: like when they change, and that there's another path. I left him behind with Nadzieja, and the rest of us made for the ditches. Just for laughs we crawled on our bellies, slowly creeping forward, as long as we could be seen from the alder grove. When we reached the outpost, I screamed, '*Hände hoch!*' with all my might, to make sure he heard me, the bastard. . . ."

"Bimber and I were over on this side, Lieutenant, and we let ourselves be taken prisoner. . . ."

"What a ball we had! You've no idea. You should've seen the sergeant playing prisoner. . . . How he trembled, how he kept looking every which way! Bimber was pretty good, too. And Glosny had himself a real treat. He even gave the sergeant a kick in the ass."

"Well? Why shouldn't I? How often does a man get a chance like that?"

"You can go to hell! I'll get you for this yet!"

"And that lousy tramp," Nadzieja shouted, over the loud bursts of laughter. "As soon as he sees them coming over the ditch, he says right away, 'Coat, sheepskin coat — that's the one,' and he rubs his hands happily, the old goat!"

"The stinking bum!" repeated Hieronim.

"But that's not all. Listen to this! The minute we bring the prisoners around, he makes us give him that coat. We had to hold on to Skrzetuski with everything we had; he was fighting like hell, like it was for real."

"Sure. What's so funny about it? My sheepskin coat for that old bastard's lice?"

"We gave him the coat and tied up Skrzetuski and Bimber. In a minute he's got the coat on and he's starting to eye the shoes. He took a fancy to Bimber's army boots, so he goes to pull them off. Bimber crossed his eyes — we thought we'd break up. Only Skrzetuski kept a straight face. And then, Lieutenant, I took a rifle from Jarzabek, unloaded it on the side, and gave it to the old tramp. 'Now, kill them,' I says."

No one spoke.

"D'you think he said no? Not on your life. Only that he can't shoot so good. So I show him how to go about it, and he takes the shooter and only asks if he could also take the underpants of the corpses. Then, cool as a cucumber, he lifts the rifle and aims at Skrzetuski."

"That's right, Lieutenant." Skrzetuski straightened up, furrowing his heavy eyebrows solemnly.

For a time everyone was quiet. Zbirek had now crawled off his cot and stood in front of Skrzetuski, his eyes shining. No one stirred, only the lieutenant, who had also gotten up from his bench, swayed rhythmically back and forth, from heel to toe, so that the water gurgled softly under the floorboards.

"He was aiming at me to kill, sir. Cold shivers went down my back, I can tell you, even though I knew it wasn't loaded. You should've seen him! That pile of rags, that half-dead slob! Hairy mug, tiny gray eyes, almost kindly, you might say. But he didn't bat an eye. He was aiming straight for the heart. . . . Only then Glosny. . . ."

"Yes, me, Lieutenant. It wasn't fitting to take it any longer. I grabbed the rifle from his hand and jammed him in the teeth. He didn't say a word. He sat himself down, wiped his nose, and gazed up at us, like he was stupid or something."

"They untied Bimber and me. So I go up to him and say, 'You no-good bastard, so you were going to kill a Polish soldier. . . .' D'you know what he answered? That the lieutenant made him."

"I'll be damned!" Hieronim slapped the table with his palm.

"It's hard to believe," said the lieutenant.

"Ask Glosny; ask Nadzieja. That's exactly what happened, I swear to God!"

Nadzieja suddenly burst into a whinnying laugh. "And that look on his face! He sure was mixed up: What gives? Here are the Krauts, there the partisans; a minute ago they were about to kill each other, and now they're pals. . . ."

"First they give things away; then they take them back," added Skrzetuski.

"One minute they make him shoot; the next they knock his teeth out," shouted Glosny, trying to make himself heard. "A real circus!" They went on, slapping their thighs in merriment, almost choking from laughter.

Hieronim came up behind the lieutenant and pulled at his sleeve. "Well then . . ." He pointed down with his thumb. "Into the hole?"

A reddish glow came over the officer's cheeks. His face appeared stiff under the luminous veneer. Only the lips moved as if directed by some separate mechanism. "Yes," he said, "there's no point in fooling around."

Zbirek stepped forward and halted directly in the beam of sunlight that slanted across the room. "Sir, let me do it." Standing erect, he waited for an answer.

The masklike face bent down almost imperceptibly. The gleam of light now fell on the forehead; a shadow covered the eyes. "Why?" asked the lieutenant.

"Please let me," repeated Corporal Zbirek in a high-pitched, stubborn voice.

The lieutenant shrugged his shoulders. "All right."

The others were leaving, but Zbirek remained standing erect.

"Sir, could I borrow your good pistol?"

The officer reached out, drew his pistol toward the edge of the table, but at the last moment, forestalling Zbirek's move, he covered it with his hand.

"You have your own revolver."

They all stood looking at the stooped back covered with a faded green jacket. The old man didn't hurry with his work; he groaned a bit as he pushed the shovel down with his foot, although the earth was not too hard in that spot. The blade cast aside pieces of moldy wood, decayed roots and dry forest sand. All was quiet. The late-afternoon November sun hung low, deep in color, lighting up the tree trunks with a resinous glow. The frosty air seemed all the more penetrating. Breath formed little clouds of transparent mist.

The old man continued to interrupt his digging, resting himself against the handle, and his surprised gaze moved from one face to another. His narrow eyes, practically hidden behind the bushy eyebrows, didn't seem frightened. They sparkled with an almost friendly grin. One might have thought that he was flattered to be the center of all the silent attention. No one any longer shouted at him; no one gave him anything or took it back. Here they all were, in one friendly group: soldiers in German uniforms, and "bandits" dressed in various costumes, in soft, four-cornered caps, in jackets, sheepskin coats, military tunics; some armed, some unarmed. He gazed at them for a time, then glanced in the direction of the ditch to watch others approach, hopping awkwardly over wooden planks; again he was swinging the spade once or twice, and then resting some more.

It was a secluded spot. A band of swampy meadows circled around in a wide loop; through the center, a glossy stream coiled like a silver snake. The peninsula formed by the loop bristled with a dark thicket of young spruce trees, from which arose a narrow bluish streak — the smoke from the camp kitchen. On that side the terrain gradually sloped upward from the valley. Along the edge, a clump of alder trees, their deep green still untouched by the frost; then anemic little birches, shedding golden leaves; elms and young oaks; and, further up, pines, at first only here and there, but later thickening into a deep forest, where the darkness of the night was already beginning to set in. Overhead, the sky seemed transparent, light, and cool in the diluted sunlight. The serenity of the evening brought blessed peace. The old man didn't hurry. He dug a small hole, no deeper than up to the middle of his calf, and now, having come upon a thick root, he was helplessly poking at it with the shovel.

"At this rate we'll be here till midnight," said Sergeant Skrzetuski. "One of you boys help him out!"

The old man handed over the shovel with a certain reluctance. He mumbled something to himself, lingered a bit, but finally gave up and, walking a few steps away, sat down on the ground. He began rummaging through his pockets slowly and with great care, obviously looking for something; with stiff fingers he dug out all kinds of rubbish and tufts of dirt, which he carefully scattered. Zbirek came closer, leaned against a nearby tree and watched him intently. But the old fellow paid no attention. Abandoning his search, he pulled down his hat, since the setting sun was beginning to hurt his eyes, and settled down to study Wons's work from under the shabby brim.

Private Wons was a sturdy fellow with a short neck and a large round head. He knew his work. After two fast blows, the root jumped like a living thing. Now the digging went ahead smoothly. Wons took off his coat; the shovel flew up and down with the regularity of a machine. Sand whistled through the air; metal sparkled with a blood-red flame reflected from the sun. Murmurs of praise arose in the group. His face was turning purple and shiny, but the private never slowed down. He was already up over his knees in the hole. But the blade of the shovel made a different sound now: it slid in softly, and came up with a slushing noise. The sand was no longer flying—it fell on the ground in wet slabs. Wons straightened up. "Water," he said.

Suddenly the old man scrambled to his feet, went over to the edge of the hole, and peered inside curiously. He was obviously displeased. His head moved from side to side; lost in thought, he rubbed his scraggly beard. Then he turned around and started walking away, as if he had decided to leave.

"Stop!" screeched Zbirek, quickly reaching for his gun. Several rifles lifted up; one of the "Germans" was already rushing after him. The old man stopped and calmed them down with a motion of his hand. "It's damp," he said in his rasping, cracked voice.

"So what if it's damp?" shouted Skrzetuski angrily. "What difference does it make now? You come back here!"

"Wait a moment," rasped the old man, not in the least dismayed. He bent down, and slowly began picking up something from the ground. "It's no good when it's damp," he mumbled peevishly. "It's got to be dry."

They couldn't comprehend this. They gathered around him, staring in amazed silence. But he kept on combing the grass with his fingernails, groaning, rustling through the underbrush. Finally he straightened up with an armful of dry leaves and small twigs. He walked back down to the hole, and proceeded to empty his load into it. No one interfered. He repeated this two or three times, and then crawled into the hole himself, disappearing inside it. They leaned over to look. The old tramp was stretched out at the bottom, squirming to make himself comfortable on his acrid-smelling bed, his arms tucked under his head. He looked like a dirty rag doll.

One of the men giggled, and then everybody burst out laughing. The rag doll stiffened, looked puzzled at the noisy voices. After a while, small wrinkles formed around his beady little eyes; the mouth, surrounded by dirty gray whiskers, opened slightly; the parted lips exposed several greenish stumps. As if helpless in the face of the general merriment, the old beggar also smiled. Only Sergeant Hieronim refused to join in.

"Enough!" he said in a sharp, commanding tone. "Get out of that hole. You've been clowning around long enough."

The soldiers, ashamed, moved aside, and the old man scrambled over the edge of the hole. A few leaves and twigs had stuck to his grubby clothes and some had become entangled in his beard. His hat, sweaty and frayed at the top from wear and begging, had slid to one side, giving him a fanciful, grotesquely macabre appearance.

"Do you know why this thing is going to happen to you?" asked Hieronim in the same crisp voice.

For the first time a look of alarm came upon the beggar's face. He threw them quick, furtive glances, first right, then left, as if looking for a way out. He didn't say a word.

"Didn't you lead the Germans into our camp?"

The old man nodded with unexpected eagerness.

"Weren't you going to kill this sergeant?"

He pondered this for a moment, first looking at Skrzetuski, to whom Hieronim was pointing; then his eyes fell on Glosny, and he showed a sign of relief.

"Herr Lieutenant told me to," he said.

"And so you would've killed him?"

"He didn't let me."

Hieronim looked helplessly at his companions. "All right," he murmured, "that's all."

Zbirek stepped forward. Arms behind his back, legs wide apart, he swayed gently back and forth; he looked more than ever like a frog.

"Say your prayers," ordered Hieronim, turning to the beggar. But, before the dirty, trembling hand could reach the forehead to make a sign of the cross, Skrzetuski spoke up in his formidable basso.

"One moment. Maybe you have some other wish."

Slowly, the old man finished crossing himself, mumbling something incomprehensible; he did not answer; he did not understand.

"Perhaps you'd like something," repeated Skrzetuski, louder.

The man stared at him, then began rummaging through his pockets again.

"He wants a smoke," someone guessed.

The beggar nodded.

Several men offered whatever they happened to have: one a tobacco pouch, another a box. The old man took a large pinch of dark, moist tobacco from Wons, holding it uncertainly in his open palm. With his free hand he browsed through his pockets.

"Any of you have a piece of paper?" asked Skrzetuski.

They all searched their pockets, but nobody had cigarette paper. Finally Hieronim got an idea: he pulled out of his wallet a crumpled-up one-zloty bill and handed it to the old man. The beggar took it, curved it skillfully along the middle, forming a small trough, packed the tobacco inside, and folded the thick roll with his thumbs. But his movements were becoming slower and slower as he went along, and when finally the only thing left was to lick the edge, he stopped altogether, lost in thought, and gazed at the unfinished cigarette.

"Well, Grandfather," said Skrzetuski gently, "it's getting dark."

He didn't hear him. Despite all the intent, staring faces, he was entirely alone with his awed uncertainty.

With a deep sigh he unrolled the cigarette, gathered the tobacco firmly into his left fist, folded the bill in half, and carefully tucked it away, into some secret hiding place in the lining of his coat, a place that was hard to find. For a long time he fumbled with his clothing, his head down, his back bent.

Hieronim touched Zbirek's elbow. With a slow, fluid motion Corporal Zbirek brought his right hand out from behind his back.

"Why are they screwing around out there all this time?" grumbled Biskaj. "I'll be serving dinner in the dark. What's all the fuss? Wham-bang, and that's all there is to it!"

They were standing on top of a mound, which was also the roof of a storehouse, in a grove of young spruce trees, no taller than a short man. Across the swamp they could see the majestic pines, their crowns still aglow with the slowly fading light. A thin, grayish mist was now rising from below, sending up waves of chilly dampness.

"It's all because of the boredom, sir," deliberated Biskaj. "They'll try to make a game out of anything that comes along. And no wonder. It's so dead around here a man could hang himself. Well, that's life. . . ."

From across the ditch came the dull sound of a rifle shot; and then another.

They looked at each other. Biskaj rubbed his frozen hands. "Well, I'll go and light the stove, so the guys won't gripe like they did the last time." He ran down through the bushes and disappeared in the clump of trees surrounding the kitchen.

The lieutenant was now alone. He drew his head deeper into the turned-up collar of his leather jacket. He waited. From the direction of the ditch he could already hear the voices, the crackle of dry twigs, the rustle of underbrush. The first stars had appeared in the darkening sky. The voices were approaching rapidly. It was already possible to recognize which voice belonged to whom, though without distinguishing the words. The camp was also coming to life. Those who had stayed behind were now emerging from their underground shelters, their hazy silhouettes making their way through the thicket. Then, right next to him on the path, he heard Hieronim's voice:

"You're a mean little bastard, aren't you, Zbirek."

There was more admiration than contempt in the statement, so Zbirek answered boastfully, "Today I was in the mood for something like that, my friend. I felt I'd go nuts if I couldn't blow off some steam. There comes a moment . . ." His last words dissolved in the cool breeze, treble and strident.

"Anyway, he saved himself a zloty, eh?" someone said, with a laugh.

The lieutenant walked down toward them. The entire group had now emerged from the shrubbery and was being greeted by those coming from the camp. The air was filled with a humming crescendo of voices. The men were describing what happened, talking about the bedding of dry leaves, about Zbirek, about that last cigarette.

"Have you brought his documents?" asked the lieutenant.

"Yes, sir," said Hieronim. "I took his German identification card."

"Good. We shall have to prepare a report for the Underground district authorities."

One more figure emerged from the bushes: it was Wons, the shovel thrown over his shoulder. "All done," he said.

"Sergeant Skrzetuski, have the men get ready for dinner!" The lieutenant turned around and walked toward his quarters. Hieronim rushed ahead of him and lighted his kerosene lamp. Lying on the table was a weather-beaten German identification card with bent edges, limp as a rag. The two greasy covers were stuck together and it was necessary to pry them apart with a fingernail. The lieutenant looked for a long while at the photograph inside. A broad face, thick nostrils, little eyes squinting as if in defense against the glare of a cruel and strange world. One might have imagined that the entire face had once been covered with long hair which age and wear had rubbed away in spots — on the temples, the forehead and the cheeks. These smooth places stood out amid tufts of hair.

" 'Alojzy Szynalik,' " read the lieutenant aloud. " 'Occupation — none. Born in Gidle, in the year 1878.' Not as old as I thought," he said. "Only sixty-six . . . but he looked . . ."

"Eh, just like any old bum," put in Hieronim. "An old filthy bum, sir, that's all; a typical tramp."

The lieutenant sat down, still holding the identification card under the lamplight. He looked at it intently, as if the few official words concealed some fascinating story.

"I've seen all kinds," continued the sergeant, "but you know, sir, if I'd been told about him, I wouldn't have believed it." He shook his head. "Already standing over his grave. Death just about grabbing him. And he gets stingy about a dirty piece of money, damn him. A human being, a man. . . ."

The lieutenant stirred, turned around impatiently, looked at Hieronim for a moment through narrowed eyes, with distaste.

"Yes," he said shortly. He got up, hands in his pockets, and began walking back and forth on the shaky boards. The water under the floor gurgled in rhythm with his steps.

"Open the typewriter," he said. "Perhaps we have time before dinner to write a report about that wretched creature . . . that tramp . . ."

He stopped walking and, while Hieronim was removing the typewriter cover, pondered a moment on something, head lowered.

"It was wrong," he said suddenly. "It was wrong — that business with Zbirek. I shouldn't have let Zbirek do it."

Hieronim's fingers were already poised over the typewriter keys. He smiled. "It was all right, Lieutenant. Otherwise he would've made our lives miserable for weeks. I know his sort."

"Please write! Headquarters of the 'Acacia Unit,' November 18, 1944. To the Commander of the Forest Battalion, to be transmitted to the divisional commander: Today we have executed a beggar, Alojzy Szynalik, born in Gidle in 1878, as a dangerous informer for the Germans. The proof of his guilt . . ."

The typewriter clacked rapidly with a metallic sound, and the roller banged at even intervals. "The proof of his guilt . . ." repeated Hieronim.

"Yes. The proof of his guilt . . ."

They heard a gay whistle at the entrance. Zbirek walked in. "Your plates, gentlemen. I'll bring you dinner, to show the kindness of my heart."

Hieronim gave the lieutenant a meaningful wink.

"Corporal Zbirek" — the lieutenant touched the young man's arm with his fingertips — "tomorrow you will report back to the home base."

Zbirek's eyes fluttered in surprise. "Eh, Lieutenant, I don't need a rest. . . ."

"You don't think so?" The lieutenant walked away one step and gazed distractedly through the window into the blackness outside. "You'll report to the home base," he repeated in a colorless tone.

— *translated by* BARBARA VEDDER

(From *Buty*. Published by "Wydawnictwo Literackie," Krakow, 1956.)

Conrad in the Ghetto

BY JERZY ZAWIEYSKI

JERZY ZAWIEYSKI was born in 1902. He is best known as a playwright and in his dramatic work often used classical and Biblical symbolism in treating contemporary events. Zawieyski is also the author of novels, short stories, essays and prose poems. He is interested in problems of education, family life and child psychology. In 1957 he became deputy to Parliament (Sejm), representing the Catholic group Znak, and is also a member of the State Council. His major plays are *The Comeback of Przelecki* (1937); *The High Wall* (1956); *Crossroads of Love* (1957); *Reprieve of Jacob; The Perfect Husband;* and *Socrates*. The more important novels are *Where Are You, Friend?* (1930); *The Way Back Home* (1942); *Hubert's Night* (1946). His *Collected Plays* were published in 1957. He lives in Warsaw.

I WENT UNWILLINGLY to open the door; I felt sure that it was a mistake, as often happens here, and that it would again be someone asking for my neighbor, Mr. Konieczny, who is never at home. When the bell rang again, I opened the door hastily, pen in hand, mentally concluding the second part of the sentence which I had begun.

It was dark in the passage (it was an afternoon in autumn). I put on the lamp in the hall and by its light saw an elegantly dressed woman, still young, waiting with a flirtatious smile on her face for me to greet her.

"Don't you recognize me?"

"No. Please refresh my memory."

"I'm Dora Rosenblum. Henry's wife."

That's how it began, just as it used to in the stories of olden days — "One fine day in autumn . . ."

I had not seen Dora for almost twenty years, not since the days when I used to visit her and her husband (the poet Henry P., now deceased) in the Warsaw ghetto. So how could I have recognized her immediately? It was only when she mentioned her second husband's surname — and her late husband's first name — that it all came back to me.

No sooner had Dora come in than she burst into a flood of complaints. First of all, she said that she had been looking for me for a long time and only by chance had discovered my purposely concealed address. Then, when she had finally tracked me down, it turned out that she was told that I had gone away, which, according to her, was untrue. She complained, too, about the city. Complained? No. She cursed those who had so designed the reconstruction of the city: nothing was in its place, whole districts were new, and you got lost at every turn because the streets had changed their direction.

"So how can one say that it is the same city? Why has it the same name? It's a lie!" she said, flying into a rage. "Invent whatever you like, but don't parody the old city! Where has it gone? Where?"

It was a long, slow business before her anger subsided and she came to the real purpose of her visit. Dora had come from Tel Aviv to find Henry's grave, and to see to the publication of his poetry. But she had not discovered his grave, and in the matter of having his poetry published, she had also encountered difficulties. On the site of his grave, in the courtyard of a house in the former ghetto, there stood now a block of flats containing thirty-eight apartments.

"Thirty-eight!" she exclaimed excitedly. "What is this — America? How do people here find the way to their flats?"

As she had not succeeded in finding Henry's grave, she no longer wished to wait for a decision about the publication of his poetry, which was not properly appreciated by the publishers here.

She spent the whole evening with me. From the years of our youth she slowly came back to me as she sat opposite me talking about her life in Tel Aviv, about her husband, whom I knew of old, and about her children, now growing up. She and her husband were running a small textile factory, as they had formerly done here. They were doing quite well.

"But what of that?" Dora threw out her arms in a gesture of despair.

I did not understand. Was she referring to the grave which she had failed to find? To Henry?

During this conversation it was not Dora I was thinking about. It was Henry — and, because of him, I was thinking of Daniel.

"Daniel, Dan, Danny." In my thoughts I repeated the name of the six-year-old boy who had died in the ghetto and for whose death Henry was no less to blame than I, but my guilt was the greater. Perhaps, indeed, I am completely weighed down with it. For had it not been for those letters, those ridiculous, idiotic letters!

And this is the story — a story that gives me no peace — which came to life with the arrival of Dora Rosenblum.

Daniel appeared on the scene in the final stage of my friendship with Henry, when it was at its climax, as it were, a few weeks before his death.

I got to know Henry quite by chance, in the army, during our training. Fate ordained that we should occupy bunks in the same barracks. Only Henry had the top bunk and I the one below. I had already read his poems in the literary magazines; consequently, when I heard the familiar name, I eagerly held out my hand to the poet.

Afterwards — many years later — we would often, when we talked, go back to our time in the army, which seemed much more interesting in retrospect than it had been in reality. Our chief recollection was of how we both used to go about exhausted all the time and half-asleep, and how we made use of every free period to have a nap — no matter where, no matter how. Henry, for example, could sleep, or rather doze, even during roll calls, when anything could happen. Once, in a moment of regained consciousness, after taking a nap while at ease during a drill period, Henry, as though pronouncing a metaphysical truth, declared that everything is Sleep and Yawns, "and a monstrous Kip," he added after a moment's thought.

Such then were the impressions which we took away with us from our army service, a trifle ghostlike, a trifle nightmarish, but not so much so that we could not still, years later, discuss them feelingly. The one and only occasion when Henry roused up was when he heard our corporal bawling at the soldiers. This corporal came from Silesia, and his father had played the trombone in a circus. He had at his command an NCO's vocabulary of the highest order. It was not, however, the individual words that set the stamp of originality on his speech: it was the combinations of words, the unexpected, amazing magnificent juxtapositions. The man's speech aroused in Henry, the poet, disingenuous admiration. He exaggerated, of course; but then exaggeration, of good and ill alike, was a trait of his personality.

Henry, then, loved Corporal Przyciasny's extra-subtle turn of phrase, while I, for my part, loved the ceremonial marches to the city. Not a bad city — Torun. Copernicus's old city. From the barracks you went by a circuitous route over the bridge on the Vistula before you got to the marketplace. That was where parades and inspections were held. The band used to march before us, while the section was under the immediate eye of its squat, swarthy corporal.

"He *is* the army!" I would say in admiration as I studied him on our marches, during training exercises or even in the barracks.

But it was later on, after we had left the army, that Henry and I went over all this, when I went to see him at his home.

Henry's home!

His mother had died when he was born: that he might live, his mother had to die. This was the bitter comment which Henry's father used to make. Henry's father was a short, thickset, gray-haired man. He had been for many years a confidential clerk in the Commercial Bank. Nowadays not many know the meaning of this title, but in those days, in that far-off world before the Second World War, the post of confidential clerk was quite an important one. Old Mr. P. had his own favorite pursuits, which had nothing to do with the bank or banking. He liked philosophy, and of all the philosophers he was keenest on Friedrich Nietzsche.

It may be that he did not read Nietzsche carefully and failed to perceive in his philosophy all the somber, suspicious aspects which were aimed at his race and thereby directly at him. Henry, too, was fond of Nietzsche. Did he, too, not read him carefully? But who at that time was aware that a criminal police-state system might derive support from a few sentences torn from their context, from a few fragmentary theses? On Henry's desk stood a bust of Nietzsche, which, for my sins, I had once taken for a bust of Pilsudski. Henry for a long time teased me about this mistake, while old Mr. P. never again spoke with me about serious matters. The remaining member of this "Nietzschean" household was Miss Roza, Henry's aunt. She took the place of a mother to him and brought him up from infancy.

My recollection of Henry's home is made up of the sadness and loneliness of two old people, together with an atmosphere of refined intellectual pleasures. If I called on him before midday, I always found him in bed surrounded by books. His health was poor, and he had to spend much time in bed, always anxious lest his temperature might go up. His illnesses were invented by Aunt Roza; she treated, with remedies of her own contriving, not only Henry and old Mr. P., but also acquaintances near and far. Despite her special and, one might call it, hermetic medical knowledge and superior intuition, Miss Roza died suddenly of aneurysm of the heart, as it used to be called. By that time, Henry had completed his law studies and was just finishing his bar practice in preparation for entry into the legal profession. One year after Miss Roza, Henry's father died, in consequence of what had seemed a trifling complaint. A spot had formed on his tongue. Mr. P. ignored it. Meanwhile it turned out that the spot was a cancer.

Thus Henry was left alone in the world. I lost touch with him for several years, and when I again located him, Dora was already on the scene.

Henry had moved and was living in a five-room flat on one of the main streets. He was a practicing lawyer, but it was obvious that he had not abandoned poetry. In his study, which was furnished with easy chairs and settees, as befitted a lawyer dealing with important cases, there stood a row of bookcases filled with works entirely unrelated to his profession. On a high pedestal the bust of Nietzsche stood in the middle of a wall, between the bookcases. Henry was lost amid the cumbersome, ugly furniture — the atmosphere of solid affluence which Dora had created. How had the marriage come about? Probably through Henry's poetry, for Dora had long been among the admirers of his gift. She had come to him once with a slim volume of poems, asking if she might dedicate them to him. She found him in a deep depression, sick and unable to cope with life. She made up her mind that she was needed. And so she stayed. She had recently inherited a textile factory and a large sum of money. She was an enterprising and courageous woman and managed the factory herself, and this probably influenced Henry's decision to entrust himself to her care. He did not need to worry now about his legal practice; he could occupy himself with writing and his intellectual life. Nietzsche continued to be his favored thinker, while among writers his only rival was Conrad.

Conrad! It was thanks to him, among others, that little Daniel met his death. For if Henry had not reread Conrad there, in the ghetto, would Daniel have come to knock on my door? But I do not wish to anticipate events before concluding the story of Henry.

What, then, do I know about Henry? In truth, so little that despite the bond of friendship which united us, perhaps I ought not to write about him. But he will lead me to Daniel and that is why I want to divulge that fragment of truth about him, as known to me, which will justify events still to be told.

It must be remembered that Henry was a poet and that, because of this, perhaps, he failed to come to grips with the world and did not understand other people's affairs. Sometimes I managed to watch him unobserved, during periods when he was engaged in writing. He reminded me of an unleashed spaniel, vigilantly and eagerly following the scent of game. If he happened to be out of doors, he would stop and note down the word which he hunted; if indoors at home, it would seem to me that he was ill, in a fever, or else that he had not yet awakened after sleep. He derived his literary pabulum from every quarter. From every quarter? No, only from dreams, from his own visions, or from the mystery which resides in recording the world in the first person.

This tendency to see nothing outside oneself and to be incapable of understanding people, necessary no doubt for writing poetry, was gradually becoming a facet of his nature, an inhuman facet, I make so bold as to call it. Henry passed people by and failed to comprehend the world, although he was neither bitter against it nor in revolt. Is it any wonder that he failed to understand the history of his own times, or, to be exact, regarded the world as unworthy of notice?

Let us not hold that against him. He was like other poets of his time.

Let us remember only that it was poetry that gave his life its purpose; thus we will better understand his behavior in the period of the war and the ghetto. During the time which I am now describing, Daniel was not yet in the world, and I am writing about Henry in order to come to Daniel. Thus, although Daniel did not yet exist, events had begun which were later to destroy the little boy — events which can be expressed by the names Nietzsche and Conrad. It might seem that these are symbols, existing only in the realm of literary tastes.

So it might seem. Yet Nietzsche provided the inspiration for a system which built — if it built anything at all — the crematoriums in the concentration camps. And Conrad? Little Daniel knew nothing of either Nietzsche or Conrad.

Conrad then. Besides Nietzsche, Henry read Conrad with pleasure and delight. And, probably, reading him, he did not interpret his meaning aright, since later . . . But there is time enough for this "later," and, by Heaven, there is no call for haste.

In order to raise her social standing in the circle of small-scale manufacturers, Dora used to put on frequent and sumptuous receptions. To these I would sometimes be invited. Henry, of course, was the chief and sole attraction at these occasions. It was touching to see the adoration accorded the poet by people occupied solely with swelling their bank accounts, solely with that unclean, if not positively dirty, business. If he so much as deigned to speak, silence and rapt attention ensued. The program at Dora's receptions was always the same: as soon as everyone was assembled in the ugly green drawing room, Henry would read his latest poems aloud. And Henry, as I observed, enjoyed the most lavish flatteries paid him, even — oh horrors! — the comparison of his poetry with that of Goethe! Why with Goethe's it was impossible to discover. (Nor did Henry know why this company should have thought of Goethe.)

After a few glasses of vodka had been downed, in the interval between courses, Henry would give a second piece. This was by way of being an act of rebellion against Dora's friends, so he explained it to me. But nobody took it in this way — on the contrary. His second reading was considered a splendid joke. Henry, slightly tight, would bang on his plate, take a slip of paper out of his pocket, and read out neither more nor less (only skillfully arranged in sequence) than a catalogue of the barracks phrases used by our corporal. "There's poetry for you! There's real poetry!" He would shout this in ecstasy, amid general laughter and the plaudits of the assembled company.

But how else could Dora's guests react to the corporal's "poetry"? And could they realize that Henry was expressing his rebellion? I always had the impression that, contrary to his intention, he sustained a painful defeat by reciting from the corporal. Possibly Henry sensed this too, since more often than not, he would vanish immediately from the dining room and shut himself up in his own room, on the pretext of having a headache. Dora's friends continued to amuse themselves, probably feeling relief at being freed from the burden of this fantastical poet, the supposed new Goethe.

Of the guests only one abstained from applauding Henry when he recited the corporal's poetry. This was Samuel Rosenblum, who had recently become a partner in Dora's firm. Did he perhaps understand the significance of the recital? Or did he think that Henry had exceeded the bounds of decency?

When I asked him why he was not amused by what Henry read at the table, he replied simply, "It bores me."

Mr. Rosenblum was always silent and preoccupied, his brows knitted on his low forehead. But one time I heard the sort of confidences which he addressed to Henry's wife. It was at the end of one of these showy parties, already getting on toward morning. I was sitting in an easy chair, listening to a technical discourse from the director of a chemical factory, when there reached me the words which poor (as he struck me) — poor, tormented Mr. Rosenblum was uttering.

"They're all rotten to the core. Rotten, did I say? In plain terms, it's like a lot of swine wallowing in the mire. I'm not talking about that filth that Henry read out. All around. Look at that Mrs. Goldberg and that Zimmer of hers, Dora! Perhaps I'm supposed just to look at you and be content, Dora, while they can do what they like? I shan't be stealing you from him — he hasn't got you as it is. Tomorrow — tomorrow week perhaps — we'll make a business trip to Vienna. We must! No? Why not? Do let's go! Dora, Dora . . ."

Henry's relations with Dora's partner were on a correct footing and, knowing Henry, I can risk the assertion that it never occurred to him that Mr. Rosenblum might be Dora's lover. It was not until they were all three together in the ghetto that Henry's eyes were opened.

Again I lost track of him for a while, and the occasion of our being reunited was associated with Conrad. It was in a well-known café patronized by writers. Henry had matured; he had put on weight and become bald, but, although he had aged, he had lost none of the charm of his poetic nature, somehow so childlike and impulsive. He was just telling me excitedly how he was working on a film script, when suddenly in the middle of a word he stopped, seized me by the arm, and, looking in the direction of a man who was coming into the room, whispered:

"Conrad!"

And so it was. Just as if a well-known photograph of Conrad had come to life — wearing a black overcoat, with a hat, and carrying a stick. The supposed Conrad walked slowly, with dignity, as befitted one of his small stature. We thought that we could see the Malay isles, or that any moment the unhappy Lord Jim would appear, or Heyst perhaps, or Lingard.

"Conrad" looked around the room for a minute, then sat down near us, where there was a table free. We watched him in silence, our hearts standing still. But then up came rushing a stoutish individual and shouted to him from across the room:

"Mr. W., will you go at once to the warehouse. A fresh load has arrived from Lodz."

Our reverie was cut short. It was a sad moment.

I began to see a lot of Henry again. Not at his home, in the study with the easy chairs, but more often than not in that same well-known café. This was now the period when Nietzsche, brought out into the light of day by the new politicians, uttered a threat only later to be recognized.

During that time I had been in Nietzsche's native land. I returned from it with the feeling that I had been on a journey to hell. Henry listened unenthusiastically to my impressions; some of the things which I had seen there he took jokingly as manifesting stupidity not unmixed with a certain piquancy. I think now that Henry, who had failed to comprehend Nietzsche and Conrad, failed still more dismally to comprehend his own time. But did others comprehend it any better? I too succumbed to the collective unconcern, although the recollection of what I had seen in Nietzsche's native land oppressed me like an incubus's importunities. To all outward appearances things could not have been better. There were visits by ministers and marshals and diplomats, and there were diplomatic hunting parties, at which toasts of friendship were exchanged.

"Look! Our president, Moscicki, and that fat German slob Field Marshal Goering." Henry would wave the paper in front of my face. "Do you see? This means something, doesn't it?"

"My dear fellow, let's talk about serious matters. There's a new book by Lesmian out. Have you seen it?"

It was at about this time that Daniel was born. Yes. He was already alive and kicking, growing up to meet his fate. His place in the world was a mean and humble one, in a shed in a yard, in one of those suburban holes which it is a pitiful irony to call a town. One Sunday toward the end of the last years, or months perhaps, of that era in which the world was walking upon a precipice, not seeing it or wishing to see it, it was possible to read in the papers that in the land of Nietzsche Jews had been forbidden to enter public places, such as theaters, cinemas and concert halls. A decree was also issued which obliged Jews to wear the Star of David on their arm.

I was sure that anyone reading this must feel shame that anywhere in the world such a thing could be thinkable, above all in Europe! And that this was being done by the compatriots of Goethe! Of Thomas Mann! Of Bach! I hurried to town, thinking, of course, about Henry and imagining his dismay.

The café was packed, and I managed with difficulty to get to Henry's table. On all sides I heard the laughter of lively, cheerful people. Henry, like the rest, was enjoying himself hugely, Dora was laughing her high-pitched laugh, and even Mr. Rosenblum had succumbed to the general atmosphere of gaiety.

I showed Henry the paper.

"Rubbish! Nonsense!" he cried, with a loud guffaw.

I went out of the café quickly; then I ran through the streets, as if I were running away. For I was running away. I was running away.

Carnival time came around; again there were repeated visits by ministers, again toasts and speeches. And certain speeches, of course, were taken seriously by nobody.

In his yard, beside the gutter, Daniel was growing. He was four, then five, then six. Then came what had to come.

A few weeks after the outbreak of war, one cold, rainy day, following my return from travels in the East, I saw Henry in the distance down the street. On his left sleeve was an arm band with the Star of David.

I visited Henry in the ghetto a few days after our encounter in the street. The heat of the fires in the city had not yet died. Streetlamps, bowed toward the ground, still swayed in the breeze. The rubble had not yet been cleared. Those who had stayed on in the first days of the war, those who had not marched off to the East, remembered with horror the siege of the city, especially a certain Monday, a few hours before the capitulation, when it seemed that the sky had been transformed into a hell, as fire and iron rained down from the silvery airplanes overhead. In the rare intervals of quiet the Lord Mayor's voice could be heard — a hoarse, rasping voice which appealed for calm, offered counsel, but above all gave an assurance that someone was keeping watch and that someone existed. That someone existed, just that. From time to time the radio emitted a tragic tune, the same that the French sent the city in the time of the 1831 November Uprising — the "Warszawianka." * The song wreathed itself about the deserted, empty, dead-looking city, calling now only to the paving stones, to the ruins, to go and fight at bayonet point. Fight whom? A fiery abyss?

Now, after the disaster, an amazed human silence filled the streets. It was the end of November, frosty already and presaging an early, hard winter. Henry was living in the heart of the Jewish quarter in a gloomy house, the stone courtyard of which was filled with lofty outbuildings. When I knocked on the door on the third floor, he drew me into a dark passage, cluttered with cupboards, then led me through another, somewhat lighter passage to his apartment. In the first large room, I came upon Dora and Samuel, who were sitting at a table playing patience. We greeted one another more effusively than usual, like people who have survived a common disaster. A second room, which was small and narrow, was occupied by Henry. I noticed at once a great change in him. He was slimmer and seemed younger. The arm band with the Star of David hung on the door handle. I looked around the room: a bed, a small table, chairs, and around the walls large cupboards, on top of which there were boxes reaching up to the ceiling. There was little room to move, and the room was dirty.

* "The Warsaw Song."

From time to time we punctuated our labored silence with exchanges of information about everyday matters. After a while Dora brought in tea, a strong, fresh brew, made from a supply laid in long before. Contrary to her wont, she did not try to disturb us but retired quickly to her own room.

"They live in there; I live in here," said Henry, with a bitter smile.

I had not raised the subject, in order to avoid giving away what I had known all about long before. Henry's fate since the war began had been quite simple: the house in which he lived had been bombed, so he and Dora had gone straight from the shelter to relatives of Samuel's. And so they had come to stay here as a threesome, not knowing what would happen next.

I expressed the generally accepted conviction that it would last only till spring. Henry smiled and shook his head in disagreement.

"The war will last for years," he said.

I made light of this, as if it were a specimen of the perversity which is understandable in high-strung people.

So we sat in silence till dusk, which fell early. Henry lit a candle, since there was no electric light now in that quarter, and at my request he read his latest poem aloud. It was a poem about his father. At the end Henry said that the spot on old Mr. P.'s tongue had come at the right time. That, I think, was the only allusion to the times through which we had been living.

At that period one often saw people with arm bands doing manual labor or being conveyed — or, rather, unceremoniously driven — to work. So Henry seldom went out of the house. What did he do? What did he think about? His poem about old Mr. P. suggested to me that Henry was now at last coming to terms with the past. Probably he had been roused from his dreams with a greater sense of alienation than others, with a greater sense of dread. At that time everyone was busy looking for scapegoats, raking through recent history. Whom did Henry blame? Did he remember that day when I brought him the news about the Star of David? When I visited him in his crowded, dark, dirty room I had no wish to go back to the past. The subjects of our conversation were political news and news from the front, and banalities. Politics consisted of the frequent lengthy speeches churned out by those conducting the war. The news from the front irritated us more, because there was no sign of any offensive getting under way. We lived in daily expectation of this. Happenings in the city and the country were the only reality. The prisons were permanently filled, and the camps, prepared beforehand in the land of Nietzsche, were engulfing great numbers of innocent people. The whole country had impressed upon it the existence of the camp at Oranienburg, to which forty professors from the Krakow Jagellonian University had been sent. A still greater impression was made by the news that these men, while on muster parade in the frosty weather waiting for they knew not what, would exchange talk about their latest scholarly researches. Thus hope came to the whole country, and a model of unshakable resolve was established: notions abandoned in the days of unconcern and license returned. The appeals of poets, humanists and preachers for man to rise above his limited humanity again became alive. Henry acknowledged that a moral rebirth of mankind was being achieved, although unhappily through a bloody harvest of misfortune.

Even then, when our misfortunes had scarcely begun, we devised various systems of consolation, having no inkling of the gradual pressure exerted by evil. So also today, years later, we do not know if the measure of evil has been fulfilled without residue. From that bloody seed time has there come forth that of which Henry and I used to talk? Today there exists no longer either the quarter where Henry lived or the narrow, crowded room in which we comforted each other with visions of the future. Today bright, spacious new blocks of dwellings, erected by the faith and hope of those who came through, rise up on the very spot where he once lived; but would it be going too far to express a fear that misfortune is still lying in wait to descend on us, this time without any hope for the future? And, by Heaven, have we learned any more than that evil is infinite and that it exists not beyond but within the human kind? Henry happily was spared confirmation of the full extent of mankind's capabilities. His death, like old Mr. P.'s spot, came just in time.

Meanwhile, on the threshold of a new epoch, we both lived on illusions, believing, for example, in the power of the type of culture expressed by the professors imprisoned in Oranienburg. But could there be any other symbol for us? If the authority of statesmen had been overthrown, if military heroism had yielded, if on the streets of our capital only a tragic foreign song about our way of dying remained — what other choice had we?

After a while Henry began to occupy himself with translating Rilke; he had always liked and admired the poet, and he had known German well since childhood.

We were seeing less of each other now that life provided us both with so many day-to-day cares. I was incomparably worse off materially than he, and I had difficulty in getting through the first terrible winter of the war. I availed myself of an invitation from friends, and I was to go away to the country from mid-December until the end of March. Henry regarded this as a fortunate solution of my problem.

I went away. I returned, however, not in March but in October.

A few days afterwards I went to visit Henry. Alas! It was too late. The ghetto was now walled off and surrounded by barbed wire. I could not get through to him. But he reached me — through Daniel.

A trifling thing happened: I lost my food ration cards. I searched for them at home, in the street, in the shop; I searched the staircase; I ransacked the papers on my desk. I went outside several times, in case someone had found them and might be looking for me. I had just come home after a vain search, when by the door, in the dark passage, something moved. In the corner a child was sitting, a little boy, staring at me.

"What are you doing here?" I asked in amazement.

The child pulled out a battered envelope, on which I made out my name. I took him by the hand and led him into my apartment. I was in a bad mood, and, with the letter in my hand, I continued to search for the lost food cards. When finally I gave up and came back to the room, the little boy, slumped against the stove, seemed to be asleep. But he woke up at once. He had a bold, inquiring look.

The first sentences of Henry's letter informed me that the boy was from the ghetto, that his name was Daniel, and that from now on he would act as courier between us. For, wrote Henry, only a nimble and crafty six-year-old shrimp such as he could get past the wire and through a hole in the walls without attracting the notice of the guards.

It was a long letter. I deferred reading it until later, intrigued by this singular courier.

"Your name's Daniel, then?"

The little boy nodded.

"And what do they call you at home?"

"Where?"

"At home," I repeated.

"I haven't got a home," replied Daniel, looking me in the eye.

I noticed that his voice sounded harsh, as if he were hoarse.

"What about your mummy and daddy?"

Daniel hung his head and fingered a hole in his stocking. Feeling that I must have hurt him with my questions, to make up for it, I started telling him about a certain Wladek, with whom I used to go fishing.

But Daniel displayed no interest in my story. I suggested, therefore, that we should have something to eat, and I began making tea. After a while Daniel followed me into the kitchen. Again I talked to him, as if to a grownup, about my stay in the country and about the children whom I had met there. This time he listened.

Tea was now ready and the bread cut, and there was also some gingerbread. Daniel, to my astonishment, asked of his own accord where he could wash his hands. He returned presently with hands clean and face washed. He was grinning contentedly. Now at last I had a good look at him for the first time. He had large black eyes with an expression of touching seriousness. His hair, long uncut, fell about his head in curls and ringlets. His most surprising feature was his voice, which contrasted with his childish good looks. I remember how difficult it was that first day to start up a friendship between us. Only when we were in the kitchen did he begin to talk about himself. I learned that he had three elder sisters, Leah, Sarah and Manya, and that his father had been killed by the Germans because he would not leave his workshop in a small place near Warsaw and go to the ghetto. It happened before the eyes of the entire family. His mother went to work somewhere different every day and only came back now and then, once or twice a week, to the apartment of a washerwoman, who lived in the basement of the house where Henry lived. His sisters were also working, but where, Daniel did not know. He himself stayed here, there and everywhere, but most often with Mr. Samuel Rosenblum's relatives.

Daniel talked about all these matters with quiet dignity, not at all like a six-year-old child. When we went back to the room, he announced that he had to go now.

"What about the letter?" I said, pointing at the reams of paper from Henry lying spread out. "I must read it and send a reply."

"I'll come tomorrow at midday. I have to go somewhere else now," he said.

He was going two streets farther, as it turned out, to run another errand. But he would not say to whom he was going or what he had to deliver there. He had nothing on him. He added that he would stay the night at the place he was going to. When I bent down to kiss Daniel good-bye, I could feel papers rustling beneath my fingers down his back. He had them under his pullover and jacket.

"Aren't you afraid of the Germans?" I asked seriously.

"I can always give them the slip!" Daniel boasted. "I've given them the slip once already. I hollered and made off."

We parted until the next day.

After Daniel had left I continued to watch him out of the window; I saw him quickly running past pedestrians. I wanted to start reading Henry's letter, but I kept thinking about this unusual courier from the ghetto, who, with illegal papers concealed down his back, was running through the streets to meet someone and execute the commission entrusted to him.

I took up Henry's letter. I read it. I read, not believing what I was reading. I reread this letter of Henry's written from behind the walls. It was an impassioned, though distant, letter, and in it I found something of the attitude of the Oranienburg academicians, something of the perversity of the poet defending the honor of a humanist down in the ghetto. The letter was about Conrad.

Henry was rereading his favorite writer and this time, according to him, reading him properly, apparently for the first time. Behind the walls, cut off from the world, he understood better the meaning of Lord Jim's Patusan — Patusan, the ghetto of loneliness. The whole letter was the result of his reading.

He and Lord Jim were united by similarity of experience, although Henry, as he admitted, had not run away from any *Patna* in order to save himself. But at the same time he posed the dramatic question: had he not run away? Had not both he and others? Had we not deserted the ship when the storm drew nigh?

Henry directed these questions not only at himself but also at me, making me, too, responsible for our ship.

He devoted a large portion of his letter to the great dialogue, as he called it, between the criminal Brown and Lord Jim. Henry asserted, like Marlow, that this dialogue was one of the cruelest duels that had ever been fought on earth. The dialogue was watched by Fate, cold and indifferent, for only it knew how the struggle would end.

He reported that during one of the numerous checkups he had had a conversation at his place with a Gestapo officer, an educated Bavarian, who was an admirer of Rilke. It was precisely the dialogue described many years earlier by Conrad, which that great writer, unaware of what might happen on earth in time to come, had placed in a tropical land with the attractive name of Patusan. In his letter Henry continually stressed the analogy, saying "here in Patusan" or "in our Patusan." He promised to write about his talks with the Gestapo man in his next letter.

What did Henry want? Seemingly — so I understood his letters then — he wanted to perish, holding converse with the criminal Brown, to die with honor and a clear consciousness of his own death, since he saw no deliverance after death.

It was just this that aroused my opposition. How could Henry want this? Terror was spreading ever wider; executions were being carried out in the streets, and camps were being set up, not somewhere in the land of Nietzsche, but here, in our own country. People were being picked up everywhere, from their homes, in trams, in cafés. The ghetto, Henry's Patusan, was walled up, and only someone like little Daniel could get through a hole to the city. We were all living on the thirst for revenge. We impatiently awaited an offensive in the West. We knew that the ghetto's walls of shame would crack.

It was from these realistic premises that my letter to Henry stemmed. It began with the words: "Ruler of Patusan, dear Lord Jim!" I wrote this partly in irony because of his absorption with Patusan, and partly in acknowledgment of his inventive interpretation of Conrad; but I also described quite forcefully the reality in which we outside the walls were living. I defined the attitude common now to many in these words:

"The one really worthy answer to the barbarians is a gun in one's hand!"

Again at the end I banged out the word "gun"; then I put this anti-Conradian letter into the envelope which I was to hand to Daniel the next day.

But Daniel did not come at midday, as he had promised. He did not come until nightfall was far advanced. He was different, gayer than the previous day, relaxed and talkative. But, despite this, he would not say why he was late or where he had been or what he had been doing. He ran all around the apartment, then washed his hands and face in the bathroom, delighted to be able to do so. He would not eat anything, however, as he was in a great hurry to get to Henry before the curfew hour.

I put my letter into the inner pocket of Daniel's jacket and again down his back I could feel a packet containing papers.

I, too, began to read Conrad, following the same lines as Henry in his Patusan. But I read him differently, with resistance, polemically. More than once — why I cannot now understand — I threw the book from me almost with hatred. But I went back to it again when my antagonism had died down. At that time, in 1940, nobody was reading Conrad; probably nobody in our wounded city thought of reading him over again. Was it otherwise behind the walls? Was Henry alone in his passion for penetrating to the nerve of history?

In Henry's courtyard (this is connected with Daniel) not a blade of grass would grow. Only later — oh God, that courtyard! — but let us not anticipate events. We are waiting then for Daniel, and whatever we say about the poet concerns also this child. Especially that barren stone courtyard as severe and harsh to the eye as only prison courtyards are.

Daniel came a few days later, just before the curfew. He did not knock, did not ring, but scratched on the door.

"Well, here I am!" he said as he came in.

This time he was distracted and restless. He had to touch every single thing on my desk and on the shelves and look it over, asking all the while, "What's this? What's this for?" Then he did not listen to my explanations and at first would not answer when I asked him something. Later, when he finally sat down in an arm chair, I could see that he was bored as I told him about a journey I had made to Africa some years ago. Perhaps it was too difficult, because he showed no interest either in the monkeys which had removed my helmet and scampered off up a palm tree or in the Negroes whom I had visited in their village and who might have eaten me.

Suddenly Daniel interrupted my story and said, "And I've been in Pyry. There the cabbages grow as big as . . . oh, as big as that table."

I seized upon this visit to Pyry, but Daniel changed the subject to practical matters. "I'd like some cabbage," he announced. "Is there any?"

Fortunately there was cabbage. There were also various delicacies which I had saved for him.

In the kitchen Daniel felt more comfortable than in the other room, where apart from the books, desk and settee there was nothing of interest to a child. Here, however, the sideboard and its contents sent him into raptures. I let him do whatever he liked, because his very presence gave me pleasure. Was this because it was Daniel in particular, or because there was a child around me? Perhaps both. Probably even then I loved my little courier. That evening I became conscious of the fact that I could take him to myself and thus save him from an evil fate. For what might be in store for him down there outside the walls? Lately news had been going around that the Germans were removing people from the ghetto to the camps. They might take Daniel too. They might catch him carrying some secret literature, or they might intercept my letter to Henry, or one from him to me. I knew inevitably that Daniel faced death, since these criminal "Browns" did not spare even children.

I resolved to save Daniel.

"Do you like it here?"

He shrugged his shoulders and after a while said yes, he did.

"Perhaps you'd like to stay?"

"For good?"

"Yes, for good."

"No! I don't want to!" cried Daniel, stamping his feet. Then he burst into tears. For a long time I tried to calm him, and of course I withdrew my proposal. He sat down under the stove, with his back turned to me, and sobbed quietly. He refused to undress for bed and would not lie on the sofa, preferring to sleep where he was, under the stove. I spread rugs on the floor, brought cushions, then went back to my work at the desk. Presently he wriggled under the blankets fully clothed, except for his little shoes, which he placed beside him.

I did not give up, however. I decided to ask Henry for help.

I began reading the letter which Daniel had brought.

Once more it was about Conrad. But this time Henry described his conversations with the Gestapo man; he had taken a fancy to Henry and visited him, invariably drunk, at various times of night and day, but more often than not in the night or at daybreak. The Gestapo man was called Rudolf Stein, but Henry saw in him the criminal Brown, coming to destroy Jim — that is, himself, Henry P., in Patusan, the land of loneliness. So at unexpected hours, their interviews continued — a savage duel between Henry and Stein, Lord Jim and Brown, perhaps even between Faust and Mephistopheles. Henry wrote that his life now consisted of waiting for his Brown, a waiting equivalent to waiting for death. On the table, at which their great dialogues took place, there was always vodka and beer, and a gun.

A gun! The word which I had used carelessly had come back in Henry's letter.

So, with vodka and a gun in front of him, Stein told Henry all about the great crimes committed by Jews in history. He told him that he, Henry P., the poet who translated Rilke, had poisoned men's souls with his poetry. He was guilty of a crime — deeply serious because it was a spiritual crime and infinite in its consequences. Stein hoped his pupil understood this and the duty Providence had laid upon Nietzsche's noble people to exterminate a race so criminal and perfidious. Stein, who loved Rilke, who loved poets in general, who loved music and everything of the spirit, everything beautiful — Stein, a worshiper of Bach, was obliged to be here, in this Philistine, louse-ridden, half-savage country and had to be here in the ghetto to carry on apostolic conversations (were they not apostolic?) with a poet-criminal!

More than once Stein burst into tears over his lot, poured himself more vodka, and took up his gun, aiming it at Henry.

The worst of all, according to Henry, was Stein's lyrical-*cum*-emotional outbursts. He had a wife called Else and a daughter named Luise. Stein suspected Else of being unfaithful to him with Erik, who worked in the military administration. When Stein talked about this, he trembled with indignant rage; here he was having to talk to Henry, when at that very moment Erik was probably lying serene and happy in the embrace of his Else. What had the poet to say to that? Could he give him any advice? Henry tried to assure Stein that it was inconceivable that Else could prefer anyone else to such a splendid officer and subtle connoisseur of the arts as he, Stein. Stein genuinely seized upon this apparently, for he clapped Henry on the back, put away his gun, and took his leave.

Dora and Samuel Rosenblum, closeted in their relatives' overcrowded room, used to wait for Stein's departure, and then put Henry to bed, for after these visits he always looked as if he were on the point of death.

At the end of his letter he again touched on Lord Jim's sufferings and his sense of guilt, which seemed so much the greater since the *Patna* did not sink. But our *Patna*? Our *Patna*? he beseeched. I decided to write about this too. In my letter I wanted also to raise the separate question of Daniel.

I spent a long time writing to Henry. The quiet of the house and city contrasted with the horrors of the second year of war. Next morning about noon our little courier set out to take my letter to the ghetto. This time he carried no illicit literature; this I had discovered by making a thorough search the previous evening.

He was in a better mood. He had slept well and was washed and fed. I wanted to see him off when he left, but he objected. However, I accompanied him down the stairs to the gate, then watched for a long time, until the droll, enchanting little figure disappeared from view.

The house seemed empty after he had gone.

I cannot now reckon up the number of visits from Daniel; neither can I reproduce from memory all of Henry's letters. I do know that on occasion, Daniel dropped in for just a moment and that he did not always bring news from my friend. But this happened probably not more than three times, if that. Daniel would scratch on the door, then come in with his little triumphant cry, "Well, here I am!"

He would roam about the apartment for a while, always making a visit to the bathroom, then he would have something to eat and make a speedy departure, indifferent to my appeals to him to stay longer.

One of Henry's letters concerned only Daniel. It was a reply to my plea for the little boy to stay with me permanently, or with my relatives who lived nearby. Henry did not regard my proposal with enthusiasm. He said I should realize that we needed Daniel — "we" meaning he and I. The boy was irreplaceable as a means of communication with the outside world and indispensable to many others in the ghetto. Above all, however, Henry went on, this little shrimp was able to produce a soothing effect on him during the fits of depression which came after Stein's visits — the child knew when to come, what to say, how to behave; he knew how to chase away the ever-present specter of death.

"I sometimes think of him as my own son," Henry wrote.

His son! I guessed immediately that this was the real reason why he did not want me to take Daniel. Afterwards I often reproached myself for not being able to muster up the strength to carry out my resolve. But how could I deprive Henry of his one solace? The one solace of his nightmarish existence, taken up with waiting for visits from Stein.

So I let things stand. Daniel was becoming attached to me and probably enjoyed dropping in, just as the fancy took him, without warning, if only for a brief visit. I discovered, moreover, a mutual pastime which Daniel liked — drawing. Who could draw the best duck? Or airplane? Or soldier? Or tree? We both drew with enthusiasm and of course Daniel's drawings were always much better than mine. They really were better. They were bold, unusual and had a tendency for exaggeration which bordered on the grotesque. I genuinely admired his wit and shrewd observations. Daniel might have become a real artist, for his drawings expressed something more than the drawings of the ordinary child. I often wondered what Daniel would grow up to be, if he survived — if he survived.

Fear for his life never left me. At the same time I did nothing to guard him from danger. And danger threatened him continually, every day, every hour.

One day before my very eyes I witnessed what might have been the death of Daniel.

I was riding in a tram along the main street of our city when suddenly through a windowpane I saw a group of people watching two gendarmes, armed with rifles and grenades, escorting or, rather, leading by the arm a little boy who was weeping and shouting, stamping his feet, and crying for help. I recognized Daniel. The tram was packed, but despite that I managed to jump off fairly quickly while it was moving. When I succeeded in getting near the group of people, Daniel was no longer there. The gendarmes were proceeding down the street, looking solemn and haughty, doubtless somewhat ashamed that the victim of their rough treatment was so incongruous to the physical and armed might which they were flaunting. I did not need to ask what had become of Daniel, for everyone was remarking upon the little boy's courageous escape. Why and in what circumstances had the Germans taken him? Where had he escaped to? Nobody knew.

Although he had got away, I continued to worry about him. I resolved this time not to give in to Henry. I would keep Daniel with me the next time he came. Therefore, I began to think of the details of life needed for a child in a house not prepared for a child; I arranged for a teacher to come, so that the boy should have lessons, and I came to an agreement with my relatives by which we would jointly take care of him. And I waited daily for Daniel.

At last he came. He arrived at nightfall, just before curfew time, making his special scratching noise on the door. He walked in with his triumphant "Well, here I am!" bringing a long letter from Henry, which I immediately put away on my desk for nighttime reading. I reproached Daniel for not coming sooner and also questioned him about the gendarmes. He burst out laughing, waving his hand deprecatingly, making light of the affair. A very ordinary incident, he said; there had been many like that. He knew how to shout and cry so they always let him go.

"But what did they pick you up for?" I insisted.

"Oh, because I spat at them!"

"Daniel!" I cried severely.

He threw his arms around my neck and pulled me over to the desk to do some drawing with him. After that we had supper, and after that Daniel had a good wash in the bathroom and went to bed. This time he agreed to sleep on the divan.

I decided to say nothing about keeping him with me until next day at breakfast time.

After Daniel had gone to sleep, I began reading Henry's letter. First of all he reported that Stein had gone on ten days' leave to be with his Else; that was why Daniel had not been coming to me. They had been spending the time together playing and he had had a wonderful feeling of freedom, at least for these ten days, which would be up today. Doubtless, tonight or in the early morning Stein would arrive with his gun and vodka bottle.

I looked at the date. The letter was dated the previous day, so Daniel must have left the ghetto then and had doubtless spent the night at the place with the people two streets away to whom he took the secret messages. I was disturbed by news that Henry was ill; he had a high fever, but only Daniel knew this.

"It must be kept a secret from Dora," Henry stated. I did not know why. However, at the time I did not attempt to solve the mystery, being concerned with whether Stein might now be at Henry's with the inevitable gun and vodka bottle.

His letter was once again mostly about Conrad. To be exact, the first part, which referred to *The Rescue*, contained comments about love, skillfully concealed beneath a description of the conversations of people threatened with disaster, stranded on sand banks in a shallow sea, cut off from the world. Once again a discovery on Henry's part, full of allusions to his conditions in the ghetto — the selfsame shoals, the vast expanse of waters, the condemnation to loneliness and banishment from the world.

The people in *The Rescue* were threatened with a death which hourly drew nearer. Yet their souls were filled, not with fear, but with love — in other words, filled with something diametrically opposed to that other extreme which is death. Lingard, the splendid, valiant sea wolf, experiences the birth of love, its growth, the insane passion and agony of it, to all of which he was ever faithful. Poor Miss Travers, beautiful and lonely, is only able to say to herself, "So be it," as if this sentence contained a summary and balance sheet of her entire life. The conversation between Lingard and Miss Travers, which occurs on a reef washed round by the boundless sea, on a tiny hunk of sandy soil, moist beneath their feet, is a hopeless dialogue embracing only the themes of love and death. This dialogue, according to Henry, was a tremendous testimony to the greatness and weakness of man.

"Only we who are confined to the ghetto can understand this," he wrote. "For this is, as it were, a ballad or folk tale about us, about people dishonored, to whom there remains yet one resource — to be transported by love."

I broke off reading and put the letter aside. Daniel was asleep. I could not look enough.

So this conclusion too, I thought sadly as I paced my room in the middle of this wartime night, had to occur to Henry, and release with it hopeless yearnings, truly inconceivable in his position. Henry described Miss Travers, not as Conrad described her, but as if he were describing his dreams of a unique woman created in his imagination to the specifications of his own longing. What could this be if not that which he called "a tremendous testimony to the greatness and weakness of man"?

In the next section of his letter there were a few sentences about Dora and Samuel, who were now — and perhaps for the first and last time — experiencing after their fashion a "transport of love." Isolated, like everyone down there in Patusan, they had only themselves, the solace of their bodies, and fear and despair in the face of death. But they did have themselves. Henry acknowledged that they were good to him, kind and solicitous. And Miss Travers? Conrad had given him her to mock and deride, especially now that right before his eyes he observed Dora and Samuel every day.

Henry ended this truly heart-rending part of his letter with the remark that he lived continually stretched out between the two great, cruel dialogues which Conrad had created for him. These were the dialogue between Brown and Lord Jim, and the dialogue between Lingard and Miss Travers. On the one hand, Patusan, the land of loneliness — on the other, the reefs, the sandy islets, surrounded by the waters which cut men off from the world.

"And I know that no rescue will come my way," he wrote in conclusion.

The second part of his letter began with the words:

"I've got it! I've got it!" This section was a confused, intricate discourse, full of triumphant cries of discovery, about "Heart of Darkness."

Henry had buried himself in the gloomy recesses of something which he called the soul of criminals, hence also the soul of Stein.

"At last" — Henry stressed the words with exclamation marks — "I know why it is that Stein gets drunk, why he comes to me at night, recites Rilke, and pulls out his gun! At last I know whence he derives his vision of the extermination of the Jews, of the extermination of those who are lower than his race! I have discovered the heart of darkness of Stein and the Steins. It was they who produced Bach and Goethe, they who created the science and subtle cognitive tools of man, but this is only appearance! Only appearance! ! Kurtz's heart of darkness is within them, tragic and insane! This is why they know dialectics so well, and every contradiction and every abyss of the soul, these people who have been expelled from Paradise, fettered by a mission, brimming over with contempt, sensitive and subtle, sentimental, endowed with the gift of tears."

"I've got Stein!" cried Henry. "I've got him firmly in my grasp!"

And in the same vein he continued writing with passionate satisfaction about the complexities of the soul of Stein and the Steins.

For Henry, Lord Jim, the discovery of knowledge about the Steins had come, seemingly, too late, and it had now become for him a source of inexhaustible grief.

I spent almost the entire night writing to him. I began the letter several times, and kept tearing it up, starting my reply afresh. But no, it was not a "reply," for how could one make an answer to the ravings of a soul thirsting for the "transport of love," or for the discovery of the heart of darkness in the intricacies of the Steins? I wrote a letter about hope. I sent him news from the front and a bit of political news, assuring him that the coming spring would be the last spring of the war. Once again it was an anti-Conradian letter, a letter about hard realities, but, my God, didn't it, too, cling to myths? If only the myth of this spring being the last, because it was unthinkable that things could go on any longer. In those days nobody, unfortunately, thought otherwise.

The morning brought a disappointment to Daniel and me. It was drizzling and spotting with rain; the wind was whistling, and there was a soughing in the trees, not at all like December. Daniel's good spirits departed as soon as he looked out of the window. I recognized the uselessness of discussing my proposal about staying. Once more I postponed the matter till his next visit.

At breakfast Daniel made faces, and spilled the milk; nothing suited him, and he hardly touched his food. He took my letter and, as usual, set off in great haste. Despite his protests, I wound a woolen scarf around his neck against the cold. Off he went. This time he consented to be seen to the tram.

Thus quickly — perhaps too quickly? — we have completed our journey to the end of the lives of Daniel and Henry. I never saw Daniel again, although I waited for him impatiently, almost desperately.

One evening, on returning home, I found a letter stuffed in the door handle. It was from Dora. Henry had died a week ago of typhus. Daniel was also dead, she wrote, and his death had been witnessed by all of them from the window. Daniel died by the hand of Stein. Having returned from leave, Stein had come to see Henry that rainy day when Daniel went back with my letter. On the door of Henry's apartment there hung a notice, terrible to all Steins, saying: "Typhus." Stein retreated in fury; he was drunk already and staggered on the stairs. In the courtyard he encountered Daniel, who, at the sight of Stein, began to run away. Stein chased him and, when he caught him, drew out his revolver and fired. He took the letter, which was protruding from

Daniel's pocket; then he unfolded a large sheet of the *Völkischerbeobachter,* covered the body with it, and went off, reeling and swearing.

I have said already that when Dora visited me for the first time after the war, I had a lot of work on my desk. I was, in fact, in the process of putting together a piece about those days, and Daniel and Henry had kept recurring in my thoughts. Could I now, after Dora's visit, not bear witness to their lives? I am always with Henry and always with Daniel, who were crushed beneath the wheels of history.

What more can I do for them today? May they, I beg, accept from a Christian a fervent Requiem for them both.

— *translated by* MARCUS WHEELER

(Original title, "Requiem dla Nich Obu." Published in *Przeglad Kulturalny,* No. 11, 1961.)

Death Passed Here

BY BRONISLAW TRONSKI

BRONISLAW TRONSKI, a journalist, was born in 1921 in Wilno. He was actively engaged in the Home Army's armed resistance during Hitler's occupation of Poland, and in 1944 took part in the Warsaw Uprising in the ranks of the same Home Army. After the war he graduated in law from Warsaw University. In 1957, his book *Death Passed Here* was published. For some time he was a foreign correspondent in the Far East for the Warsaw press and the radio. His book *On the World's Roof,* published in 1940, is an account of his experience in Tibet.

In the following excerpt the author recounts some of his personal experiences during the Warsaw Uprising in 1944. The group of insurgents about which he writes in the entry dated September 7, 1944, were boys and girls who had fought the bitterest battle of the uprising in the beleaguered Old Town, then had crossed through the sewers into Midtown, the next part of the city to be attacked by the Germans. The men in the group were wounded or sick, and the girls, acting as couriers or nurses, totally exhausted. In this excerpt they are trying to join their unit, which is already engaged in another fight raging in the Czerniakow district near the Vistula River.

September 7, the thirty-eighth day of the Warsaw Uprising
Midtown and Czerniakow

ON THE STREET, the tumult of battle swept over us; the noise from explosions was louder here, and thick clouds of fire and smoke hovered in the sky over the crowded mass of buildings. Shots sounded from all sides. Soldiers, nurses, and civilians cautiously crept by us, sticking close to the walls. The streets looked different from the week before. Fresh rubble littered the road, and the calm had disappeared from the faces of the passers-by; no longer were there elegant women strolling along in high heels, and eager spick-and-span young men in officers' boots. Ashes which had once been curtains hung dolefully over the windows of a building near a deep, gaping bomb crater.

We plunged into a labyrinth of cellars, brushing past feverish figures, passing groups of insurgents who hurried in all directions. A young liaison girl with a bag thrown over her arm told us that she would help us reach the Third of May Avenue through a tunnel. She knew the way very well indeed, and in a few minutes we found ourselves at Number 36. Here there was an atmosphere of peace and order. The building was undamaged, the soldiers seemed relaxed and indifferent to the long-drawn-out whistle of bullets. Luck was with us. Our Iza spotted Barbara sitting on the stairs with a group of other girl couriers. Together they set off to take care of the necessary formalities. Barbara suggested that we wait in the doorway of the neighboring house, Number 34, as soldiers were not allowed to gather here, and if the officer on duty showed up, there would be hell to pay.

Number 34 also housed military offices. In the doorway we met a group of soldiers. A tall, stubble-chinned second lieutenant with a bandaged arm was telling about the German attack on Krolewska Street from the Saski Gardens. With his good hand he pulled a newspaper out of his pocket, and not without pride showed a communiqué saying that all attacks had been repulsed.

"The only trouble is we're short on ammunition," he said. "Everything would be fine if it weren't for this damned shortage. We'll probably manage for a while, but we have to use it sparingly. They promise us a drop today, tomorrow. And the Krauts are pushing through the Zelazna Gate to the Grzybowski Square too, but there also they have a shit of a chance. Our boys are well dug in. Here, in Midtown, it's not so hot . . ."

The violent sound of shots from somewhere in the Lazienki Park tore through the doorway, along with the scream of exploding mines, followed by grenades going off like echoes in the Three Crosses Square.

"The Krauts took two houses in Warecka Street today," said a man with a deep bass voice, paying no attention to the detonations. "They surprised our boys just before dawn, as patrols were being relieved. They also attacked from the Krakowskie."

"It's not that bad." An insurgent with cavalry insignia defended the situation. "Even today we'll smoke them out of there. We'll have a little game with them." He laughed and whirled his "Bergman" around.

After a moment the second lieutenant appeared, and, as if on command, a part of the group silently followed him out into the street. The rest moved into a circle around us.

"Hi, Old Town. Where are you off to with these bandages?" said one of them, addressing us. There was no irony in his voice; he added, "They are regrouping us in Czerniakow. Is that where you're bound for, too?"

"Yes," I answered, a little arrogantly. "Only, if you would lend us some 'gats' — we have nothing to spray the Germans with."

I was reminded of the pile of arms we had to leave behind before going down into the sewers.

"There was a cretin who stripped the detachment down to the bone. God damn his black soul . . ." swore Tiger, spitting to the side. Then he checked himself as Iza and Barbara slid into the soldier-filled doorway, laughing, and began to search for us.

"Group 'Forester.' Gr——" they called. But we were upon them already. Iza showed us a new document with the stamp of the Polish eagle, and, raising her arm with a swagger, she proclaimed in a carrying voice:

"I hereby pronounce you knights of Czerniakow."

On the corner of Ujazdowskie Avenue we slid by the ruins of the Queen Hedwig High School. At our left the partly destroyed St. Alexander's Church looked like a temple moved bodily from the Greek Acropolis. Continuing along the barricade separating a street from the square, jumping over trolley tracks ripped out of the asphalt and bent into crazy shapes as if they were made of wax, we stumbled upon the iron fence of the Deaf and Dumb Institute, and only then did we pause for a moment on a buttress amidst the hum of shrapnel striking the earth like penknives thrown in some children's game.

Breathing heavily, I leaned on a dust-covered bush. I felt that my right leg was sinking in muck. Examining my leg with some trepidation, I found no scratches, so that apparently only my sweaty foot had softened the pussy bandage. I let out a sigh of relief. A panting group of soldiers passed up and disappeared into the communication trench leading down the street.

We followed in their wake. Stooping, we plodded on, wanting to get out of the exposed area as soon as possible. The trench zigzagged drunkenly, bypassing large tree trunks, disappearing behind elevations, and reappearing again like a brook somewhere below in a thin rusty line. Suddenly there was a pileup. The nurse called China Doll tripped on roots lining the trench, and went down headlong. The man behind her — we nicknamed him Wilno — fell too, wrenching his wounded shoulder in the process. With all my strength I dug my feet into the ground in order not to crash into the pair, while on my back I felt the weight of Iza's body.

A group of "elephants" * was making its way up the trench, groaning under the weight of crates. Seeing what had happened, they threw their burden on the high bank and cursed. A few tried to help China Doll and Wilno get up. Bullets, which began to whizz by overhead, forced them down to the ground. The crates contained bottles with highly explosive fluid, and a thin officer screeched:

"Crates into the trench; take them off quickly, or everything will blow up!"

"That's all we need," I thought feverishly, getting up on my knees and trying to drag Wilno up. With his good hand he grabbed my belt, which allowed the China Doll to disentangle her legs from the roots. She jerked to her feet and lurched forward; after her crept Wilno, cringing with pain, then the rest. The "elephants" got busy with their crates. After we had passed them, they dragged themselves up the hill, paying no attention to the bullets which crossed over the trench constantly.

With no further incident we arrived at the building of the Social Security Office. Tall, spreading gray walls surrounded by barricades

* Civilians who volunteered to carry provisions and supplies from burnt-out houses for the insurgents.

made one think of a fortress. Soldiers filled the rooms and hallways. The upper-story windows housed firing posts. The guard at the barricades checked our pass and showed us the way through courtyards swarming with people, bustle, mutinous excitement. We couldn't find out where the colonel was. Only farther up the street did we run into our old pals, Slow and Blackie. Their faces were ashen and drawn. Blackie's nose seemed to have lengthened, and Slow's cheek bones stuck out. "We probably look no better than they," I thought, shaking hands with them and asking about Colonel Radoslaw's quarters. Slow was now one of his bodyguards, and so in a few minutes' time, unmolested by anyone, we found ourselves in the smallish room of the leader.

He stood surrounded by several officers. He gave us an indifferent look, or perhaps did not see us at all, being absorbed in his thoughts. His was a worried, hard face. Slow saluted and reported our arrival. I moved to the front and held forward the document, which a tall, slim officer in a "tiger skin"* grabbed and handed to the colonel. After a cursory glance at the paper, he gave it back to me, speaking with undisguised irritation:

"What are we to do with the likes of them? How did they make their way here? I forbade them to send me wounded men!"

The words hurt me. But I controlled myself, and said calmly:

"Colonel, sir, we only complied with the order to join the Czerniakow detachments. Most of us can take part in any action right away. We are soldiers from the Old Town, and we know our duty."

Apparently, the colonel considered the interview finished, because he whispered something to the slim officer in the "tiger skin," and the latter showed me out, asking me to stop with my group temporarily at Slow's quarters.

The boys were waiting impatiently at the door. When I told them what had taken place, they looked disappointed; Tiger grumbled, "Why the hell did we trudge here? Damned shame we didn't stay in Midtown."

But Porebski, adjusting his glasses, said, "Well, the colonel needs battle-ready men. And that his remark should cut us to the quick—that's our personal matter . . ."

He didn't finish the sentence, because the guard asked us not to block

---

* Camouflage jackets used by armored units.

the passage, and also Slow was urging us to go on to where his company was quartered. Grenades were exploding all the time, giving off the characteristic sharp metallic sound, and raising dust which parched throats. No doubt, here too it was going to "be hot," although Hitler's air force in this section wasn't as active as in Midtown.

Meeting soldiers from the old flame-throwers' company brought on many reminiscences. Polek, with his inseparable "Bergman" slung over his neck, looked as pugnacious as ever, and the already healed scar on his cheek fit his martial countenance to a tee. Vel, his arm in a sling, was already adorned with sergeant's stripes, and swaggered a bit. Cypka, her hair flying wildly, milled frantically among the soldiers, batting her lashes at one and all.

There was a terrific mess in the room. Shoes, blankets, pillows, and half-opened suitcases were strewn all around. A body stretched out on the bed shook it with a penetrating snore. It was the colonel's adjutant, and he had not slept for the past two nights. At the table sat several fellows drinking black coffee and eating dumplings with sugar. My mouth watered at the sight.

Before I had a chance to introduce myself to anyone, I was called before Captain "Horodynski," a tall, lean-faced, well-mannered man. He informed me that we would be attached to a reserve battalion, and led me to Number 2 Okrag Street, where we were to be quartered on the ground floor of an apartment house, in a room darkened by an equally tall neighboring building.

Right away, Roch set off on a "reconnaissance," taking with him a very young soldier boy whom he knew from the Old Town. Among the insurgents stationed here were many familiar faces from over there. Perhaps that is why I felt at home in this part of the city which I knew so little.

As usual, Roch didn't come back empty-handed. For supper, we could feast on sweet, meaty onions.

"Vitamins, vitamins," he repeated, proud of his spoils, amidst general cries of delight and loud smacking of lips. From his pockets he also pulled out a good supply of candles and soap, which he handed over to Iza's care. Some, tired from the long and trying day, lay down on the floor and kept still; others continued to discuss the possible course of events. One of our men groaned quietly, shrinking to the darkest corner of the room. His knee was swollen, and every movement caused him pain. The fetid odor of puss made me nauseous; the broken windows did not relieve the stuffiness in the room.

I went out into the street. The remains of units decimated in other parts of the city were marching by. I directed myself to the adjoining building and looked out at the deserted yard bordered on the right by a blank wall. The Vistula River lay straight ahead. One could see the roughly drawn outlines of the Poniatowski Bridge and the contours of its turrets. Against the background of a darkening sky, colorful streams of bullets burst forth from these turrets, sinking into the blanket of roofs. From Praga, a suburb on the other side of the river, could be heard the monotonous hum of artillery fire pounding somewhere far away.

I breathed in the throbbing autumn air. At one time, on such evenings I used to like walking in the park, listening to the wind in the trees; I liked to dream about the future.

— *translated by* MARIA DE GORGEY

(From *Tedy Przeszla Smierc,* a journal. Published by "Czytelnik," Warsaw, 1957.)

Verbrennungs-Kommando Warschau

(*Excerpt*)

BY TADEUSZ KLIMASZEWSKI

TADEUSZ KLIMASZEWSKI was born in 1919 in Warsaw. Before the war he studied law and economics at the Academy of Political Sciences in Warsaw. In 1939, he took part in the defense of the capital in one of the Workers' Battalions of the Polish Socialist party.

In 1944, he was in the ranks of the Home Army. Deported to Germany after the Warsaw Uprising, he worked in a quarry in Thüringen. After a lengthy stay in Sweden, France, Africa, Madagascar and Indochina, he returned to Poland in 1951.

The following books of his have been published: *I Ran Away from the Foreign Legion, Verbrennungs-Kommando Warschau* and *There Is a Sleeping Car on That Train.*

The people described here are civilians who, after having been rounded up by SS men in a bombarded house during the Warsaw Uprising, were formed into a slave unit to burn corpses and pull down barricades under fire. In his preface to this documentary record, the author has this to say: "Following the 1944 Uprising in Warsaw, I was deported to Germany, and I did not return to Poland until after a long stay abroad. Once back home, I carefully avoided memories relating to a time of horror and degradation. But in March 1958 I read a notice in the daily *Express Wieczorny* calling for witnesses to come forward and testify to the crimes committed in the suburb Wola by the units of General Reinefahrt. I responded immediately. Later on it transpired that the appeal had been prompted by a group of progressive film producers from Germany who were looking for evidence with which to indict Reinefahrt. Meeting them, as well as my fellow witnesses, revived the past I had tried to forget."

THE BUILDING bore no scars of battle. Only the windows were broken by explosions of bombs which had fallen heavily on the surrounding houses. On the edge of the sidewalk, a toppled tree blocked the entrance with its wilting greenery; a massive iron gate hung open part way.

Lieutenant Thieschke moved ahead of the SS men. For a moment his flapping jacket caught in the protruding branches.

"Take this crap away!" he hissed.

At a sign from the sergeant, a few people standing nearby removed the broken branches. Only then could we see the body stretched out on the ground right in the doorway. It was a man in overalls. Thick dark hair fanning out around his head was glued to the pavement by the puddle of sticky blood.

Thieschke paid no attention to him. Taking a big step, he ambled over the corpse and disappeared in the hall. Like an inseparable shadow, the sergeant hurried after him.

We didn't have long to wait. From the hall burst a short hoarse command, and our column set off down the dark corridor ending in the lighted quadrangle of the courtyard. A blinding glare greeted us there, along with an insufferable stench.

As far as the eye could see, the courtyard was littered with corpses. They lay in the blazing sun — some piled in heaps toward the center, others lying nearby side by side, still others at the edge of the yard with arms outstretched toward the walls, as if in a last desperate effort to escape.

The Germans must have thrown grenades at the crowd herded into the yard, because the masses of corpses were horribly mutilated, and the yard was full of craters and gaping holes. Some of the victims, whom death hadn't found instantly, lay strewn about in disorder, cowered in fear or pain, or else stiffened grotesquely in a last muscular spasm.

The walls of the yard were pockmarked by shots, and the ground was littered with scattered objects — bunches of keys, ripped briefcases, bags, rolls, bits of bread ground into the earth, hats, berets. This mass murder must have been committed a few days before, because the August sun had already bloated the bodies. Thousands of fat blue flies swarmed down on the puddles of dried blood, the gory gashes of wounds, the sightless eyes.

We stood staring, unable to speak or to breathe the thick, jellylike air quivering with the buzzing of flies. A nameless horror, an animal disgust swept over us.

Apparently our faces must have expressed the unspeakable feelings, because even Thieschke and the SS men surrounding him turned away from us and slowly left the yard. The sound of their boots scraping on the pavement became fainter and fainter, until it disappeared completely. We were alone.

We stood motionless. Not one head turned away or trembled; we were afraid to look at one another; we were afraid of our own fear — bordering on madness.

A sudden sob, spasmodic, unrestrained, tore through the silence. We turned to see the engineer crying like a baby, not even bothering to cover his face.

"Men, men, don't take them away." His words came through sobs. "I beg you, don't do it. Leave them, let them lie here. The war is nearly over. They must be left here; let the others see, let them see. You can't touch them, understand?" He jumped up with a sudden burst of strength. "They must lie here! We'll bring people here from all over the world; let them see!"

The Kapo was the first to come to. Gently taking the engineer by the hand, he said, "Calm yourself, enough of this. Don't be an old woman!"

The engineer pulled his hand away brusquely. Anger flashed in his half-crazed eyes. His sobbing died down; now words came in a venomous hiss:

"Ah, so you're the one who's 'covering their tracks.' I understand, you know . . ." But his voice broke, his face crumpled. We led him back to the wall, as far from the corpses as possible, and sat him down on the ground. His head fell, and he froze in a crouching position, as if caving into himself.

"He'll get over it," muttered the Kapo walking away. "He's too sensitive, that's his trouble," he added.

When we returned, people were still standing around irresolutely. The Kapo gave no order. Slowly, he stooped over the closest cadaver, and gently, as if he were lifting a wounded man, took him under the arms. Slowly, the lifeless face turned toward us, its blackened lips falling open hideously. A shiver of revulsion went through the Kapo, but he forced himself to control it.

"He's too heavy, help me somebody . . ."

The angular form of a blond man bent down obediently. Carefully, the men approached the tangled heap of bodies.

"Well, let's get to it" came Edek's stifled voice. Moaning like an old man, he came closer to the corpses.

"Well, go on, what are you gaping at?" he sputtered out furiously.

When we returned for the next load, the men had already formed into pairs. Almost all of them took part in the work. The few whose insides were being ripped apart by vomiting were sent by the Kapo to carry wood. From abandoned offices and shops they hauled tables, doors, parts of cupboards, to cover the first layer of bodies, and then another layer of bodies was placed on the wood.

Minutes dragged by like hours. The ghastly smell of the disturbed bodies had long since passed the limit of endurance, but the men endured it — they had to. We worked in complete silence, clenching our mouths and noses, to inhale less of the poison that permeated the air. Our senses dulled. Disgust, pity, hate, fear — all these combined into an oppressive mist, which dimmed our thoughts.

At first we were at pains to find the "best," the least mutilated, the most human cadavers, but after a time it was all the same. Our unprotected hands no longer searched for the "better" ones, they tugged at the encrusted clothing, grabbed the decaying limbs. Masses of disturbed flies, buzzing angrily, infuriated by the interruption of their feast, attacked our sweaty bodies, settling on our lips, cramming themselves into our eyes. Our anguish was increased by the rising heat, which in this yard, enclosed on all sides by scorching walls, poured over us as in a

Turkish bath. But still our hands reached out for new loads, our muscles flexed. To hold out, at all costs to hold out against being pushed down into the swarm of bloody, rotting bodies. Who knows, maybe today or tomorrow or the next day or next week a chance of escape will come.

In the meantime the pile grew, rising into the sky. Occasionally, during brief moments of respite my eye wandered over the workers. I saw the sunburned figure of the Kapo, his stubborn features and muscular arms in feverish strain; the face of the blond man, which usually wore a broad smile, now resembled a gray blotch; the tall silhouette of the lawyer glided by as in a hypnotic trance. The man with the funny snoot seemed almost indifferent — working steadily, he was greedily inhaling cigarette smoke. The soft, effeminate body of the teacher dripped with perspiration, but his face seemed expressionless — it was dull, empty, with the chin thrust forward. His small, delicate hands no longer hesitated — they grabbed the cadavers at random.

It must have been noon already when we heard the familiar grating of boots at the entrance, and the lieutenant appeared, the inseparable sergeant at his side. Pistol holsters swung from their loosened belts, now and then hitting against the wooden grenade handles.

Thieschke stopped, his legs wide apart. His body swayed back and forth slowly and deliberately. For a moment his wandering gaze rested on the heaped up pyre, and his morose face lit up with a smile of satisfaction. He whispered something to the sergeant, whose bulging eyes were glued to him obediently. Suddenly, Thieschke made a wry face, and his lips twisted into the wicked grimace that I had noticed that morning.

"Kapo," he called with faint surprise in his voice, "what's that man doing over there?"

For a moment we interrupted our work to follow the direction of his pointing hand. Over by the wall sat, or rather half lay, the engineer. Tears had left furrows on his dust-covered face. His reddened eyes, opened unnaturally, were riveted to the growing pile of corpses.

"Why doesn't he work?" asked Thieschke slowly, a dangerous note rising in his voice.

"He is sick," answered the Kapo. "The air here isn't too good."

Thieschke waved his hand carelessly, chasing away a fly from his face. His brow wrinkled slightly, and his lips parted in a sarcastic smile.

"Oh, is that so?" he drawled. "Well, if he's sick, he must be taken to the hospital. . . . Send him to me at once!" he added sharply, and turned on his heel.

We led the engineer to the doorway. Thieschke looked at him as though he were a useless object.

"He can stay here," he muttered, motioning us away.

When we returned, the pyre was practically ready. Four men stood on the third tier, pulling up the remaining dead.

A group of us started to throw earth on the black blood stains; others poured gasoline along the bottom of the heap.

At the moment that the pyre was ready to be lit, we heard footsteps in the corridor. It was the Kapo and two others dragging still another body.

"Give him here quick!" shouted the last man on top, who was about to jump down.

All eyes turned on the corpse being hoisted on to the pyre. The engineer's body appeared strangely soft and fluid. His dangling gray head turned to reveal a face still wet with tears; red drops of blood seeped from the half-opened lips and fell onto the hands of the Kapo.

— *translated by* MARIA DE GORGEY

(From *Verbrennungs-Kommando Warschau,* a war memoir. Published by "Czytelnik," Warsaw, 1960.)

A Day at Harmenz

BY TADEUSZ BOROWSKI

TADEUSZ BOROWSKI was born in Zytomierz in 1922. Under the Occupation, he worked as a mason but took part in the Resistance, and at the same time studied Polish at the Warsaw University operated by the Underground. His first book of poems, *Wherever There Is Earth,* was printed by an Underground press in 1942. Arrested in 1943, he was sent first to Auschwitz and then to Dachau, and was finally liberated by the Americans. In 1946, together with two other former prisoners, he published *We Were in Auschwitz.* After returning to Poland, three more books appeared: *Farewell, Maria* (1948), *A World of Stone,* and a collection of articles, essays and stories which had been published previously in the Warsaw press. Between 1949 and 1951 he was actively engaged in public affairs on the side of the Communists, and in July 1951 he took his own life by turning on the gas – a fate he had miraculously escaped in Auschwitz. Andrzej Kijowski (*see* "Travel by Air" in this book) wrote of him: "There is only one author in Poland in recent years who has caused authentic moral indignation . . . because he had the courage to identify himself with the evil he describes . . ."; and another critic, Grzegorz Lasota, quotes Borowski as saying of his own work that it was "a journey to the utmost limit of a certain kind of morality." Lasota goes on to comment: "The Auschwitz cycle . . . as someone justly remarked, not only demonstrates the bankruptcy of one kind of morality, but it also reverses the relationship between the executioner and his victim. The writer, quite as if he wanted to exclude the figures in SS uniforms from the field of human judgment, indicts only the victim." His story, "A Day at Harmenz," appears both in *We Were in Auschwitz* and *Farewell, Maria. The Collected Works of T. Borowski* was posthumously published in 1954.

I

THE SHADOW of the chestnut trees is green and soft. It sways gently over the ground, which is still damp after being newly dug over, and it rises over the head in sea-green cupolas scented with the morning freshness. The trees form a lofty palisade along the road, and their crowns dissolve into the hue of the sky. The heavy, noxious smell of marshes comes from the ponds. The grass, as green as velvet, is still silvered with dew, but the ground is already steaming in the sun. It will be hot today.

But the shadow of the chestnuts is green and soft. Covered by the shade, I sit in the sand and with a large adjustable wrench I tighten up the fishplates of the narrow-gauge railway line. The wrench is cold and fits comfortably into my hand. From time to time I strike the rail with it. The harsh metallic clang spreads over all Harmenz and returns from afar in a dissimilar echo. A group of Greeks are standing close by me, resting on their spades. But these men from Salonica and the vineyard slopes of Macedonia are afraid of the shadow, so they stand in the sun, after taking off their shirts, and tan their incredibly thin shoulders and arms covered with innumerable scabs and sores.

"You're working hard today, Tadek. Good morning. Aren't you hungry?"

"Good morning, Mrs. Haneczka. Not at all. And to tell the truth, I'm banging the rails so hard because our new Kapo . . . Excuse my not getting up from the rail, but you understand, there's a war on, *Bewegungarbeit* . . ."

Mrs. Haneczka laughs.

"Of course I understand. I shouldn't have recognized you if I hadn't known it was you. D'you remember how you sat in the lupines and ate the potatoes that I stole from the chickens for you?"

"Ate them! But Mrs. Haneczka, I devoured them! Look out, here comes an SS man." She poured out a handful of grain from a sieve for the pullets that came running toward her; but then, after looking around, she waved her hand unconcernedly.

"Oh, it's only our chief. I can twist him around my little finger."

"Around such a small finger? You're a very brave woman."

I swung the wrench once more against the rail, making it give off part of the tune "La donna è mobile."

"Don't make so much noise, man. Would you really and truly like something to eat? I'm just going to the house. I'll bring you something back."

"Mrs. Haneczka, I thank you most kindly. I think you fed me quite enough when I was poor."

"But honest," she said, with a touch of sarcasm.

"Well, helpless, at any rate," I retorted to the best of my ability. "But as for my helplessness, I had two fine pieces of soap for you, called by the finest of all names — 'Warsaw' — and . . ."

"And someone's stolen them, as usual?"

"Someone's stolen them, as usual. When I had nothing I slept in peace But now it doesn't matter how I tie up the packets with string and wire, they always untie them. A day or two ago someone organized * a jar of honey off me, and now the soap's gone. But the thief will be sorry for himself when I catch him."

She laughed aloud.

"I can just imagine," she said. "Child, you needn't worry at all about the soap — I got two fine pieces from Ivan today. Oh, I almost

* In the camp slang, to "organize" was an expression for "to steal."

forgot: hand him this little packet, will you . . ." she said, laying a small packet at the foot of the trees. "Just see what fine soap it is."

She unwrapped the paper; it seemed strangely familiar to me. I went and looked at it more closely: on both of the large pieces of soap was the cameo of the King Sigismund column and the word "Warsaw."

I handed the packet back to her without a word.

"It certainly is fine soap."

I looked across to the field where men were working in scattered groups. In the last group, right by the potatoes, I caught sight of Ivan: he was vigilantly walking around his group of men like a sheepdog around the flock; he shouted something which I could not distinguish at that distance and waved his big peeled stick.

"The thief will be sorry for himself," I said, not noticing that I was talking to empty space, for Mrs. Haneczka had already gone. As she went she called back:

"Dinner as usual under the chestnut trees."

"Thank you."

I started to knock the wrench again against the rails and to tighten up the loose bolts. Mrs. Haneczka always caused a real sensation among the Greeks, for she brought them potatoes from time to time.

"Mrs. Haneczka good, extra first class. Is she your Madonna?"

"Why Madonna?" I flew into a passion, hitting my finger with the wrench by mistake. "She's an acquaintance, a 'comrade,' say, *filos, compris, Greco bandito?*"

"Greco not bandit. Greco good man. But why don't you eat any of the food she brings? Potatoes?"

"I'm not hungry. I've got something to eat."

"You're not good, not good." The old Greek porter from Salonica, who knew twelve Southern languages, shook his head. "We're hungry, always hungry, always, always . . ."

He stretched out his bony arms. Under the skin lousy with scabs and rashes, the muscles played with a strangely distinct movement, as though each was quite separate; a smile softened the tense expression on his face, but the lurking bitterness in his eyes could not fade.

"If you're hungry you ask her. Let her bring something for you. But now work, *laborando, laborando,* for I'm bored with you. I'm going somewhere else."

"That's just it, Tadek, you're making a mistake," an old heavy-bodied

Jew said, stepping out from the others. He rested his spade on the ground and went on, standing over me:

"After all, you've been hungry too, so you can understand us. It wouldn't cost you anything if she brought a bucket of potatoes."

He drawled the word "bucket" dreamily.

"Becker, you can stop bothering us with your philosophizing and occupy yourself more with the earth and your spade, *compris?* And understand this: when you're dying I shall finish you off myself, get that? And d'you know why?"

"Well, and why?"

"Because of Poznan. Or isn't it true that you were the camp senior in the Jewish camp outside Poznan?"

"Well, and what if I was?"

"You killed people. And you hanged them on a post for stupidly stealing a bit of margarine or a roll of bread."

"I hanged thieves."

"Becker, they say your son is in quarantine."

Becker's fingers clutched the haft of his spade convulsively, and his gaze began to appraise my body, my neck, my head . . .

"You drop that spade; don't look at me so murderously. Perhaps it isn't true that your son has given orders for you to be killed because of those in Poznan?"

"It's true," he said thickly. "I hanged my second son in Poznan, but not by his hands, only by his neck, because he was stealing bread."

"You swine!" I burst out.

Now Becker was calm and self-controlled, an elderly, grizzled Jew, with a disposition to melancholy. He looked down at me almost with contempt and asked:

"How long have you been in the camp?"

"Oh, some months."

"You know, Tadek, I'm very fond of you," he said unexpectedly, "but you haven't ever really known what it is to be hungry, have you?"

"That depends on what you mean by hunger."

"Real hunger is when a man regards another man as something to eat. And I've been hungry like that. Get me?"

As I was silent and only knocked the wrench against the rail and automatically looked to the left and right to see whether the Kapo was coming, he went on:

"Our camp — there — was quite small. Right by the road. People traveled along the road, well-dressed people, and women too. For instance, going to church on Sundays. Or young couples. And farther on, there was a village, just an ordinary village. There the people had everything, just half a mile from us. But we ate turnips. . . . There were times when our people felt like eating a man alive. And so wasn't I justified in killing the cooks who bought vodka with our butter, and cigarettes with bread? My son stole, and I killed him too. I'm a porter — I know life."

I looked at him curiously, as though I'd never seen him before.

"How about you? Did you never eat more than your own ration?"

"That was different. I was the camp senior."

"Look out! *Laborando, laborando,* quick!" I snarled suddenly. For an SS man on a bicycle had appeared around a turn in the road; he rode past us, eyeing us closely. At once the backs were bent lower; the spades held constantly at the ready were raised heavily, the wrench knocked against the rail. As the SS man vanished beyond the trees, the spades dropped and were still, and the Greeks lapsed into their usual torpor.

"What's the time?"

"I don't know. It's a long time yet to dinner. But you know what, Becker? I'll tell you this in parting: there's to be a checkup in the camp today. I hope you'll go to the furnace, together with your sores."

"Checkup? How do you know . . ."

"Why are you so scared? There's going to be one, and that's that. Why, are you afraid? The wolf carried . . ."

I laugh malevolently at my wit, and go off humming the fashionable tango called "Cremo." Empty human eyes, suddenly voided of all content, stare fixedly into the distance.

2

THE RAILS of my narrow-gauge railway crisscross all over the field. At one spot I had taken them right up to a heap of burned bones which a lorry had brought from the "cremo"; I had run the other end to the pond, where these bones were to be deposited finally; elsewhere I ran the rails up to a mound of sand, which was to be spread level over the field to give a dry base to the very marshy soil; elsewhere I laid them along an embankment of grassy earth, which was to go to the sand. The lines run this way and that, and wherever they intersect there has to be an enormous turntable, which is shifted from one spot to another.

A crowd of half-naked men surrounded the turntable; they bent down and clutched it with their fingers.

"Hooh! Up with it!" I snarled, suggestively raising my hand like an orchestra conductor, to achieve a better effect. The men tugged again and again; one of them fell heavily over the turntable, unable to remain very long on his legs. His comrades kicked him, and he crawled out of the ring; raising his tear- and sand-stained face from the earth, he groaned:

"Too hard, too hard . . . It's too hard, comrade."

He thrust his lacerated hand into his mouth and sucked greedily.

"Get back to work. Get up! Now, once more! Hooh! Up with it!"

"Up with it!" the group repeated in a harmonious chorus; they bent as low as they could get, and thrust up their backbones, as jagged as those of fishes; they strained all the muscles in their bodies. But the hands clinging to the turntable hung limply helplessly.

"Up with it!"

"Up with it!"

Suddenly a rain of blows fell on the ring of straining backs, the bowed shoulders, the heads bent almost to the ground, the peeling hands. A spade haft drummed on a forehead, broke the skin over the bones, and beat hollowly on the bellies. A violent activity set in around the turntable. A horrible human howl suddenly burst out and broke off; but the turntable moved upward and, swaying heavily, hung over the heads of the human beings, threatening to fall at any moment.

"You dogs," the Kapo shouted at them as he went off. "I'll give you a bit of help."

Breathing heavily, he rubbed his crimson, swollen face with his hand and ran an absent gaze over the gang as if seeing them for the first time. Then he turned to me.

"You, railway man, it's hot today," he said.

"It is hot. Kapo, that turntable has got to be put down by the third incubator, hasn't it? How about the rails?"

"You're to run them right up to the ditch."

"But there's an earth embankment in the way."

"Dig through it. It must be finished by midday. And by the evening you'll make me four stretchers. Someone may have to be carried back to camp. It's hot today, isn't it?"

"Yes. But Kapo . . ."

"Railway man, give me a lemon."

"Send your 'boy' along to me. I haven't got one in my pocket."

The Kapo nods his head several times and goes off, limping. He goes to the house, for food. But I know he won't get anything there, for he beats up the prisoners. We laid the turntable down. With a terrible effort the rails were carried up; they were levered into position with a pick, and the bolts were tightened up with bare hands. The hungry, feverish bodies crawled about, disorderly, hunted, bloodstained. The sun rose high and scorched more and more pestilentially.

"What's the time, mate?"

"Ten," I answer without lifting my eyes from the rail.

"Lord, Lord, still two hours to dinner. Is it true that there's to be a selection in the camp today, that we shall go to the furnace?"

They all know already about the selection. They stealthily dress their wounds, trying to make them cleaner and fewer; they tear off the bandages, massage their muscles, splash themselves with water so as to be fresher and nimbler for the evening. They fight for existence fiercely, heroically. But others no longer care. These men move around only to avoid being beaten; they devour grass and sticky clay in order not to feel hungry; they go around in a daze, already living corpses.

"We're all for the crematorium. But the Germans will be *kaput.* When the war ends, the Germans will go to the crematorium. Every one of them! Women and children too. Get that?"

"You get it well, Greek. But it isn't true — there isn't to be a selection, there's no need to worry."

I dig through the embankment. The light, convenient spade works of itself in my hands. The clods of damp earth yield easily and fly softly into the air. It is easy to work when one has had a quarter of smoked bacon with bread and garlic for breakfast and drunk a can of evaporated milk.

In the meager shade of the brick incubator the Kommandoführer, a little sickly SS man with an unbuttoned shirt, was squatting. He was worn out from crawling among the diggers. He could use his riding whip painfully. Yesterday he gave me a couple of strokes across the shoulders.

"Plate layer, what's the latest news?"

I swing my spade and flatten down the top of the earth.

"Three hundred thousand Bolsheviks have fallen at Orel."

"That's good, isn't it? What do you think?"

"Of course it's good. For the same number of Germans also fell there. But the Bolsheviks will be here inside a twelvemonth if they go on at this rate."

"Do you think so?" He laughs malevolently and asks the sacramental question:

"How long to dinner?"

I take out my watch, an old rubbishy silver one with absurd Roman figures. I'm fond of it because it's like the watch my father had. I bought it for a packet of figs.

"Eleven."

The sickly German got up from under the wall and calmly took it out of my hand.

"Give it to me. I like it a lot."

"I can't, because it's my own; I brought it from home."

"Well, if you can't, you can't."

He swung his arm and flung the watch against the wall. Then he sat down in the shade again and tucked his legs under him.

"It's hot today, isn't it?"

Without speaking I picked up the watch and in my fury began to whistle. First a foxtrot about merry Joan, then an old tango, then the "Song of Warsaw" * and the "Cavalry Squadron" song, and finally a repertoire from the political left.

I was just whistling the "International," mentally repeating "This is our last and decisive fight," when suddenly I was aware of a tall shadow and a heavy hand fell on my back. I raised my head and was struck dumb. An enormous, bloated crimson face spread over me, and a spade haft swayed ominously in the air. The immaculately clean camp clothes showed up strongly against the green of the distant trees. The small red triangle with the figures 3277 sewn to the chest swayed strangely and grew before my eyes.

"What are you whistling?" the Kapo asked, looking me straight in the eyes.

---

* A famous revolutionary song dating from the Polish Insurrection of 1831.

"It's an international sort of song, Mr. Kapo."

"But do you know the song?"

"Well . . . a little . . . from various people," I added prudently.

"But do you know this?" he asked.

In a hoarse voice he began to sing the "Red Flag." He threw down the spade haft, his eyes glittering restlessly. Suddenly he broke off, picked up the haft, and shook his head half in contempt and half in commiseration.

"If a real SS man were to hear you, you'd be dead by now. But that . . ."

The sickly fellow by the wall laughed broadly and good-naturedly.

"And you call this penal servitude. You should have been in the Caucasus like me."

"Kommandoführer, we've already filled in one pond with bones; but how much had been filled in before, and how much has gone into the Vistula, neither you nor I know."

"Hold your tongue, you pig-dog." He rose from under the wall and reached for his riding whip.

"Collect the men and go to dinner," the Kapo said hurriedly.

I dropped my spade and vanished around the corner of the incubator. In the distance I heard the Kapo's voice, hoarse and asthmatic:

"Yes, yes; they're pig-dogs. They all ought to be beaten off their feet. You're quite right, Herr Kommandoführer."

3

WE GO off by the road that runs through Harmenz. The lofty chestnuts rustle; the shade is still greener, but dryer somehow. Like withered leaves. It is the shade of noonday.

As we emerge onto the road we have to pass a little house. Its windows have green shutters with little hearts roughly cut out of their centers, and white half-drawn little curtains. Under the window delicate little roses of a pale, dead color are climbing up, and strange, violet-colored little flowers are growing in little boxes. On the steps of the little veranda intertwined with dark green ivy a little girl is playing with a large sulky dog.

The dog is obviously bored; it allows itself to be tugged by the ears, only shaking its head in an endeavor to avoid the flies. The girl is in a white dress, and she has bronze, sunburned arms. The dog is a black

Doberman with a bronze dewlap. The girl is the daughter of the Unterscharführer, the boss of Harmenz. And this little house with its little roses and curtains is his house.

Before we reach the road we have to cross several yards of clinging, sticky mud mixed with sawdust and watered with disinfectant fluid. This is to avoid bringing any infection to Harmenz. I pass cautiously around the edge of this filth, and we come out all together onto the road, where great caldrons of soup have been set up in a row. A lorry has brought them from the camp. Each gang has its own caldrons marked with chalk. I walk all around them. We've arrived in time—no one has stolen any from us yet.

"Take our five . . . good. Those two rows belong to the women, and we mustn't monkey about with them. Aha, here's one," I talk aloud to myself and pull out a caldron belonging to the next gang, putting one of ours, only half the size, in its place. I write new marks on it with chalk.

"Take them away," I shout to the Greeks, who stand gaping at this procedure, wide-eyed with understanding.

"Hi you, what have you changed the caldrons for? Wait, stop!" yell the men of the second gang, who are arriving for their dinner, but have got here late.

"Who's changed them? Shut your mouth, man."

The others run up, but the Greeks drag the caldrons over the ground, groaning, swearing in their crazy language, urging one another on, and disappear beyond the pale which separates the world from Harmenz. I follow up behind them. I can hear the others already at the caldrons cursing me by all the devils and scattering my family vigorously to all the four corners of the world. But everything's okay: today it's our turn, tomorrow theirs; first come best served. Our gang patriotism never goes beyond the bounds of sport.

The soup gurgles in the caldrons. The Greeks set them down on the ground at every few paces.

They pant violently, like fish flung up on the shore, and with their fingers surreptitiously collect the thin little trickles of sticky hot grease oozing from under the loosely screwed-on covers. I know how it tastes, with its mixture of dust, dirt, and the sweat of hands; for I myself was carrying these caldrons not so long ago.

They set down the caldrons and gaze into my face expectantly. I go solemnly up to the middle caldron, slowly unscrew the screw, hold my hand on the cover for an endlessly long half second, and raise it. A dozen or more pairs of eyes fade with repugnance: nettle soup. A thin white liquid is gurgling in the caldron. The yellow disks of margarine are floating on its surface. But by its color they all realize that whole, unchopped, hairy nettle stalks the color of decay and stinking horribly are lying at the bottom, and that the soup is the same right to the bottom: water, water, water. . . . For a moment the world goes dark before the men's eyes as they move up. I put the cover back on the caldron. Silently we carry the caldrons down the slope.

I walked in a great arc across the field towards Ivan's group, which was tearing off the surface of the meadow by the potatoes. A long row of men in striped camp clothing was standing motionless by the black ridge of earth. From time to time a spade was shifted, someone bent, froze still in this movement for a second, straightened up slowly, shifted his spade, and was frozen for a long time in a half turn, in an uncompleted gesture, like the animal called the sloth. After a time someone else stirred, swung his spade, and fell into the same impotent torpor. They were working not with their hands but with their eyes. When an SS man or the Kapo appeared on the horizon, or from some shady niche where the damp cool of fresh earth reigns, the foreman scrambled up heavily and the spades clattered with more life, though they remained empty as long as it was possible to get away with it; the men's limbs had the movement of figures in an old film: absurd, angular.

I made straight for Ivan. He was sitting in his sheltered spot and carving ornaments — squares, love knots, little hearts, Ukrainian phrases — in the bark of a stout pole with his pocket knife. An old, trusted Greek was kneeling beside him, stuffing something into his bag. I managed to catch sight of a white feathered wing and the red head of a goose tightly bent over its back before Ivan noticed my arrival and threw his coat over the bag. The pork had gone soft in my pocket, and I had an ugly stain on my trousers.

"From Mrs. Haneczka," I said curtly.

"Didn't she say anything? She was to bring me some eggs."

"She told me to thank you for the soap. She liked it very much."

"That's good. I bought it from a Jew in 'Canada' * yesterday. I gave three eggs for it." He unwrapped the pork fat. It was crushed, melting with the heat, and yellow. I felt sick at the sight of it, perhaps because I had eaten too much smoked bacon that morning and it kept rising in my throat.

"Oh, the whore! Is that all she's given for two such fine pieces of soap? Didn't she give you any cake?" Ivan looked at me suspiciously.

"Oh, you know, Ivan, she really has given you too little. I saw the soap."

"You saw it?" He fidgeted restlessly in his shelter. "I must go and drive the men to work."

"Yes, I saw it. And she did give you too little. You ought to have more. Especially from me. I'll try to see that you get it."

For a moment we looked hard into each other's eyes.

4

RIGHT ABOVE the ditch, flags were growing, and on the farther side, where a stupid, bewhiskered guard was standing, with a couple of triangles on his arms to indicate long service, there were raspberries with pale leaves, as though dusted over. At the bottom of the ditch muddy water was running; green slimy monsters ran riot in it, and occasionally a black wriggling eel drew itself out of the slime. The Greeks eat them raw. I straddled across the ditch and slowly worked my spade along the bottom. I stood carefully, so as not to get my boots wet. The guard came closer, and stood watching silently.

"What's going to be done here?"

"Banks; and then we shall clean out the ditch, sir."

"Where did you get such fine boots?"

My boots really are fine; hand-sewn, with a double sole, and holes ingeniously punched in the uppers, Hungarian fashion. Friends brought them to me from the loading bay.

"I got them in the camp together with this shirt," I replied, showing him my silk shirt, for which I had given at least a pound of tomatoes.

"Do they give you boots like those? Look at the ones I've got on."

He showed me his boots. They were creased and split, with a patch on the right toe. I nodded sympathetically.

---

* "Canada" is a designation for the state of those who were well off in the camp.

"Wouldn't you sell me your boots?"

I gave him a look expressive of utter surprise.

"But how can I sell you the camp property? How can I?"

The guard rested his carbine against the bench and came closer, bending over the water, which reflected him. I reached with my spade and disturbed the reflection.

"Everything's allowable if no one sees. You'll get bread — I've got it in my haversack."

That week I had received sixteen rolls of bread from Warsaw. In addition, a pair of boots like mine were a sure thing for a liter of vodka. So I laughed indulgently.

"Thank you, but we get such good rations in the camp that I'm not hungry. I have enough bread and lard. But if you have too much bread, give it to those Jews working over there by the embankment. Say that one that's carrying the turf," I said, pointing to a thin little Jew with bleary, rheumy eyes. "He's a very decent sort. And after all, these boots aren't all that good — the sole's coming away." There was in fact a crack in one sole; sometimes I hid a few dollars there, sometimes a few Polish marks, sometimes a letter. The guard bit his lips and stared at me with knitted brows.

"What did they put you inside for?"

"I was walking along the street and there was a roundup. They picked me up, put me inside, and brought me here. For no reason at all."

"You all say that."

"Oh, that's not so, not all of us. A friend of mine was arrested because he sang badly. You understand: *'falsch gesungen.'* "

The spade which I was stirring constantly over the bottom of the slimy ditch came up against something hard. I tore it up: wire. I cursed vigorously under my breath, but the guard stared at me dumfounded.

"What, *falsch gesungen?*"

"Well, it's quite a long story. One day when hymns were being sung during a service in Warsaw my friend began to sing a national hymn. And as he sang very badly they put him inside. And they said they wouldn't let him out till he had learned music. They even beat him up, but nothing came of it; he's sure to be kept inside till the end of the war, for he's quite unmusical. Once he even mixed up a German march with Chopin's 'Funeral March.' "

The guard hissed something and went off to his bench. He sat down, picked up his carbine thoughtfully, and, playing with the bolt, went through the motions of loading and firing. Then he raised his head as though he had remembered something.

"Here you, Warsaw man, come here; I'll give you this bread, and you can pass it on to the Jews," he said, reaching for his haversack.

I put on the most pleasant smile I could. The guard line ran along the farther side of the ditch, and the guards were permitted to fire at prisoners on that side. They get three days' furlough and five marks per head.

"Unfortunately, we're not allowed to come over there. But if you like, you can throw the bread across; I'll catch it, I really will."

I stood in an expectant attitude; but the guard suddenly put the haversack on the ground, started up, and reported to the passing commander of the guard that "there was nothing special to report."

Janek was working at my side; he is a very charming child of Warsaw, who simply cannot understand the ways of camp life and probably never will. He was diligently shoveling up the slime, piling it neatly and carefully on the farther side, almost under the feet of the guard. The guard commander came closer and scrutinized us as one examines a pair of horses drawing a cart, or cattle grazing in a field. Janek smiled broadly at him and nodded collusively.

"We're cleaning out the ditch, Rottenführer: there's a lot of mud in it."

The Rottenführer started and stared at the speaking prisoner with the same astonishment that one would have if a draft horse suddenly started to speak, or a grazing cow began to sing a popular song.

"Come over here," he told Janek.

Janek put down his spade, jumped the ditch, and went up to him. The Rottenführer raised his hand and slapped him in the face with all his strength. Janek staggered, clutched at the raspberry bushes, and slipped down into the slime. The water bubbled; I choked with laughter. But the Rottenführer said:

"I don't care a damn what you're doing in the ditch, you can do nothing at all for all I care. But when you speak to an SS man take your cap off and stand to attention."

He walked away, I helped Janek to scramble out of the mud.

"What did I get that for; what for, what for?" he asked in astonishment, not in the least understanding.

"Don't get in the way of the hunter," I said. "But now clean yourself up."

We were just finishing the work of cleaning out the ditch when the Kapo's "boy" arrived. I reached for my bag, and set aside a roll of bread, lard, and an onion. I took out a lemon. The guard on the farther side looked on in silence.

"Boy, come here. I've got this. You know who it's for."

"Good, Tadek. Listen, have you anything to eat? Something sweet, or an egg. No, no, I'm not hungry; I had some food in the house. I got some omelet from Mrs. Haneczka. She's a fine woman. Only she's always asking things about Ivan. You know, when the Kapo goes to the house they don't give him anything."

"Let him stop beating people, and they'll give him something."

"You tell him so."

"What are you his 'boy' for? You don't know how to organize things. You look and see how certain people catch geese and cook them in the barracks in the evening, while your Kapo eats soup. Did you like yesterday's nettles?"

The "boy" gave me an inquisitive look. He was a young but very crafty lad. He was German and had been in the army, though he was only sixteen now. He engaged in smuggling.

"Tadek, tell me straight out; we understand each other, don't we? Who are you putting me on to?"

I shrugged my shoulders.

"No one. But you keep a close eye on the geese."

"Well, you know, another goose disappeared yesterday, and the Unterscharführer was so mad he beat the Kapo and took his watch from him. I'll go and look."

We went off together, for it was time for dinner. Piercing whistles came from the direction of the caldrons, and hands were waving. Implements were flung down wherever the prisoner happened to be. The spades were left sticking into the embankment. From all over the field exhausted men dragged slowly towards the caldrons, trying to extend the blessed moment before dinner, to prolong the hunger which shortly they would be satiating. Ivan's belated group dragged along behind all the others. He stopped at the ditch by my "guard" and had a long talk with him. Snarls and shouts urged him to greater haste. As he went past me he flung at me:

"It looks as though you won't hunt down anything today."

"The day isn't finished yet," I retorted.

He gave me a malevolent sidelong and challenging glance.

5

IN THE empty incubator the "boy" is setting out the utensils, wiping the stools, and laying the table for dinner. The group secretary, a Greek linguist, is huddled in one corner, trying to make himself as small and inconspicuous as possible. Through the wide-open door one can see his face, the color of boiled lobster, with watery eyes like frog's spawn. The prisoners are seated in the yard, on a little square surrounded by a high rampart of earth. They have sat down just as they were standing, in fives, in ranks and groups. They sit now with legs crossed, bodies erect, their hands dropped on their thighs. They may not move a limb while dinner is being served. Later they will be able to stretch themselves out on their backs and lie on the knees of their comrades, but woe to them if they break the neatness of the rows. The SS men are sitting negligently on one side, in the shade of the rampart, with their machine pistols laid nonchalantly across their knees. They take bread out of their wallets and haversacks, carefully spread the margarine, and eat slowly and solemnly. Rubin, a Jew from "Canada," has seated himself beside one of them and is talking quietly to him. He is arranging some affair, either for himself or for the Kapo. The Kapo himself, huge and crimson, is standing by the caldron. We run to and fro with plates in our hands like highly trained waiters. In perfect silence we hand out the soup; in perfect silence we wrest the billycan from hands of those who are trying to scrape up a little more from the empty bottom, or to prolong the moment of eating what clings to their plates, and stealthily to run their fingers over the bottom. The Kapo leaps away from the caldron and rushes among the ranks — he's spotted someone. With a kick in the face he bowls over a man licking his plate; he kicks him again and again in the genitals and goes off, treading on the knees and the hands, but carefully avoiding those who are eating.

All eyes strain in the Kapo's direction. Two more caldrons: second helpings. Every day the Kapo gets a tremendous kick out of this moment. His ten years in the camp entitle him to enjoy this authority over human beings. With the end of his ladle he points to the men who have earned a second helping; he never makes a mistake. The second helping is given to those who work better, to the stronger, the healthier. The sick, the feeble, or the emaciated man has no right to a second plate of water and nettles. The food mustn't be wasted on people who will be going to the incinerator before long.

By virtue of their office the foremen are entitled to two full plates of soup together with potatoes and meat scooped up from the bottom of the caldron. With a plate in my hand I look around me undecided; I feel someone's gaze fixed on me. Becker is sitting in the front row. His goggling eyes are fixed greedily on the soup.

"Here, eat this; you never know, it may do you some harm."

He silently seizes the plate from my hands and begins to eat voraciously.

"But put the plate down beside you for the 'boy' to collect; or you'll be getting one in the mug from the Kapo."

I give the second plate to Andrzej. He brings me apples in return. He works in the orchard.

"Rubin, what did the guard tell you?" I ask in an undertone as I go past him to get into the shade.

"The guard says they've occupied Kiev," he replies as quietly. I come to a halt in my astonishment. He waves me on impatiently. I go into the shade, fold my coat under me so as not to soil my silk shirt, and stretch myself out comfortably for a doze. We rest as much as we're allowed to.

The Kapo went to the incubator, and after eating two plates of soup he dozed off. Then the "boy" took a piece of boiled meat out of his pocket, cut it up on bread, and began to eat it ostentatiously in front of the hungry crowd; he savored the meat with bites of onion, treating it like an apple. The men had lain down in serried rows on their coats and dropped into a heavy, restless doze. We lie in the shade. Opposite us a gang of girls in white kerchiefs has settled down. They call to us across the intervening distance, and convey a whole story with their eyes. Some of them nod their agreement. One of the girls is kneeling by herself, holding a large, heavy beam extended on her hands above her head. Every minute or so the SS man guarding the gang slackens his dog's leash. It leaps up to her face, barking furiously.

"A thief?" I conjecture sluggishly.

"No, they caught her in the Indian corn with Petro. Petro fled," Andrzej replied.

"Will she stick to it for a full five minutes?"

"She will. She's a tough girl."

She didn't stick to it. Her arms sagged, and she flung down the beam and broke into noisy sobbing. Petro turned away and looked at me.

"You haven't got a cigarette, have you, Tadek? Pity — that's life!"

He wrapped his head in his coat, stretched himself out more comfortably, and dropped off to sleep. I, too, had just settled down to sleep when the "boy" tugged at me.

"The Kapo wants you. Look out, he's in a bad temper."

The Kapo had waked up, and his eyes were red. He rubbed them and stared fixedly into space.

"You" — he touched me menacingly on the chest with his finger — "what made you hand over your soup to someone else?"

"I've got other food to eat."

"What did he give you for it?"

"Nothing."

He shook his head incredulously. His enormous jaws worked like those of a cow chewing the cud.

"You won't get any soup at all tomorrow. They'll get it who haven't anything else to eat. Get that?"

"Very good, Kapo."

"Why haven't you made the four stretchers I ordered you to? Have you forgotten?"

"I haven't had the time. You saw what I did this morning."

"You'll do them this afternoon. And see you don't lie on one of them yourself. I can arrange that for you."

"Can I go now?"

Only then did he look at me. He fixed on me the dead, empty gaze of a man torn out of profound thought.

"What are you doing here?" he asked.

6

A STIFLED CRY reached me from under the chestnut trees. I collected my wrenches and spanners, arranged the stretchers one on top of another, and told Janek:

"Janek, take the box; for Mummy will be angry." I went off to the road.

Becker was lying on the ground, hawking and spitting up blood, and Ivan was kicking him haphazardly in the face, the belly, the genitals . . .

"Look what this viper has done. He's eaten all your dinner. The blasted thief."

Mrs. Haneczka's billycan with some gruel in the bottom was lying at Becker's side. The Jew was smeared all over with the stuff.

"I shoved his muzzle into the billycan," Ivan said, panting heavily. "Finish him off, I've got to go."

"Wash the billycan," I told Becker, "and put it under a tree. See the Kapo doesn't catch you. I've just made four stretchers. You know what that means, don't you?"

On the road Andrzej was exercising two Greeks. They didn't know how to march. The Kapo had broken two sticks over their heads and had told them they had to learn. Andrzej had tied a stick to each of their legs and was explaining as best he could:

"You devil's children, you go like this: this is your left, that's your right. Left, left . . ."

The Greeks open their eyes wide and march around, shuffling their feet along the ground in their terror. A great cloud of dust rises high into the air. By the ditch where the guard is standing, the one who wanted my boots, our lads are working, "planing" the earth, delicately beating it down and smoothing it with spades as if it were pastry. As I strike across their path, leaving deep tracks, they bawl:

"What's the latest, Tadek?"

"Oh, nothing much; they've taken Kiev."

"But is it true?"

"A funny question!"

I shout this at the top of my voice as I pass to one side of them and walk along by the ditch. Suddenly I hear a shout in German behind me:

"Halt, halt, you, Warsaw man."

A moment later, unexpectedly in Polish:

"Stop, stop!"

My guard comes rushing after me on the other side of the ditch, carrying his carbine as if going into an attack. He is highly excited.

"Stop, stop!"

I stop. The guard forces his way through the bramble bushes and rattles the lock of his carbine.

"What was that you said just now about Kiev? You're spreading political rumors. You've got a secret organization here. Your number, number, give me your number!"

Shaking with fury and indignation, he holds out a scrap of paper and searches for a pencil. I felt that I was being drained. But I recovered a little.

"Excuse me, guard, you didn't understand. You don't understand Polish very well. I was speaking of the stick* Andrzej has tied to the Greeks on the road. And saying that it was very funny."

"That's right, guard; that's just what he said." There was a harmonious chorus of agreement. The guard took aim with his carbine as though intending to hit me with the butt end across the ditch.

"You're mad, mad. I'll report it this very day to the political arm. Your number, number."

"One hundred and nineteen, one hundred . . ."

"Let me see your arm."

I hold out my arm with the number tattooed on it, feeling sure that at this distance he cannot read it.

"Come closer."

"I mustn't. You can report me if you like, but I'm not White Vaska."

A few days previously, White Vaska had crawled over to a birch growing along the guard line, in order to cut some branches to make a twig broom. You can exchange such a broom for bread or soup in the camp. The guard took aim and fired; the bullet passed through his breast and came out between the shoulders. We carried the lad back to the camp.

I walk away feeling mad, but just beyond the embankment Rubin catches up with me.

"Tadek, what on earth have you done? And what will happen now?"

"Why, what d'you think will happen?"

"But you'll tell everything; you'll say that I . . . Oh, you've done a fine thing. What made you shout so loud? You're out to destroy us."

"What are you afraid of? None of our people will blab."

* An untranslatable play on words. The Polish word for stick is pronounced like the first syllable of "Kiev."

"I know and you know, but *sicher ist sicher*. Sure's sure. You might give that guard your boots; he'll agree for certain. I'll try talking with him. Let me try. I've done trade with him."

"Well, that's fine; now he'll tell all about that too."

"Tadek, everything's black before us. You give him the boots, and I'll have a talk with him. He's a fine fellow."

"Only he's lived too long. I won't give him my boots — that's too great a loss for me. But I have a watch. It won't go and its glass is broken, but what are you going to do? After all, you can give your own; it didn't cost you anything."

"Oi, Tadek, Tadek . . ."

Rubin puts the watch away. In the distance I hear a shout: "Railway man!"

I ran across the field. The Kapo's eyes had acquired an ominous expression, and foam was showing in the corners of his lips. His hands, his enormous gorilla arms were swinging rhythmically, but his fingers twitched nervously.

"What were you up to with Rubin?"

"Didn't you see it yourself? You see everything. I gave him my watch."

"Wha-at?" His hands slowly began to rise towards my throat.

I was petrified with fear. Without moving a muscle (he's a wild beast, the thought flew through my mind), not shifting my eyes from his face, I burst out in one breath:

"I gave him my watch because the guard wants to report me to the political arm for carrying on secret work."

The Kapo's hands slowly lost their tension and fell to his sides. His jaw hung loose, like a dog's when it finds the heat too much for it. As he listened to my story he irresolutely waved a spade haft.

"Go off to your work; I expect you'll be hauled off to the camp today." At that moment he made a lightning movement, started to attention, and dragged the cap off his head. I jumped away, struck in the back by a bicycle. I tore off my cap. The Unterscharführer, the boss of Harmenz, leaped off his bicycle, crimson with nerves.

"What's going on in this crazy gang? Why are your men walking about with their legs tied up over there? This is work time."

"They don't know how to march."

"If they don't know, then kill them. But do you know that another goose has disappeared?"

"What are you standing there for like a stupid dog?" the Kapo snarled at me. "Andrzej is to bring them to order. Get moving!" I flew along the path.

"Andrzej, finish them off. The Kapo's ordered it."

Andrzej seized a stick and struck out violently. One Greek put up his arms to defend himself, started to howl, and dropped to the ground. Andrzej laid the stick across the man's throat, stood on the two ends, and began to rock himself. I went away quickly.

In the distance I saw the Kapo and the SS man go to my guard and have a long talk with him. The Kapo gesticulated violently with the spade haft. He had his cap drawn down over his forehead. When they went off, Rubin went up to the guard. The guard rose from the bench, drew close to the ditch, and finally stepped onto the dike. A moment or two later Rubin nodded to me.

"Thank the guard for not going to make a report about you."

Rubin didn't have the watch in his hand.

I thanked the guard and went back to my work. On the way the old Greek, Ivan's confidant, stopped me.

"Comrade, comrade, that SS man's from the camp, isn't he?"

"Well, what of it?"

"Is it really true that there's going to be a checkup today?"

And in a strange exaltation the grayhaired, withered Greek, a merchant from Salonica, throws down his spade and raises his hands above his head.

"*Nous sommes des hommes misérables. O Dieu, Dieu!*"

His pale blue eyes gaze up into the sky, just as blue and pale.

7

We were hoisting up the little truck. Filled to the brim with sand, it had gone off the rails right by the turntable. Four pairs of emaciated hands pushed the truck backward and forward, rocking it. They rolled it sideways, raised the front wheels, and got them back onto the rails. We set the little wheels underneath and were on the point of getting the truck back onto the rails when we suddenly let it go and straightened up.

"Checkup!" The words quivered and whistled in the distance.

The truck falls back helplessly and digs its wheels into the earth. Someone flings down the now unnecessary crowbar; we pour the sand out of the truck straight onto the turntable. After all, it can be cleared away tomorrow.

We go off to the checkup. But after a moment or two we realize that it must be too early for that. The sun is still high in the sky. It still has quite a way to travel to the crowns of the trees on which it rests its rim at checkup time. The human faces are anxious and questioning. We stand in fives, we form a line, and we tighten up our sacks and belts.

SS men and our guards come from the direction of the house. They form a ring around us some distance off. We remain standing. At the end of the gang are stretchers with two corpses.

There is more traffic on the road than usual. Disturbed by our early departure, the people of Harmenz are moving about. But old "campers" see the situation clearly: there is to be a checkup in the camp, without doubt.

Mrs. Haneczka's bright kerchief appeared and disappeared more than once.

She turned inquisitive eyes in our direction. She set a basket down on the ground and, leaning against the barn, stood gazing. I followed the direction of her gaze. She was looking anxiously at Ivan. The Kapo and the sickly Kommandoführer had come up together with the SS men.

"Spread out in open order, and put your hands up," the Kapo said.

Then we all understood: we were to be searched. We unfasten our jackets, open our sacks. The SS man is efficient and swift. He runs his hands over our bodies, reaches for the sacks. In mine, in addition to the rest of my bread, an onion or two, and some ancient bacon fat, he found an apple which obviously had come from the orchard.

"Where did you get that?"

I raised my head; it was "my" guard asking.

"In a parcel, Mr. Guard."

He looked me ironically in the eyes for a moment.

"I ate apples exactly like that after dinner today."

Out of our pockets they dig pieces of sunflower heads with seeds, cobs of Indian corn, herbs, sorrel, apples; again and again a short human bellow bursts out as someone is beaten up. Suddenly the Unterscharführer strode into the very middle of the rank and drew aside the old Greek with his large well-stuffed sack.

"Open it," he said curtly.

The Greek opened the sack with trembling hands. The Unterscharführer looked inside and called the Kapo over.

"Look, Kapo — our goose."

He drew a goose with enormous, wide-spreading wings out of the sack. The "boy," who had run across to the sack too, shouted triumphantly to the Kapo:

"There it is; didn't I say so?" The Kapo raised his stick to strike.

"Don't hit him," the SS man said, holding back his arm.

He drew his revolver out of its holster and turned to face the Greek, waving the weapon eloquently.

"Where did you get this? If you don't answer, I'll shoot you."

The Greek was silent. The SS man raised his revolver. I glanced at Ivan. He was very pale. Our eyes met. He compressed his lips and stepped out of the rank. He went up to the SS man, took off his cap, and said:

"I gave it to him."

All eyes were turned on Ivan. The Unterscharführer slowly raised his riding whip and struck him across the face once, twice, three times. Then he began to beat him on the head. The whip whistled and the prisoner's face was covered with bloody weals; but Ivan didn't fall. He stood with cap in hand, erect, his arms down his sides. He made no attempt to avoid the blows; he only swayed with all his body.

The Unterscharführer let his hand drop.

"Take his number and report him. Kommando, about turn and back to work."

We went off with a regular, military step. Behind us we left a heap of sunflower heads, heaps of herbs, rags, and bags, crushed apples, and, in addition, a large goose with red head and spreading white wings. Ivan marched at the end of the gang, with no one supporting him. Behind him on two stretchers followed two corpses covered with branches.

As we passed Mrs. Haneczka I turned and looked at her. She was standing pale and erect, her hands pressed to her breast. Her lips were quivering nervously. She raised her eyes and looked at me. Then I noticed that her large black eyes were filled with tears.

After the roll call we were driven into the barracks. We lay on our bunks, peering through the chinks and waiting for the end of the checkup.

"I feel just as if I was to blame for all this checkup. The astonishing fatalism there is in words. In this damned Oswiecim even bad words have a power of their own."

"Don't take it to heart," Kazik replied. "Better give me something to put in the pasty."

"Haven't you any tomatoes?"

"Not every day's a holiday."

I pushed away the sandwiches he had made.

"I can't eat anything."

Outside, the checkup was almost finished. The doctor, an SS man, after taking the numbers and noting the total of those chosen, went on to the next barracks. Kazik got ready to go out.

"I'm going to buy some cigarettes. But you know, Tadek, you're an innocent; if anyone had eaten my gruel I'd have made mincemeat of him."

At that moment a huge grayhaired cranium appeared from below over the edge of the bunk, and blinking, disconcerted eyes stared at us. Then Becker's face appeared, furrowed and looking even older.

"Tadek, there's something I want to ask you."

"Speak up," I said, leaning across to him.

"Tadek, I'm going to the cremo."

I bent still lower and gazed closely into his eyes; but no, they were calm and empty.

"Tadek, I've been hungry for so long. Give me something to eat. Just for this last evening."

Kazik brought his hand down on my knee.

"Do you know this Jew?"

"It's Becker," I answered quietly.

"You, Jew, climb up onto this bunk and eat. When you've eaten enough, take the rest with you to the cremo. Climb up on the bunk. I don't sleep here. I don't care if you are lousy."

"Tadek." Kazik clutched my arm. "Come on. I've got a beautiful apple charlotte in my barracks, straight from Mother."

As we climbed down from the bunk he touched me on the arm.

"Look," he whispered.

I looked at Becker. His eyes were closed, and he was vainly groping, like a blind man, feeling for the boards with one hand, to climb up to the bunk.

— *translated by* HARRY STEVENS

(From *Pozegnanie z Maria.* Published by Panstwowy Instytut Wydawniezy, Warsaw, 1961.)

Portrait from Memory

BY STANISLAW STANUCH

STANISLAW STANUCH was born in 1931 in Polish Silesia and is the son of a schoolteacher. He was graduated from the School of Journalism, Krakow University, in 1954. A book reviewer and reporter, he published his first novel, *Portrait from Memory* (an excerpt follows), in 1959. Earlier short stories were published in 1955. He now lives in Nowa Huta, near Krakow. Reference is made to his work in an essay by Stefan Kisielewski in another section of this anthology.

"What am I to do? Tell me, Nikolai Styepanich, I beg of you: what am I to do?"

"I don't know. I cannot advise you, Katie; honestly speaking — I don't know."

A. CHEKHOV

I STOPPED in front of a tall door. It was not an ordinary door. It was covered with leather. Touching it, I felt a thick layer of wadding. Moving my fingers, I hoped for a moment that I would find a harder spot on which I might knock. This had not been foreseen. The door provided insulation from any noises by which people in the large waiting room might wish to draw attention to themselves.

I pressed down the handle. The man sitting behind the desk in the middle of the large hall looked up from his papers. On meeting my questioning and humble gaze, he raised his eyebrows. In his eyes I could read first an effort to detach himself from the thoughts which were obviously preoccupying him, then interest. This was immediately stifled. I said "Good morning." His eyebrows did not move; they continued to express astonishment. I thought that perhaps his status did not allow him to ask questions, or to demand an explanation of why I had burst into his room. There was no contact between us. I was straining my leg muscles to remain firmly on the ground and to prevent myself from floating suddenly in the air, filled with the realization of my nonexistence. We remained facing one another, tense.

The seconds which had passed since I had pushed open the door were enough for me to discover under the wrinkles and the gray hair of the sitting man a likeness to someone in the photograph hidden in my pocket. Formerly that photograph had lain on my father's desk. For many years he had been conscience-stricken at not having taken it to be framed. At such moments, he took it in his hands, explained to me its most interesting details, and put it back on the desk in what seemed to him the most conspicuous place, in order — so he said — not to forget to take it with him to town the next day. I knew precisely how he wanted it framed: with a black rim of shiny tape around a sheet of glass. I also remember the empty space on the wall over my father's desk waiting for years to receive the photograph. Now that photograph was in my pocket — still in the same condition in which my father received it years before from the photographer and in which I found it on his desk when I had to leave home — to remind me, in company with a few other trifles, of what I had left behind without any hope of return.

This now yellowing piece of paper showed some young people sitting in a semicircle. The chairs must obviously have been placed on the steps of the building in the background, because the sitters were on three different levels. All were lifting their heads slightly upwards; all had solemn, frozen expressions like those to be observed in cats when you stroke them. This pose was emphasized perhaps by their high, tight collars. They sat legs crossed. With one hand each held a saber, lifting it slightly and pushing it forward, while the other hand was slipped under the military tunic, a Napoleonic gesture. In front of them stood a heavy machine gun, of the old Maxim type, pointed toward the camera. Against the wheels was propped a small board with the inscription: "Officers' corps of *N*th Infantry Regiment." On the back of the photograph were signatures and the words of a collective dedication. The date transported one to a remote past.

The continued silence of the man looking at me made me realize that nothing would free me from the necessity of an explanation. I shut the door and walked up to his desk. Nervously fingering the photograph hidden in my pocket, I told him as distinctly as possible my name and embarked on a lengthy explanation of my visit. The expression of astonishment, expectation and alertness disappeared from the face of the sitting man. It became benevolent and friendly. I then scored a small victory; he smiled and half rose from his chair, inviting me with a gesture to be seated.

The previous day, I suddenly had the idea of visiting that man. In the middle of the large city I was sitting alone on a bench in a side street. The lamplight filtered through a trembling curtain of leaves. I floated in an enormous emptiness. A question suddenly caught up with me. Its final sense frightened and robbed one of freedom. "Here I am," I thought. "I have lived in this world for twenty-six years and then what? Nothing. Have I achieved anything? Have I thought anything sensible? I have not. Twenty-six years ago someone threw me into the current like a leaf and I am still floating — but there is not, there's never been, any sense in it."

On that day, when the lack of sense had become so obvious, I clutched at distant memories as at a plank thrown into the sea, and, as along a gangway, I began to enter my unknown self, condemned, it seemed, to oblivion. I wanted to escape as far as possible, to rush forward toward a point where decisions are simple, and intentions accompany us into sleep, tucked under the pillow. With increasing fear I listened to the distant sound of city bells, distilled from the silence, carrying memories of other bells, streets and landscapes stored unnoticed through the years. I discovered that my memory was not as pure as before.

That day I could not get rid of a desire for justice and a few other abstractions which sometimes seem indispensable for living. And yet — like all people of my kind — I believed that my lot was sufficiently hard and that I should not worsen it by my own actions. I doubted also, most of all, whether I would succeed in finding a sense in my life, whether it mightn't prove to be a brittle, unimportant knickknack, a meaningless enclosure in the dossier of the world's affairs. I chose carefully some motifs, examined them from all sides, wishing to make them as weighty as events, to find in them some decisive influence on my life. But perhaps because I clung too close to the verge, or because worry arising from a feeling of responsibility had robbed my sight of acuity, the anxiety and insecurity did not leave me. I saw only chaos, a tangle of uncoordinated events, decisions, failures — not a trace of a pure current. In the end I was filled with contempt for myself and at a loss to know what the outcome of it all might be.

My future superior, looking through my testimonials and references, observed: "You seem to have forgotten to enclose a short biography." He was clearly well disposed toward me. He therefore looked through the scattered bits of paper once more to make sure that this, for him, indispensable document was not there. He did not wish to hurt me. This is probably why he did not notice how much his words had disturbed me. Friendliness, sympathy, pity — these were feelings which at that time compromised in my eyes everyone who wished to show them to me. In the period preceding my nightly decision to look for work, I had believed that the situation in which I found myself resulted from the hostility people felt toward me. I had attributed hatred to all who cast eyes on me. If reality did not confirm my beliefs, I could make facts fit my fancies. Therefore, I especially hated people who wished to show me kindness, pity or sympathy, suspecting that this was a device of hypocrites who wanted to confound me with greater cunning. Was I guided by pride? Difficult to say. In any case I did not see a place for myself in that community because — as I genuinely believed — "I would be unable to become as vile as they."

When the man sitting behind his desk repeated his question about my biography, I answered, "Unfortunately, I cannot include this document." As he insisted, and I did not wish to cause offense, I explained: "It cannot be done. I don't know my life story. Even if I tried to write down certain facts of my life, very little would result from it. I don't know their true meaning; I am not sure which should have the first and which the last place. How to define the direction in which I move, apart from the obvious one, common to all of us, which therefore does not need to be described? I don't yet possess a key to my life. Therefore to write the life story which you require of me would only be possible after my death. If it were possible at all. We are alive," I explained, "but how can we discern what is only function and what is sense? Each day we make several hundred thousand various gestures; we move our jaws, we grasp objects with our fingers, we go out shopping and to the movie theater, we get up, we sit down, we smile, we breathe, we weep. How to recognize what is a reflex of the muscles and what is a tendency, an idea — not to speak of a division into good and bad acts?" I said all this, believing that the sincerity and naïve modesty in my words would be highly appreciated. I was quite unself-conscious because I was convinced of the depth of my philosophy. His reply was a sigh and a nervous tic at his forehead. But as he must still have felt some sympathy for me, he added:

"If your poor father had known your opinions he would be very sad. . . ."

At this point, we bowed to each other in silence, and I briskly left his study.

No sooner had I shut the door than I wanted to go back. I even hesitated for a moment, still holding the door handle. My doubts originated from the assumption that our misunderstanding had arisen, perhaps, from the excessive brevity of my pronouncement. At the same time, I felt on my hand a grip of somebody's fingers. It was a man who, without looking at me, impatiently pressed down the handle and pushed open the door.

I went and sat on a bench in the small square facing the main door of the building. I decided to rethink once more what I should tell this chief of a department when renewing my application for work. "For such a conversation," I thought, "the best place would be a café. There I might develop my views with greater precision, in greater detail, support them with valid arguments." This was a good idea. Cheered by it, I even saw the official's point. Without this more detailed argument, my behavior might indeed have seemed strange to him. "I must wait until he has finished work," I thought, "then ask him to have a cup of coffee." To tell the truth, I silently hoped he would find a way out of the situation and advise me on various matters. This seemed to me at the time much more important than the job I had expected to get. Now, I had a few free hours before me. The wonderful sunshine and the green trees around me gave me courage and hope necessary to delve bravely into matters and events with which I was to supplement later my too brief answer.

Wishing that my statement about the impossibility of my life should strike him as plausible, I decided to include my childhood in my indictment; to look in it for the reason why I suddenly found myself among people — fettered. Yes, if I was to convince him, I must confess to him with complete frankness everything that was worrying me, that I often could not explain to myself, and that obviously had a logic and a meaning, since it did not leave my memory. Was he to be told about the daily returns home? Yes, he was. He should indeed know it if I expected help. It was true that recently the returns were the worst. Where these were concerned, I had to apply certain rules against which — although sometimes I revolted — I was nevertheless powerless.

Nobody, for instance, could force me to return home at night, particularly at the time of the new moon. Even the most important things had to be arranged so that I could be in my room before dusk. This did not help much, of course, because other times also seemed dangerous to me. Therefore, whenever I was late, before I decided to enter the dark tunnel of the corridor leading to the yard, I at first paced for a long time up and down on the pavement on the opposite side of the street, observing the front windows and watching the traffic at the entrance to the house. Only when it seemed to me that I could risk it, did I cross the courtyard and climb the stairs to the fifth floor, pausing frequently to listen.

Perhaps this has been so with me since the day when I clearly realized that I had been disgracefully deceived? I bear no grudge for it. And perhaps I had become mistrustful even earlier, when I was still a child, when I had, within a few minutes, to doubt the whole of my life? Ah, how well do I remember the details of that education. I had been taught in all seriousness: don't kill, don't steal, love your neighbor. I fulfilled all these commands. More from lack of opportunity than from an innate distaste for evil, but this is my private affair. Suffice it to say that I tried not to kill, not to steal, and to love my neighbors. These of course are simple, elementary, easy rules — especially when one's horizon encompasses only one's home, and especially when one's family is sufficiently cooperative.

At that time I pronounced with an especially insistent pathos the word "life." It contained magic for me, and it did not mean much more than hope. People often said to me:

"When the Germans have gone, we shall live like human beings; we shall be free, always. When the Germans have gone, you will see, we'll be happy."

I believed it. And the Germans really went. But before they did I saw them from the window, as in disorderly gangs, with fear in their eyes, they marched through the village, only to return later on, propelled from place to place as in an enormous stewpot. Soldiers, wrapped tight from the cold, walked in small groups at the edge of the road, looking around them. Their returns became so frequent that soon I could clearly recognize the most characteristic silhouettes, announcing with a shout to my family their reappearance. My observation post was at the window of the mill, in which we took refuge as the front line approached. Like all the refugees who filled the large house, we thought that it was safer in the village than in the market town situated at an important strategic point. The monotony of refugee life was broken by some men who, in the last phase of the German retreat, suddenly appeared from the forest and spent their time gaily, playing cards, drinking vodka and pawing girls in various dark corners of the mill.

One afternoon, a boy of sixteen or seventeen came to the door, dressed in a German uniform. He spoke Polish. He was tired and dirty, and one could read from his face that only extreme necessity had made him overcome his fear and detach himself from his unit. He immediately said that he was from Silesia, that he had been forcibly drafted into the Wehrmacht. He asked for a glass of water. There was commotion among the partisans. Then their faces suddenly became serious, and they looked at each other in silence. After a short consultation, one of them beckoned to the stranger. They walked down to where the machinery of the mill stood. The members of the household followed. They stopped in the middle of the room. I remember to this day the drafty hall with the machinery in it, a number of wooden shelves and the threshing floor which, from sacks being dragged across it, had lost the natural color of earth. It had become gray. The men's steps made an immediate mark on it. I don't know why I watched with special attention these dark marks in the shape of a human foot. When I lifted my head, I saw fear in the eyes of the newcomer, and guns in the hands of those men. Having surrounded the young soldier in a circle, they ordered him to prove that he was a Pole. One of them separated himself for a moment from the group and set the mill machinery in motion. The hall was filled with its monotonous clatter. Meanwhile the prisoner knelt, sang a hymn, repeated every Catholic prayer the partisans could think of and sang something again; and the more it became obvious that he was a Pole, the tighter grew the circle of men around him. At last he was ordered to lie down, which he did without stopping to beg and plead. At the back, some of the men were meanwhile trying to lift the enormous millstone. Just when the men leaned panting over the sixteen-year-old lad, seeking a convenient angle, somebody grabbed me by the scruff of my neck and pushed me roughly through the door.

Returning to my position at the window to watch again the retreat of the Germans, I looked at the glasses of unfinished drinks on the table and at the softly crying women. I stood at the window, but the sight of passing soldiers could not hold my attention. My thoughts became scattered, nervous. One idea kept obstinately returning: does a man whose head is crushed choke slowly or does he die at once? This was not, however, a suitable moment for questions and answers. I wanted to stop thinking, for I felt my stomach rising to my throat, but at the same time, I had to probe ever deeper into the details of that other boy's death. At last I began to retch. When I came to, it was evening. I lay in bed, clinging to a wall of thick beams which were shaking slightly. After a while, I recognized the monotonous noise of the mill machinery at work. My sickness returned. I waited long into the night until the stoppage of work restored peace to the house. Since then, the slightest sound, the faintest noise, disturbs my sleep, and I have the unpleasant, growing feeling of being surrounded. Until now, too, when somebody gives me an ardent assurance that he will keep his word, I repeat the phrase: "When the Germans have gone?"

On another occasion I was returning home. It was an ordinary evening, like any other evening in the youth of any of us, especially when the moon is full, in early spring, when we are not burdened by any complicated experiences and when we feel purity growing within us. We then think about the world with gentleness and feel impatient about the next morning coming in only a few hours. We go to bed at once, but cannot sleep for a long time.

So I was returning that day, when suddenly, looking in the darkness for the gate in the wooden fence around our house, I noticed a strange silhouette on the porch. I drew back. I have always been afraid of stumbling against a strange body on the porch, or experiencing in darkness the unpleasant feel of a strange hand on my face. Ah, this can be forgiven to people as young as I was then. I could not free myself from that fear; my imagination provided so many frightful situations that all objective arguments proved fruitless. Now, however, there was no doubt: there was a soldier with a gun in front of the house. This rather reassured me. The front had recently passed through our village and made us familiar with such sights. In any case, a soldier meant once again trust and a feeling of security. No sooner did I approach him, though, than the sentry barred my way with his rifle. For a moment we stood facing each other in silence. For the first time in my life, I found it difficult to admit that this was my house. When at last I gave the necessary explanation, there was no retreat.

The doors were ajar; lights were lit in all the rooms and in the hall. I heard the sounds of bustling activity. On my forehead I felt the coolness of a wall. Somebody standing behind me was feeling my body, putting hands in my pockets. My personal belongings were thrown on the table, revealing their futility. Just like the other members of my family, I had nothing to confess, I could not think of any guilt to declare. The searchers knew it too. They had no intention of proving anything. They did their job rather on principle. When the secret policeman thought I was hiding something or being slow in obeying his orders, he would come up to me and with a greedy, skilled movement would twist my ear. This "fatherly" gesture was accompanied by peals of laughter. I was ashamed of that situation, as if I were stripped naked in a public place. And meanwhile the silliest ideas kept coming into my head.

Asked what was the reason for my stupid expression, I told my thoughts to the officer. For the first time in my life, I was slapped. Soon everybody got bored with pretending to play cops and robbers. Our guests became pleasant and polite, and their faces resumed once again their gentle expression, which inspired trust. They seemed a little ashamed of what had happened and made some general remarks about military necessity. Tea was served, and we sat around the table in harmony and in good humor. Then they all left, to the assurances by the family that everything was in the best of order and their next visit would be an honor for the house.

After that, I was unable to treat the house as before. It ceased to be a home where you ran sometimes when escaping from a dog, a gang of angry boys or an approaching storm. It had suddenly become the last resort. *At any moment, somebody might get in and make himself comfortable, might bar the entry or exit for me. And, what is worse, I could never foresee who it would be and when he would materialize. I became nervous, and that state, like illness, spread over ever new areas. As before, I never trespassed against the law, but now* I was never sure. *Of course, I had sublime and vile moments, moments pleasant and painful — I was alive, as they say — but always and first of all:* I was prepared. *I don't remember ever afterwards feeling safe when returning home. I might say: "This is me; that is my girl; we are in love." But in reality I did not believe what I said, what I heard, what I thought, or even what I did not wish to talk about. Looking into the eyes of a girl, I could not rid myself of the impression that in reality she was looking at someone else. But I never said to her: "I am tired of your insincerity." I answered a smile with a smile, a kiss with a kiss. With insouciance, achieved by a terrific effort, I spoke about the sky, the sun, beauty and love. I also chose more willingly the part of listener for myself. I thought that a lie had to be answered by a lie. I learned to perfection how to be insincere with myself; I saw guilt most readily in others. And I really did not consider myself proud. It might be said that I became somewhat selfish.*

This happened later, however, at a time when I was almost grown-up and understood the truths which — please believe me — I have no strength to confess. At any rate, these leanings led me to situations which I would willingly erase from memory. I began to find pleasure in provoking conversations about fictitious topics. They seemed to me to act as a safety valve. At a later age this developed into an unpleasant habit of talking about sudden murders, and always being ready to serve up some "real-life" examples. At the most intriguing moment of the game, I would fix my eyes on the company and ask: "It would be interesting to know how each of us would behave if our city were suddenly struck by fire or if it suffered a terrible flood. Who would rescue those being burned or drowning, and who would be content with his own safety?"

At that time, a strange duality took hold of me. I wished to be generally considered a criminal, a perjurer, a raper, a pervert, and at the same time I began to be ashamed of my own strength. Anyone who would inadvertently praise my physical attributes became my enemy. This applied to women as well. Those whom I remember with tenderness to this day had remained silent; the others had witnessed how I suddenly would run away to sit somewhere in a dark corner, living through an attack of hatred for my own arms, legs and muscles. I have really made a great effort to make my experiences a secret from my neighbors, not to differ in anything from the crowd, not to be recognized in the street, pointed at and named as myself; I took care that no one — God forbid — should wish to confide in me, choose me, recognize me from a thousand others. Some people took it as proof of my boundless conceit; others thought I was a dense person of low intelligence. In either case, they were not optimistic about my future. I did not correct them. I became reconciled to it, as finally we become reconciled even to our own infirmities. At least externally. Thus, retaining my conviction about the wrongs I had suffered, I floundered deeper and deeper, trying to brave ever new complications. Finally, this had become second nature, and I always took precautions "just in case."

Sitting on a bench in the middle of a small square, facing the entrance of the building in which the department chief worked, and engrossed in these reflections on my past, I decided in the end to limit myself only to telling him about the two above-mentioned episodes in my life. The survey I made convinced me that my distrust of his requirements was well founded. I realized the futility of attempts to describe by trite, banal phrases the extremely complicated matters of which sentences like "I was born at . . ." or "afterwards my family moved to . . ." don't give an inkling. In short, I wanted to give my future superior a kind of test during our meeting over coffee. I decided that if he proved able to answer the questions which arise for everybody on the margin of similar events, if he could give me advice, I could believe that he had understood correctly my laconic refusal to write my life story and had devised me a job in his department in full knowledge of the facts, certain of his own honesty.

Meanwhile, I noticed that the ground had begun to shake. I looked at the sky, but it was clear. When I turned my head, I saw at the end of the long road, running toward the outskirts of the city, some tanks moving slowly, one behind the other. I began to count them. Soon I got tired of that. The tanks filled the whole street. Following them, a long column of lorries appeared with soldiers packed close to one another, and lastly, a column of motorcycles, with sidecars. It took me a long while to recognize the soldiers' hats. Our garrison troops were returning from exercises. I seem to remember smiling at the passing soldiers, returning their waves, and perhaps even calling to them.

The columns of men and vehicles rolling in front of me reminded me, however, of the approaching end of office hours. Soon I saw the department chief leaving the building in the company of other men. But before I could walk to the other side of the street, they entered the waiting car and drove off at once. I stood for a moment thinking what to do, then started walking quickly towards the city.

– *translated by* CELINA WIENIEWSKA

(From the novel *Portret z Pamieci.* Published by "Czytelnik," Warsaw, 1959.)

The Crystal Stream

BY ADOLF RUDNICKI

ADOLF RUDNICKI, one of the leading writers of his generation, was born in 1912 in Zabno. His first work, a Kafkaesque novel, *The Rats,* was published in 1931. Of Jewish origin, he is the Jeremiah of the Warsaw ghetto. His major works are *The Soldiers* (1933), an autobiographical report of military service; *The Unloved One* (1937), a psychological novel; *One Summer* (1938), impressions and observations of life in an artists' colony in the country; *Shakespeare* (1948); *The Flight from Yasnaya Polyana* (1949), volumes of short stories; *The Dead and the Living Sea* (1952), a digest of previous work. "The Crystal Stream," presented here, is from *Ascent to Heaven,* published in English by Roy Publishers, New York, in 1951. *The Fiancé of Beata,* short stories, appeared in 1961. Mr. Rudnicki lives in Warsaw.

I

WHEN ABEL went out, the day after his arrival in Warsaw, he was still wearing his army uniform, though the war had ended some months before. It was obvious that until recently he had been a prisoner of war. He was tall, lean, with black eyes, a head perhaps a little too round, a face which passed quickly from moodiness to sorrow. It was this note of sorrow in his features that attracted the attention.

In Nowy Swiat Street he saw the same devastation as he had seen yesterday, on his arrival from Lodz. Only a short distance separates Lodz from Warsaw. Today the two cities are more closely linked together than in the past. Every day thousands of people travel between them on thousands of affairs; the traffic is lively and continuous. So one would think that an inhabitant of Lodz would be able to imagine what Warsaw looks like, if only from hearsay. But no. A city so completely destroyed as Warsaw defeats imagination.

From the moment the train had steamed into the outskirts of Warsaw and the first burnt-out houses had risen before him, he had sat speechless. What he saw was impossible to describe in words. After undamaged Lodz, the mind could not take in this view. Time after time he told himself: it's bound to end at the next corner. But it did not end at the next, or at any following corner; there was no end to the ruins — house after house, street after street, district after district — which had been struck by a cosmic anger, the same anger of God that thunders from the mountain tops. The empty shells, the empty windows, the mounds of foul earth inside the shells, breathed horror and filth, the dreary dreariness of corpses.

Yesterday he had spent several hours looking at what remained of the city, recalling a similar scene from his childhood after the First World War; in the silent ruins he had rediscovered a long-familiar aspect of history. But here the novelty, the incredible novelty, was that every one of the houses was reduced to a shell.

Burnt-out houses stood all along Nowy Swiat Street. And yet, they stood. The ruddy hue of certain interiors recalled the ruddiness of broken earthenware pots. Where there were missing houses, a gap of two or three in succession, it was at least possible to bring them to mind. A former resident returning to this district would still be able, after a moment's thought, to say, "My house stood here."

But when he crossed the Krasinski Square and reached what formerly had been the Jewish district he looked to the left and right of him, before and behind him, and although he had seen other parts of this "most devastated city in the world," he refused to believe his own eyes. He had expected to see destruction, but on the same scale as in the other districts; he had expected to see some traces which would enable him to re-create what had formerly existed here. There were no traces whatever. There were no buildings, not even gutted shells or the partially destroyed; there were no buildings at all. No walls, no chimneys — which cling so tenaciously to life — no outlines of streets, no sidewalks, no tramlines, no roads or squares; on no level had anything survived, to give the eye a moment's rest. Here there was not one of the elements created by organized human effort, nothing to establish that this spot had been inhabited by man. Over an area which the eye could encompass only with difficulty, where formerly the greatest concentration of Jews in Europe had been housed, there was nothing but rubble and broken brick, with here and there yellow and gray sheet iron, like untanned oxhide. Here the city had been obliterated, removed from the face of the earth, like a tent from a meadow. In other districts there were dead bodies; here there was not even a dead body. In this place the capital had been crushed to powder; not one stone was left on another. And though beneath these fields of rubble rested more dead than in a hundred cemeteries, there was nothing to suggest a cemetery. The city was deleted, and only its frail, uncertain and delusive outline loomed in the onlooker's memory. Faced with this nothingness, Abel no longer felt any urge to seek out the house in which he had lived — an urge as idiotic as it was profound. Before this place had been leveled in death, it had been leveled in suffering. There was no justification for weeping over any particular individual. He sat down on a heap of bricks. All around him was a dead silence; the only note of life was the murmur of the waters flowing through the sewers. Some distance away, several people passed in single file between hillocks of rubble. Over the city reduced to chaos hung a sky cloudy and cold.

As though in a dream, he heard footsteps. As he unwillingly raised his head, he saw a woman coming toward him. His stupefaction was followed by a realization which he could not accept. He recognized and doubted, doubted and recognized. Yet he did not stir. He stood up only when the woman, as moved as he, halted in front of him. And although he felt that he was flinging himself into her arms and crying, he stood unmoving, unspeaking. Only his pupils dilated and contracted.

She was the first to speak; just as in the old days, she hardly sounded the *b* in his name:

"Abel!"

His voice died in his throat, as it had during heavy air raids. For some time he could not even say:

"Amelia!"

2

HISTORY as we knew it in the days of blitzkriegs, the history of recent times, this ultramodern history in all the fields of struggle, on land, on sea, and in the air, was completely different in the prisoner-of-war camps. In ordinary life, when a man changed his place of residence he seemed to be changing the age in which he lived. In some cities one had only to move from one street to another to go back several centuries in history. But the prisoners of war, from being people incessantly occupied, as is the modern fashion, became people cursed with an excess of leisure. Only then could they ponder on many things for which they had never had time before.

Only when shut away in the camp — in the neat, small German town which had been transformed into Oflag 3 E, holding about six thousand men — did Abel come to realize Amelia's distinctive qualities, which in the days of freedom had ricocheted at him off other people's appreciation; he himself had never paid much attention to them. He had met her first in 1937, just about the time when he had set up as an architect. She was a thoughtful, thin, and very young girl then. As time passed she grew more and more beautiful, and one day Abel realized that her beauty was of a very distinctive kind. She was tall, dark, with a perfectly proportioned figure, a face that was wholly mild, like the faces of Madonnas, whose unprovocative femininity seems to be a contradiction in terms. Set in its frame of rhythmic curves, her face quivered with light and color like the interior of a church. Any background against which her profile happened to be set — a whitewashed wall, a scrap of sky — became a texture marvelous in itself, as in the work of an abstract painter. As they gazed at Amelia, people were speechless, as at the sight of a mountain flooded with moonlight, or of a great fire. She always reminded you of someone. Or rather, it was not that she reminded you of anyone; she awakened the age-old yearning for beauty that is innate in us all.

As long as they were together — a period of two years, one year as husband and wife — Abel was not very conscious of her beauty: as yet he had no need of it. Amelia's home — her father was a chest and lung specialist — was warm and welcoming. During the early days of their acquaintance Abel loved the family more than the girl; he himself came from a home which never knew laughter; his father hated his mother and had not spoken to her for years. Amelia conquered Abel's heart above all by her quick response to her mother's good and bad moods. The simple fact that her mother had eaten well, and had gone to see her hairdresser — which indicated that she was regaining her interest in life — or, on the other hand, the fact that she did not wish to see anyone was an experience in itself. And it was this that originally had most effect on Abel.

Once in love with the family, he deliberately ascribed to Amelia all the qualities he thought worthy of love. Because he craved for love, he persuaded himself and Amelia that he loved her. So he said many things which were not strictly true. Even as he said them he was aware of some inadequacy, of his own reservations, and he hated himself, for he was not really a hypocrite. He craved for love, but for a long time he was conscious of a gap in his soul.

The years in the camp closed that gap. His fear that one day Amelia would realize his duplicity proved groundless. In the camp he fell head over heels in love with his wife. He discovered her both as a human being and as a woman, and much in her that before had annoyed him now became something to adore. The fact that, unlike him, she was undemonstrative and inscrutable in her feelings; that she was capable of strength of character just when he lacked it; that she could bear the most unjust charges with dignity and not seek an explanation, as long as he remained angry — an art few possess; that she could be more experienced, wiser, older, though she was so much younger; that she could treat him as a sick man — in love, one party should always have the privileges of the sick. Many other fine qualities, attitudes, details, which had not been obvious to him during their everyday life together, now came to life for him, arousing tenderness and delight. Everything connected with Amelia acquired its own savor, the savor of certain early mornings, the savor of sweetness and pain. His heart ached a little at such times, as a lover's always does.

The last phase of their life together grew especially dear to him. In 1939, people were no more afraid of war than a child is of a revolver. But in Amelia's eyes Abel saw a fear of war. She would not listen when people were talking about it, she would leave the table rather than listen. After Colonel Beck's speech on the Danzig Corridor issue, in May 1939, she burst into tears.

One day Abel repeated to her what some important person had said:

Poles were not Czechs — they would shoot. When he awoke in the murderous stillness of next morning's dawn, he saw that she was not asleep. She was gazing at him intently. After that morning, whenever he woke up he would find her gaze fixed on him. When he tried to comfort her with the remark that the Germans had no food, that their tanks were made of tin, and that England would not allow them to do anything, she did not reply.

In the later days he felt sure she had a premonition of the approaching disaster. But no. Although she was living through a difficult year, she was not unhappy. The first year of her marriage was also the first of her life as a woman; she loved her husband, and she had her own home. During their last nights together she received him as a communicant receives the Host, with eyes so pure that he could not look into them.

When he was called up, she went to see him off at the station, through a city as thronged as if it were the eve of a holiday. And then he realized that her voice had taken on a new note; it seemed to flow from some unknown source. She spoke emphatically, underpinning her words, so to speak, evidently afraid she would not be able to get them out. As he stood at the carriage window and took a last look at her strong, beautiful figure, now huddled as though it had suffered an inner collapse, he felt for the first time afraid of the war. And he understood the old truth that pain affects us most through the people we love.

She was inscrutable in her feelings, she was "impregnable," and this circumstance had always intensified his own reaction; but during those last months before the war he was able to see that the fire he had laid had caught. And then he reproached himself with receiving more than he deserved.

Like the majority of prisoners of war, he lived for letters, for those official forms so well known all over Europe — the *Kriegsgefangenenpost* — of which half was allotted to the reply. Amelia amazed him. He had never expected such ardor. He remembered her as a being of perfect balance, and doubted the existence of such depths of tenderness in her as she now revealed. He doubted because he was naturally skeptical. He doubted, too, because, like the majority of men, he thought that great beauty is satisfied with itself, as if beauty were not exactly the same as comfort is to the man accustomed to comfort: the outer skin, only the outer skin.

Sometimes her replies were delayed. Then he was completely carried away by his suffering, as is so often the case with people who feel deeply. When they did arrive, he did not even need to read them. Lack of news from Amelia drove him apart from the others, made him long for solitude. The arrival of a letter, especially after an interruption in their regularity, made him seek company.

The Germans had such contempt for other human beings that they did not care what the prisoners wrote about themselves or what was written to them. The censors hardly ever blue-penciled letters, and all the men were aware of events at home. In August 1942, the camp Underground paper had an article on the slaughters in the Jewish district of Warsaw. And Abel's letters from Amelia ceased.

It was a summer night painful in its beauty. In two small, connecting rooms, nine men were lying on paillasses, but not one was asleep. Abel was sitting at the window. From time to time one of the others rose and went to him with words of comfort. Nobody had heard a word from him for two days. Nobody had seen him eat. He sat at the window day and night, his ears attuned to the inaudible cry of the murdered city. The voice of the distant suffering floated over his head as though he were a wireless receiver. He could not suppress the watchfulness and attention which is fundamental to life. As of old during his worst attacks of jealousy, so now he lacked the courage to look at Amelia's photograph — it caused him so much pain. For him a crime against Amelia summed up all the crimes against four hundred thousand human beings. During those days his face darkened. "He's fretting himself to death," the others said.

Then he received two letters from someone with the unfamiliar name of Anna Zuch. It was Amelia's new name. She was safe. She was living outside the ghetto, in the Zoliborz suburb of Warsaw. As he read the new address Abel had the feeling that she had changed her country. After the two letters there was a further interruption, and he reproached himself for having been as imprudent in replying as she had been in writing. But soon she wrote again. Her note included the words: "I have been through something during these last few months." As he read, Abel caught his breath. The meaning was clear, for it was universal.

At a later period her replies contained fewer confidences and expressions of tenderness than before. At a time of such suffering what significance — one would think — could a few tender adjectives have? None the less their absence, and the absence or rarer use of certain verbs, some change in her vocabulary, plunged him into a deep anguish of a different kind. He was nothing, less than nothing; he lived with the other Jewish officers in a separate block, 14 E, known as the *Judenblock*. Their office records were kept separately; they expected the end every day. Everybody in the camp was quite sure that Block 14 E would suffer a different fate from the others. And at home in Warsaw Amelia, hiding on the so-called Aryan side, lived continually under sentence of death, and anyone might be her executioner. And yet . . . and yet, in his thoughts, desires, and demands he never ceased to be first and foremost a man, and to think of her as a woman.

He wrote to her, saying that as he could give her nothing, he had no right to demand anything in return, and he set her completely free. To which he received a reply so passionate that he could not have hoped for anything better. But then her letters suddenly stopped. When she wrote again, despite his expectations she did not give a changed name or address, so evidently there had been no outward obstacles to her writing. But he noted that she had written with three different kinds of pencil. It was obvious that she was no longer writing at one sitting, and that in fact she no longer liked writing him letters, but had to force herself to write them.

The Catholics, who possess a long-standing knowledge of man, say that the human soul is the real arena of struggle and crisis. Abel had so often felt numb at the thought that Amelia might leave him — might perish, or might leave him, it could not be otherwise — that when her letters grew infrequent, and conversations with other prisoners forced him into the thought that it must already have happened, he bore the shock with comparative calm. Human strength is limited; suffering, like fever, has its upper limit. Tragedies arising out of infidelity were everyday experience in the camp. The women outside entered into new relations, bore children to other men, floated on the varied waves of living existence. The prisoners who were the first to suffer from their wives' "betrayal" were plunged into the depths of despair; those whose turn came later suffered less, for they had already suffered in sympathy and apprehension. That was the general law, and Abel was no exception.

In October 1944, officers who had taken part in the Warsaw Uprising arrived at the camp. The majority of them were in civilian dress, with white and red armlets. They inspected the camp with curiosity, and their first question was whether they would be retrained, and whether there would be a joint German-British attack on Russia within the next six weeks. Those who had urged them into the steps leading to their imprisonment had assured them that these questions were settled. Unlike the earlier prisoners, the insurgents were solely interested in politics. They were broken up and scattered among all the blocks.

Among these new arrivals was one of Abel's student friends, Tadeusz Mazurek. He knew a good deal about Amelia, and he thought it wrong to let people keep their illusions. Yes, there was someone else in Amelia's life. But Abel was not surprised by that news. He was surprised by himself. Before the insurgents' arrival he had been apathetic. He thought he had completely exhausted his stock of emotions, but now hell opened again before him. He was astonished at the strength of his suffering; he thought he had lost it all. He had believed himself to be reconciled to the loss of Amelia. Like the others, he had told himself: it had to be. Now it transpired that he did not know himself. In the night he started up from his paillasse with horror and defeat in his soul. He choked, as though the room were stifling. His position seemed bitter, unbearably bitter.

As Amelia was no longer his, one would have thought that he had lost all capacity for joy. But no. He was even capable of such delirious joy as is comparable only to that of a dog rushing about a yard on the first warm day after the winter. Warsaw knew that joy on May 8, 1945. Abel knew it the day the Russian forces overran Camp 3 E.

3

As SHE stood before him she repeated his name, obviously deeply moved. There was a warm light in her eyes. She had received his letter and card announcing his release, and had been tremendously pleased. She had sat down a dozen times to write a reply, and she really could not say just why she didn't. In fact, she had intended to visit him at Lodz, but always something had cropped up to hinder her. All the same, now that he was in Warsaw she did not understand why he had not called on her, instead of relying on such a remote chance as this fortuitous meeting. "You should just have dropped in."

He gazed at her, succumbing to a tumult of joy, in which forces were liberated which had been suppressed for years; he was enveloped in its gracious, its blessed, invisible ecstasy. He walked along beside her, feeling no desire for talk, which flows only when emotion grows cold. The uttered pain is a pain subdued. At its highest it is a cry, or silence. As he listened to her he was void of all desire. She was at his side.

When he regained what painters call conscious vision, for a moment he saw two faces, as though on a twice-exposed negative: the face he remembered was contained within this face he now looked at. He recognized certain intangible changes. He reflected that it was stronger than formerly. Of recent months he had often said to himself: I am behaving like a fool; by allowing myself to dream of Amelia I am killing myself. There is nothing like meeting her face to face to cure me; by the very act of living she must reveal her weaknesses and make mistakes from which she is now shielded by my yearning, by my very need for beauty. Only meeting her will cure me. I must let life kill the idea. For a lonely man there is no disillusionment to equal that of life itself; having forgotten what it is like, he will certainly find it too crude for him. But his first glance had not brought him disillusionment, not, at least, in her beauty. As of old, she was perfectly proportioned, solid, and tall. Her skin emanated warmth, well-being, and serenity; it invited caresses, like a piece of carving, like a child's bare belly. After the holocaust of a nation such women were rarely to be seen in the streets of Warsaw.

She spoke first:

"In the early days we used to wonder what we would say to the people who had spent the war abroad, and who would come back, of course, when it was over. And we used to worry over it. How could we give them some idea of the sort of life we had lived; how could we make them realize that at bottom it was inconceivable to those who had known only the prewar life? We all agreed that we would have to show them the children the Germans had photographed for publication in their press as 'the breed of the Bolshevik paradise.' Not everybody on the Polish side was friendly. Some said the ghetto walls — behind which hunger and typhus were killing the inhabitants who were packed together like people in a crowded train — ought to be surrounded with a ring of machine guns, so that if the war came to a sudden end the infection should not be spread. But when a ragged child, overgrown with filth, knocked at some house on the Polish side, and, not knowing, or barely knowing, Polish, thought it better to stand mute and humble, it was not sent away without bread."

Abel remembered that when news of the slaughter reached Block 14 E all the prisoners reacted strongly, but each of them to a different aspect of the tragedy. One said: "Driving old people into a truckful of unslaked lime!" Another: "The beautiful girls that are going under! How could any man kill a young girl?" And another: "My God, they're murdering little children."

"We couldn't explain to the children what a tree or a river was, for there were no rivers or trees. When a children's entertainment was given in a cinema the crowd wept. Korczak* told my father: 'I am an old man. I thought there was nothing else I wanted in life. But there is. I want to live to see the opening of the ghetto gates . . .' As you see, our gates have been opened," she said, pointing to the waste of rubble.

Over this soil of the most terrible of all human suffering, Abel walked, clinging to Amelia's arm, as though it were a rose garden. He drank in the sweetness of her presence, which dispelled all the horror as a memory. She was almost as tall as he, and was wearing a coat of black lamb's wool. The plate-shaped little hat had slipped down over one eye; she regarded a hat only as an ornament, like a cornice at the top of a house; he remembered that all her hats had fallen over her eyes, they had varied only in the shape of the crown.

The memory of this detail was like a new draught of sweetness to him, and he lightly brushed her sleeve with his lips again and again. Her eye was lost in the shadow cast by the brim; he saw only her nose with its slightly tilted nostrils and the provoking curve of her lips, which he badly wanted to kiss. For a long time he could not bring himself to do it. When at last he leaned across and brushed her lips with his as they walked, her smile was suddenly extinguished. That hurt him. They walked across fields of broken brick topped here and there with rusting iron. Iron rods grew out of the rubble like some new kind of bush.

It is difficult to trace the course of living conversation; it sprouts—like some men's beards—in all directions. After a moment or two Amelia turned once more to recalling the past. Every word she uttered quivered with suffering. That in turn gave Abel encouragement to speak.

When he ended, her face was drawn. The warm lights had gone. Abel was reminded of some friends he had met after six years' separation, only to discover that after fifteen minutes he had nothing more to talk about with them.

"Love . . ." She echoed him in a tone of astonishment, and apparent

* A well-known Jewish social worker, who refused to leave the children of his orphanage, and went with them to death.

dislike. For a moment he had the feeling that he had done her some wrong. "Love — that's a word I haven't heard for a long time. A word quite forgotten. A fiction . . ."

He felt as humiliated as a man who has declared his love to a woman, only to have her say, "That's nothing, it'll pass . . ." His mind rested on the word "fiction." He knew that fiction through and through . . . Set free by the Red Army, he had returned with many others to Poland. Those were wonderful days. He had stopped at Lodz. He had liked that city. During those days he had liked everything. He had taken the first job offered to him and had found pleasure in setting to work early. He had revived. The last flames of war had been flames of regeneration not only for him.

Everybody had sincerely desired a change; everybody had been yearning for light and joy after the gloom of the Occupation. But this zest had not lasted long — the depth of that night had penetrated to the bone. When the great waters subsided, Abel realized that he was still eaten up with longing, just as he had been in the camp. Freedom had not stilled that feeling. As a lover listening to a broadcast concert is conscious of the breath of the beloved who is in the hall, so Abel was conscious of Amelia in the voice of his country.

His heart stopped beating when he caught sight of a dress, a coat, a hat, similar to those he remembered from past years, though in all probability they no longer existed. A facial likeness, or a similarity of movement or gesture, no longer caught his fancy as they had when he had noticed them in fellow prisoners. Now they quickened only pain. His heart was never silent. Worst of all, he could not stop thinking and remembering.

In past days his mother, a frail little woman, had wept whenever someone mentioned jasmine to her. After six years of war he could not control his voice when he had to utter the word "love." When he saw a couple nestling against each other he could not help trembling. He could not bear to hear that someone else was happy. His heart felt like an unhealed wound, and in it was a sucking pain that never ceased. His longing turned to a nagging anxiety. He woke up again and again at night, feeling he was disemboweled of all except his pain. He was one mass of pain, and it alarmed him all the more because he did not know how to defend himself against it.

Unable to forget, he remembered. Remembering, he suffered. His body remembered, his mind remembered, and all memory was pain. He would ask himself what it could mean, but could find no explanation. He surrendered to the rapture from which he could not free himself. It was the earth to his feet, the light to his eyes, the reason for his existence. To him and within him it was the main, avid, self-sufficient reality . . . this — as she called it — fiction.

"After all, you see what is left of our life . . ." said Amelia. "This is not the result of a half-hour raid by the Royal Air Force. At night we did not go to bed, and in the morning those left alive did not see what we now see. The death agony of the ghetto, the death agony of our community, went on over years. Before the Jewish nation was sent up in smoke it was changed into mud and dung. Don't believe it when they say people know how to die. Twice during this war this city has seen that people do not know how to die. People are created to live, not to die. What people say about dying is an exaggeration, or a bitter jest, something that has as much in common with dying as the metaphorical death which young poets talk about so much.

"Millions went to their death still trading and loving, still intriguing and hating, with not one earthly feeling the less. They went to their death immersed in life up to their ears. With the taste of their own blood on their lips, they still did not feel the breath of God. To the very end they clung incomprehensibly to life. Even their death was a hymn to life. Even in the shadow of the gallows they were finicky about the food they ate."

In the old days she had talked only with reluctance and difficulty. She had never been one of those garrulous creatures. At first Abel had called her a beautiful silent child, for she had been so astonishingly taciturn. She used his forename for the first time only some months after their marriage. She was one of those women who find it difficult to become intimate with a man. But now Abel recognized that her voice, like her face, had gained in strength. It had changed.

"Death dwelt among us and changed much in our ideas of life," she went on. "When a man went away he went into the darkness, and usually did not return. We did not dare to let our feelings accumulate; they had to be spent at once. Women gave themselves to men just as though they were doing them a justice, as though they were righting a wrong. And then it appeared that there are a hundred kinds of love, and every one is good. And every one is acceptable."

Abel also knew the hundred kinds of love. During his first few weeks of freedom — those most happy and gracious weeks — he had believed that he would find a niche in life for himself even without Amelia. At first he had thought that the disaster was not so great after all, and that the Jewish intelligentsia, of whom a few had been saved, would want to build up their life again in a land which, truly, was like one vast grave, yet even that would fade in the memory. At the end of the war those few Jewish survivors who had been saved from the flood that had overwhelmed a community of three million people had emerged from underground, from the forests, from the camps. A few had returned to their former addresses. They had been received by the Poles as people who had experienced such suffering should be received. Here and there sincere tears were shed by both sides.

However, of all human feelings sympathy has the most brittle feet. As they returned after dying a hundred deaths a day for six years, many of these people, in whose presence the world should hang its head with shame, were struck down at the very doors of their homes by bullets which were not German.

Along the roads creatures who called themselves soldiers lurked in wait for them, and with a well-tried method, with *Genickschuss,* a shot in the back, murdered them. When they lay down to sleep in the villages, in small and even large towns, they were almost as uncertain of the morrow as in the time of German rule. These murders dispelled the last feeling of reluctance that troubles every man pondering on the difficult question of leaving his own country.

There was nothing else to be done; the death of a Jew had long since ceased to move anyone, so they began to flee in large numbers. And one day Abel realized that he was living in a wilderness. He met acquaintances who had closed the book of their lives, but none was opening any new book. He could see no attempts at renewal; on the contrary, they did not want to renew their life in this land. They wanted only one thing: flight. And they fled.

Abel sometimes thought that if he were living in a community whose mind was set on regeneration it would be easier for him to forget. But all around him was a wilderness; he was living in a wilderness, surrounded by stumps that were withering away. There was no life, for there were no people. Besides, he was no longer young; he was close to forty, and woe to those who in their fortieth year must begin their emotional life anew, must seek; what had he to offer to any women he came to know only now? In comparison with what he felt for Amelia all else was thin, empty. Dazzled by Amelia's brightness, he thought all others dim. All other women bored him, and he bored all other women. For so it is, that to some we are like the sea, yet to others we are like a miserable, trickling stream. There were a hundred other kinds of love — he knew that — but not one of them was for him.

"The only joy we had in those years," Amelia said, "a joy we are already ceasing to understand, though so little time has passed, was to kill a German. That was the only thing that brought us happiness. Nothing else. No one set himself any other task. It would have been imprudent, petty. Maybe there is a time which is favorable to love, but those years were not . . ."

Abel no longer pressed his lips to her coat. Her words parted him from her just as effectively as the camp had, in the past. He felt that she was right, and he felt, too, his own pettiness. And shame. Not for the first time, he thought how badly he fitted into what was happening in the world.

Nations had perished, cities had disintegrated into dust, and the gains of centuries had been lost in a single night. And what was he interested in? What really occupied his mind?

4

THE SKY was the color of soapsuds. In one spot the gate of the military prison, and elsewhere sections of the brick wall of the Pawiak prison, had escaped destruction; in the distance a church could be distinguished; only fragments of the prisons and the church had been spared. There was no means whatever of determining the spot on which their home had once stood — a handful of dust amid this expanse of rubble slag heaps. A bare beech tree stood in the cinnamon-colored gap of the Pawiak wall. Fastened to its trunk was a blackboard with a white cross; beneath it two young men were standing, bareheaded. One was talking, the other listening; they were both gazing down at a grave at the foot of the beech. Abel and Amelia walked past them, reached the highroad which once had cut right through the Jewish district, then turned back. Their feeling of exasperation persisted.

As she referred again to the fiction, to life in which nothing matters, she laughed an unpleasant laugh — the laugh of a woman false to her husband, the laugh of women delighted with the clever trick they have played. Abel caught a sudden coarseness in her tone, and recalled that it had always repelled him. He took another sidelong glance at her lips, and realized how sensuous they were. In his sudden hatred he seized her by the hands and shook her, then raised his hand to strike her. But he realized what he was doing, and was panic-stricken, afraid that out of all his years of longing Amelia would remember only that moment when his face was distorted with fury. He tried to apologize, but could only stammer. He said words which were meaningless even to himself, words which afterwards he could not even remember.

As he caught her frightened gaze he pulled himself together. For a long time he could not free himself from the effects of his outburst; he felt exhausted, alien to himself. Amelia looked at him intently; his face melted, his lips quivered. She had powers of observation at times when he was far from any such ability. They halted. She said in a quiet, slow voice:

"Abel, you have been entirely concentrated on your own life; I have not. I am no longer the woman you left behind. I am different. How can I hide it from you? Look about you; think of what happened here . . . Love! For many months the blood tingled in my veins; at night my body swelled like the earth in spring, like a river in spate; it ached as though I had been thrashed. My eyes were as restless as those of young girls who feel they are walking about the world with no skin on them. The secret of man is that he always wants more than he can achieve. Love! There is a time in our life when a single being swims in our crystal stream. And then we set ourselves the task, the difficult task, of keeping that stream in all its purity; but the heart delights in difficult tasks . . ."

Now she was speaking tenderly and warmly, she put her hand on his arm. Suddenly he observed that all the strength had gone out of her face. Her cheeks were as delicate as those of convalescence, her lips were puckered, her inscrutable eyes were tired.

"Abel, listen; I will tell you how I escaped. I was taken out of the ghetto buried under the load of a municipal dust cart. It was the only way. It took them half an hour to bring me around, I was almost suffocated. My last thought as I fainted was that I would be tipped out onto the rubbish heap down by the river. I wasn't, and I didn't die on a rubbish heap. But after that, of course everything lost all meaning. That which previously I had regarded as most precious now seemed nonsense, a tragic sneer, a fiction. Every day we died, and every day we were born again, but always we were ashamed of the sawdust in our minds. We ceased to understand the world of yesterday. We hated it, and everything that had been bad was now good, and everything we had avoided was now permissible. Once I had escaped to the Polish side of the city I no longer set myself tasks, I did not struggle, I did not go about with cyanide in my bag. Before that, I used to ask myself: 'Do you want to be like Marysia Werner?' No, I did not want to be like Marysia Werner. But then I did become like her, and did not even give it a thought. The crystal stream had dried up . . ."

She was silent. After a moment or two she went on:

"How strange it is that in the face of such destruction, such an end of the world, the heart still retains all these nuances . . . If anyone were to ask me if I regret all my self-denials, all that period when my body, like a dog on a leash, whimpered for the fiction of a crystal stream, I would answer 'No.' For in the face of this end of the world which we now see, what deserves to be called a fiction, and what does not deserve to be called it?"

They sat down on a fragment of tiled stove, first Abel, and then, after some hesitation, Amelia. Borne on a new wave of hope, he said:

"I deluded myself that you would come. Every time I went out I left a note saying where I was to be found. I regretted every wasted moment. You did not come. I wrote; you did not answer. Later someone told me you were happy, and I at once believed it. One never does doubt something which may cause one pain. That news explained everything. You didn't write, you didn't come, because you already had all you wanted. That's just the difference between the happy and the unhappy: the unhappy are never at home. Of course I could have come to you. But what for? She is happy, I told myself, so leave her alone. And I left you alone, though every day, every hour meant so much to me!

"My brother wrote to me from Casablanca; I was glad to have his invitation. I came to Warsaw yesterday in order to arrange my departure. I went and hung about your house, but I lacked the courage to go in. My first thought was : How can I go abroad? All that distance apart I shall surely wither away . . . I came here a ruin, I came with set face, incapable of a smile, with ashen lips, with a frozen heart; but now I can see what happens to me as soon as you are beside me! Without you, here or anywhere on earth, life holds nothing for me. If you leave me, you will be flinging me into my grave . . ."

He fixed his eyes on her. There was no entreaty in them; they only testified to the truth.

"Abel, in this life repetitions are never successful," she said. "They are dangerous." As he insisted, she added: "Abel, my dear, what can I bring you back? This body, this body which is like a conquered land . . ." She did not finish. She drooped her head, and sat thus for some moments. When she raised her head again, Abel saw a face swollen, quivering with emotion. Her upper lip was trembling absurdly.

"*He* has gone to visit his graves in the Polish ruins, I told myself; I too will go to visit mine in my ruins, and I came here . . . It's too late for us now, Abel. I often used to think you'd return, and we'd come together, you'd forget like thousands of others. But what one does only for the moment often lasts, and lasts for a lifetime, and it cannot be broken . . ." She added in a voice over which she had lost all control, "Now it isn't even a question of *him* any longer. I have a child six months old. And that is quite different . . ."

She said no more. And Abel, too, said nothing. He no longer asked for anything. His silence was profound, the silence that falls when all contact is broken between one and another, when one knows that the decision has already been made.

He realized that he had lost her forever. This was the end. He was surrounded by a dead sea. And there was no hope, no light. He had dreamed of Amelia as only a man long-hungering can dream; perhaps children too can dream like that. This body was no longer for him. If he had not been too ashamed, he would have asked for it as though asking for alms, but only as alms could he have received it. This body, which after him had borne with so many, and would bear with many yet, was not for him, not exclusively for him, who desired it more than could anyone else in the world.

Because she had loved him, and now had no strength, or else did not desire his love any more, so now he could never draw anything for himself from that body, except shame and degradation. For love which has once been sublime but then has lost its exaltation is only degradation. Just because he had been borne along in the crystal stream of her life she could not belong to him now, though she might belong to all others.

He buried his face in his hands. He knew that in a moment she, his life's last joy, would be departing from him. Once more he would experience nights and days of despair oozing through the chinks of life, and the old incessant sucking pain in his heart would return. He realized that fate had defeated him, and his breast ached with the pain. He felt her bend over him; he saw tears in her eyes. He felt their warmth as they mingled, hers with his, on his face. Then she left him. He did not call after her. Stunned and still, he gazed after her retreating figure, and at times a groan burst from his throat. He gazed after her until she disappeared, disappeared without once turning around. How long he sat there he did not know. When at last he began to feel cold, he rose and dragged himself away.

It was November 1 — All Souls' Eve. Warsaw was celebrating its first postwar holy day of the dead. The city was full of graves — it was one enormous grave; every few paces flowers were lying on the pavement; little funeral flags peeped out among the flowers, and candles were burning. Small boys and girls were keeping guard over the graves. They stood as motionless as soldiers. Other boys, walking in a long open file, halted before the guards and tried to make them laugh by staring into their faces. The streets were almost empty. In one street Boy Scouts were decorating a grave. The young scouts were pensive, simply pensive; their thoughtfulness conveyed no memory of the living blood of their dead. For them all that the graves implied was already history. A little farther on, at a curve in the wall, a candle was burning; several vases were standing on the sidewalk, and near them a kneeling woman was absorbed in prayer, as motionless as a chair. With wide, resigned eyes she gazed into the invisible faces of her dead. Abel halted beside her. Joined with her in resignation, before undertaking the long journey into which he took nothing save his anguished body, he said farewell to his city, his country, and his hopes.

— *translated by* Harry Stevens

(From *Ascent to Heaven.* Roy Publishers, New York, 1951.)

II

How They See Life

The Old Town Comes Back to Me

BY BOHDAN CZESZKO

BOHDAN CZESZKO was born in 1923 in Warsaw. His education was interrupted by the war, and during the German Occupation he worked as a carpenter. An active member of the wartime Communist Underground organizations, he also took part in the Warsaw Uprising. After the war he studied at the Warsaw Academy of Art. His first volume of short stories was published in 1949, and since then seven more books — novels and short-story collections — have appeared. He is the coeditor and book reviewer for *Przeglad Kulturalny,* a Warsaw literary weekly, and lives in Warsaw.

I REMEMBER the market square of the Old Town only as a colorful corner of Warsaw. It has never been otherwise in my time, and I wouldn't want to think of it as any different. In my mind the picture of the market square is associated with the legends of early childhood, forming a baroque ornamentation, rich with intricate detail. The dusty model of the corvette which hung in the entrance to Fukier's wine cellar served time and again for the distant overseas expeditions which I undertook as I dozed off to sleep. With its unusual shape it proved an excellent rival to the transatlantic liners which adorned the windows of the shipping lines. I chose a sailing ship because I felt more inclined to trust myself to the trade winds and monsoons than the incomprehensible power of steam. "I'm in no hurry," I would declare, and taking my place on the captain's bridge, I ordered the anchor to be weighed. Ten gallant lads turned the capstan (they were my friends in the courtyard), sang a monotonous song, and from Fukier's the corvette slowly sailed out of port to go to the help of Captain Grant's children.

The gray-bearded doorman, attired in a historic military uniform, who guarded the door with a halberd in his hand was my St. Nicholas, living a private life between one Christmas and another.

The prewar municipal authorities did their best to make the Old Town as much of a fairy tale as possible. From later years I remember the postal diligence which carried the tourists around. The postilions were dressed in snuff-colored liveries and blew coach horns; the stage-coach set off from the market square in an anachronistic journey through Warsaw, to finish the round trip in the fabulously colorful Old Town.

Nor must one forget the thousands of pigeons, and the pensioners feeding them with all the scrupulosity of the aged. Behind the cathedral dozed priests, neatly dressed in black, and flowers bloomed in boxes on the window sills of the canonry. This Old World atmosphere was intensified by the good-natured writer Or-Ot, who chirruped away like a cricket as he sang his warmhearted Old Town poems.

Only a step or two beyond the picturesque little shops of the market-place, on Swietojerska Street, on Freta, Krzywe Kolo, Rybaki, and Bugaj streets, the world lost its air of festivity; gloomy gray blocks of flats, with their courtyard wells, displaced the old stone buildings. The grannies sitting on low stools under the gateway arches lost all semblance of dignified, civil age and were simply bedrudged old proletarians, airing their cellar rheumatism in the sun. Unemployed men held up the walls; on the nearby Vistula in the boats loaded with sand the sand sellers bent their backs in a galley-slave labor.

During the years of the Occupation I rather avoided the Old Town; its winding, intercrossing little streets concealed too many surprises in steel helmets. Topographically the district was attractive to both the fighting sides. One evening I had an unpleasant experience there. On Podwale Street existed a wineshop marked: "For Germans only." It bore the name of "The Crooked Lantern." The doorman was the same immortal fellow with the gray beard, but now attired like a nineteenth-century patriotic Pole in semimilitary coat with loops, and four-cornered hat trimmed with lamb's wool. From inside the pub, soldiery in a state of alcoholic bestiality poured into the deep dusk of the street. They tugged at the old man's beard, pulled his cap down over his eyes, and performed all the stupid, loutish tricks which his exotic appearance provoked them into doing.

St. Nicholas had long since ceased to be a person of significance in my life, but this twilight of his incarnation filled me with bitterness.

I lived in the distant Wola working-class district, and so I became really familiar with the people of the Old Town, its streets, and the interiors of its houses only during the Uprising. I came to know the houses thoroughly, from the garrets, which afforded a sniper's view of the neighborhood, to the cellars, whose arched stone-vaulted ceilings gave an illusion of security, persuading me to sleep tranquilly. I learned all the twists and turns of the side lanes; I measured the extent of every expanse which one had to run across more swiftly than the pursuing death; I huddled against the cobblestones of the roads and the walls of the houses, longing to sink into them. I got to know the people through and through, because it was a time of sincerity. Thrust to the very bottom of hell, the "cellar rats," or the "civvies," as they were called, had nothing to hide and didn't feel like hiding anything. They were left to their own devices in the face of hunger, fire, and inexorably scything death. For three long weeks a hurricane of steel blew through the Old Town.

What could an insurgent do for them? Hand over a little sugar for a child, share his ration of horseflesh . . . They expected no comfort and did not want any; they only demanded punishment for the guilty. They turned to the People's Army men with confidence, as they judged that we knew more; but we could not give them any hopeful news, cut off as we were from communication with the world. Ours were mixed feelings; we fully realized the political significance of the London-inspired Uprising, fully realized that by taking part in it we were serving a cause hostile to communism, and at the same time we knew that not to fight would be a crime.

Not far from the spot where Hanka Sawicka lost her life in 1943, at the junction of Mostowa and Rybaki streets, a People's Army unit held a position, controlling movements, defending the district from an attack across the River Vistula. The desperate defense of this position determined the direction of the enemy assault. How many heavy attacks, supported by artillery and tanks, the poorly armed youngsters withstood almost without ammunition! Several tanks were set on fire with bottles of benzine; a house transformed into an enemy stronghold was blown up with the aid of unspent artillery shells.

By the time the battalion was tempered in battles, by the time it gained the unsought glory of one of the most valiant fighting units, it was decimated. In the Old Town all the members of the Warsaw staff of the People's Army also perished; they were killed by a bomb dropped from an airplane. Many fine sons of Warsaw's common people and many fine soldiers of the workers' movement buried themselves in the soil of the ancient marketplace. They fell on the very threshold of freedom, just before the day dawned for which they had fought for many years.

When I returned from the war I had to go out to a place in a Warsaw suburb. Dusk was falling. As I walked down an avenue I had difficulty in reading the inscriptions on tombstones I had not seen before; one of them was in the square near the Old Town. On close inspection, I discovered that it was the grave of a comrade on the staff during the Uprising. The few passers-by who saw a soldier saluting a grave without any commemoration date on it, on just an ordinary day of the week, must have thought the behavior strange, even in those strange times.

I waded through the ruins, climbing over mounds of rubble, finding the layout of the streets more by instinct than by sight. I was surrounded by a frightful landscape; in such a landscape people don't live — only the wind whistles there.

On Freta Street I came across some lights. The first was somewhere close to Krzywe Kolo; the second, by the ruins of St. Jacek's Church, signaled a soft-drink stall, a pub, and a shop selling vegetables. Another little light glimmered inside the ruins of the restaurant called "Under the Basilisk," where the People's Army canteen had been accommodated during the Uprising. At Number 16, in the ruins of a house which had been our headquarters, in the beam of an electric torch I read one of those numerous notices: "No mines"; and next to it: "Wladek, we're at Auntie Anna's, in Konstancin." * I rejoiced that evidently some of the "civvies" had survived. The little lights testifying to the existence of living people did not accompany me any farther; once more I was surrounded by the lunar landscape, and I fled from it.

During the eight years that followed, I returned to the neighborhood many times, having more and more difficulty in tracing the memorable spots. This was just as well, because why should the people of Warsaw go to the Old Town, churning over the dead in their thoughts?

However, now it is July 1953. A few days ago scaffolding was still standing on one side of the market square, but the place is slowly

---

* A Warsaw suburb.

being vacated by the artists and the conservators, who have completed the ornamentation of the façades and the reconstruction of the gilding and frescoes. Only two months ago an architect complained: "The work is limping along; I can't get it done on a really broad scale. Everything's topsy-turvy, superstructures, additions, conservators . . . it's as though something had slipped through your fingers. . . ." And now look at the old houses alive with young energy, the carpenters paneling the walls with choice woods, hammering away at the carved oaken doors. The craftsmanship is of high quality, and the materials are excellent. The men in charge of the stuccoing have finished molding the ornaments of the ceilings. In the future headquarters of the Folk Art Institute, women are painting garlands of flowers on the walls. I watch as with unusually swift, precise sweeps of the brush they produce designs which have nothing in common with graphic dryness and are infallible in color; one feels like calling it an honest work.

There are curtains and potted plants here and there in the windows overlooking the square. The people have come back for good. I recall the notices stuck on boards among the ruins: "Wladek, we are at Auntie's" . . . I would like the Wladek who already lives here to be one of the "civvies," one of the "cellar rats." I would like to shake him by the arm and cry, as I now stand in the middle of the market square, beautiful again in its colors ablaze in the sunlight: "Didn't I say that others could do as they chose, but we would come back here?"

Well, I like this city, which with the hands of its workmen has conquered its own death. It is here, and nowhere else, that I lived through my finest and my bitterest hour. Here I experienced all that a man can experience, and even that which — it would have seemed — a man is not capable of surviving. The walls of this city were my partisan forest and the grove of my young love.

I saw — bah, I felt — it being transformed into a brick-dust wilderness, on those days of that August in 1944. Here they killed my parents. Here they killed my most faithful comrades. Every one of them fell in a Warsaw street. They took bullets into their chests without kneeling. They fought for the people, and for the people they perished.

In this city I read the *Communist Manifesto* for the first time in my life. In this city my daughter came into the world. Everything that is tragic, everything that is exalted and ordinary in life, is bound up with my Warsaw. Someone has told me that the syllables forming its name mean in Chinese: "a rose in the desert."

— *translated by* HARRY STEVENS

(From *Krzewy Koralowe,* short stories. Published by "Czytelnik," Warsaw, 1956.)

The Village Wedding

BY MARIA DABROWSKA

MARIA DABROWSKA was born in Russow in 1889. Having studied sociology in Warsaw and Brussels, she began her career as a writer with a particular interest in peasant life. Her first great success, *The People from Yonder,* is a volume of short stories which reflect this interest. It appeared in 1925. However, it was her *roman-fleuve* entitled *Nights and Days* (1934) which made her famous. It is a family story concerning small country squires at the turn of the century. Her other work includes *Signs of Life* (1938); *The Morning Star* (1955), short stories; *Essays on J. Conrad* (1959). Excerpts from *The Village Wedding and Other Stories* (1957) follow. This book was published in English in Warsaw. Another story by Maria Dabrowska is in the section of this book called "Their Humor."

I

THEY WENT OUT into the night. The wind had died down. On the ground everything was black; in the sky, clouded over in places, the stars twinkled; when their eyes grew accustomed to the darkness of the night, they began to see in all directions feeble, dimly glowing lights of human dwellings. They were stumbling in the soft, loose earth.

"Aren't we going across then, not along the boundary strips?" asked Boguski, recalling the old lanes that led to old Dobrzynska's cottage. "Do we go straight ahead?"

"Better take the road," decided Susie, her voice hard and slightly hoarse. "It's a new road."

"Must be, there never was any road here," stated Michael.

"It was built this year. From the Warsaw highway right up to the co-op, from the co-op to our town road. You've come down by this road from the bus stop. Only the part to the borough council has been paved, and this stretch we are going to pave."

"Aha, you see, Susie, a new road," insinuated Michael, and when Susie made no answer, he asked, "You must be glad to be getting married."

"I'll say I am, or I wouldn't be getting married."

"You're quite a young child, though. Others at your age are learning some trade or other. They go to town and study."

After a long silence Susie answered. "Someone's got to stay in the countryside, too."

"True enough. But more learning is needed here, too."

"If necessary, married girls can go on studying."

"And that's the truth. Well, and does anybody ever come here? The traveling cinema? Got a social club here?"

"No. No cinema. They only came down once to the borough council. But there's a club. In the manor house."

"Ever go there? Do they put anything on?"

"When there's a dance, we go."

Michael searched his mind for more questions to ask; suddenly a shadow deeper than the darkness of the night confronted them. It was young Jack Boguski, Luke's son. He had just got back from the little town where he had taken fruit for sale. Jack, an enterprising fellow, bought up fruit from orchards to help raise the income. He was now on his way to Aunt Margaret's to help with the prenuptial preparations. A few words were exchanged; Jack announced that his wife, Mary, was waiting for the guests. She expected several, at least, to come. Jack was in a hurry, and so, after exchanging greetings with his paternal uncle, they continued along their several ways.

They had not gone a hundred paces when a new shadow loomed out of the night and accosted Susie. This one was a woman who asked in a choking voice:

"That you, Susie? Seen anyone? Met anybody? . . ."

"I saw nothing. Jack passed by — you know, my cousin — and we met. What's biting you?"

"No, that must have been before," stammered the woman, who was unknown to Michael. "I've been walking about here quite a while, and once as I stopped a man dashed past me. I'm telling you, he tore by like a March hare, running and groaning all the time, and he kept crying out, 'Oh my God! My God!' Who could it be? And what happened to him?"

"Ain't seen nobody. Could be he was drunk? Or you've been seeing things," Susie said, not altogether convinced.

"Jesus Christ!" the woman whispered, and disappeared into the darkness.

"Who was that? What's going on around here to drive a worried woman about at night?" asked Michael.

"That's Stephen's wife. He manages the fishery here. Director. She went to school with me — only I was starting when she was leaving. Her husband's gone to a district meeting; he can't have come back yet; and she's always afraid something awful's going to happen to him 'cause he's trying ever so hard to get people to join the co-op. She's silly to be so afraid. People in our village are not that kind. It must have been some drunk, staggering and groaning."

Suddenly, Susie, of her own accord, had something to say:

"What queer people, this granny of ours that's come down here, and my Aunt Gadek," she considered. "The way they say 'thar' and 'woine gless.' And the way they dress. Here one wouldn't be seen dead in anything like that."

"It's old peasant dress," Michael explained, "and an old turn of speech. Their village must be pretty ancient and at the back of beyond. There are villages and villages."

Susie announced: "Here we are."

Jack Boguski's kitchen was bright, clean and nice, indeed. Over a good brand of alcohol stove Mary, Jack's wife, was cooking semolina for her baby son. Susie dallied a while to cuddle the eighteen-month-old Harry, and to tell him about baby Bernadette Gadek, who had come to be Harry's "maid of honor." Jack's wife, a girl not much older than Susie, showed her husband's uncle the room where he was to sleep in their bed. There was another bed in the kitchen for themselves; for the children there was a crib for the boy and a cradle for his two-month-old sister. Mary opened her wardrobe for the uncle to hang up his overcoat. In the wardrobe there were several shelves of nice underwear and a great number of printed rayon frocks on hangers.

Pleased with his comfortable night quarters, Michael soon went to bed. For a while he could hear the young mother babbling and prattling with the children, whom she first fed and then got to bed; shortly after, all was quiet and the chink of light showing through the crack in the door went out. Rural silence enveloped the cottage, and stars peeped through the windows. But the silence did not last long because mice soon began to make themselves heard. There must have been a whole horde of them, for they scratched in every corner, made rapping noises as if they were knocking over ninepins; they scampered about noisily and squeaked, ran races under the bed, rustling straw; there must have been holes in the paillasse. But Michael Boguski was a man healthy in body and mind, and, tired after his journey, he was soon fast asleep.

At the Jasnotas', work continued full steam ahead. Leocadia had left with the guests, but her eldest son, Jack, came instead, a presentable young man, the image of his mother, with that aquiline nose, thick pink lips and chiseled features. Quite unexpectedly Gregory's wife, Agnes, dropped in too.

"I've put the boy to bed" — she spoke of her husband as if he were a child — "and I came straight here." Not by a single word did she refer to the fact that Stephen had led them up the garden path, for he had had no assurance of any accommodation for them, and they had had to call on three farmers before they and the horse and cart could be put up for the night.

Agnes, Margaret and Susie between them emptied the three-door pine plywood wardrobe, tied up the clothing in bundles, and took them into the barn. Jack, Stephen and Czesiek took the wardrobe and the beds apart; wheezing, gasping, and urging one another on, they removed all the furniture from the cottage. Some of it they put in the barn, the rest next to a small toolshed. The women meanwhile scrubbed the floor (getting splinters in their hands and groaning with pain). No sooner had they finished than the men started to repair and reinforce the floor, but there was little that could be done in such a hurry; so they just patched over the worst holes and began bringing in previously prepared planks and pegs for benches and tables. As they got to putting those together and nailing them to the floor, Margaret ran over to the Popioleks'. She hesitated at the door as it was rather late, but seeing a light, she went in. Granny Jasnota and Catherine Gadek, although fatigued, had not yet talked themselves out, or told Popiolek's wife the details of the journey and talked of Bernadette, Jim and his asthmatic father. Meg sat down on the edge of the bed and embraced her mother-in-law.

"There are so many to be welcomed here I've not had time to enjoy your being here, Mother," she complained. "And it's dog's age since we saw each other."

"Oh, so long ago, so long ago!" lisped Granny; while she spoke, her tongue kept popping out of her toothless mouth. Meg moved away from the old woman, for somehow there was an unpleasant smell about Granny.

"Oh, my God," she thought, "what's Stephen's mother come to?"

Meg recalled how, while engaged to be married, she had gone with Stephen to his native village, how she had been received there, and how she had taken to her future mother-in-law. Even though on the way down her mind had not been made up, she had liked Stephen's mother so much after meeting her that she had finally decided to marry him. For Stephen's mother had been as good as can be, nice, gay, singing, dispensing kisses; seldom did you come across an old woman so pleasant and so full of life. It was sheer delight to be daughter-in-law to such a mother. Even now you could see she had not lost her former spirit, seeing she could undertake such a journey; but, may the Lord forgive her, Meg remembered only that long, long ago she had grown to love Granny and now she had none of that old feeling left, only a fear of Granny's overwhelming senility. And she was so upset that she burst out crying.

"What you crying for, Meg? Are ye sorry for Susie 'cause she won't be a maid much longer? Oh, grief, oh human grief." And here Granny, just as was her custom of old to sing a song suited to the occasion, intoned in her quavering, rusty voice:

> For you no maiden's chaplets of roses,
> No handsome boys to lead by their noo-ses . . .

"Baby's asleep," Meg whispered, and smiled through the tears.

"Bernadette? No-o. She's such a good'un, once off and nothing will rouse her," enthused Catherine.

It was past midnight when the young men finished the seats and left. Stephen escorted Agnes to her husband's quarters; Meg and her daughters once again swept and scrubbed the floor. Around two o'clock they lay down on a paillasse and drew a blanket over themselves; Susie and Jadwiga fell asleep at once, but for a long while Meg could not go off. Diverse thoughts assailed her, and so many of them thrashed about, just as if a whole crowd of people were talking inside her at once.

"What did that Czesiek say?" her thoughts ran on. "That there was to be a band from Warsaw and his uncle Adam Rucinski was to be the leader?" She had known him a little, but that was long ago. The year Adam came to Warsaw, where for many years now he's been working as a railwayman, he used to call on her sometimes to chat with a woman from his village, although they had hardly known each other there, having then lived at opposite ends of Pawlowice. But once, returning from the family, he was sent by Meg's mother on an errand to her, and from that day on he had kept calling, then he had stopped and shortly after had married someone. Perhaps he had visited her ten times or perhaps not even that often, but she had fallen in love with him. He had known nothing about that, nor had he even guessed at it; he must have been flirting with many a one; a sociable kind of man he was. And the only one she had been in love with during her spinsterhood. This only true love was also the only grief of her youth, for apart from it she had been happy. At nineteen she had gone into domestic service with an elderly, childless couple; her masters had been so wise, so kind and quiet that she had not even felt she was a servant. Several men had courted her, but not being of a passionate nature, she had been long choosing a husband, had looked for a kindhearted type. Or it could have been that no man appealed to her after Adam Rucinski. She was getting on toward thirty-six when she had met Stephen, when he had got himself a job as the caretaker's assistant in the building where Meg was employed. He came of a poor family and, like Margaret, had sought a living in town. What had made her marry him? Most likely it must have been that he had fallen so deeply in love with her. He was so gone on her that he fainted when she told him point-blank she would not have him. She remembered what it was like to be in love with someone who did not love you. She was moved to see herself so beloved; she was getting on in years, and there was the fear for the future. Her employers were elderly; if anything happened to them she could not hope to find another place like that; and after all, one can have enough of service with even the kindest people; and no one wanted to pass a lifetime in service — a girl preferred to set up her own home. So the two had got married and, on thinking it over, decided to return to the village. Times weren't the worst then, and their families had paid them off. In Meg's native village they bought land cheaply, those ten acres of land, bare, uncared for, neglected, without any buildings. Their life together began, and it was hard, sheer murder. Stephen was a man of weak character, in poor health, not much good at work, and fond of the bottle. The worst thing was the problem of a cottage. They bought the lumber, and Luke offered to put up a cottage for them; but the timber rotted away, and nothing came of it. So they'd had to rent what they could, but no one will sublet a good room to paupers; they had to trudge miles to work, as their lodgings invariably were so far from the field; and they'd had neither horse nor cart, nor place to put the cow.

Margaret had then disliked her husband so that the very sight of him was at times painful. She would recall her days in Warsaw as a kind of paradise; she had dreamed at nights of her old employers; she had written them letters, often repented that in an evil hour she had thrown up that comfortable, clean life where she had always been respected and where, as she put it, the world had blossomed out before her like a rose. Now she was a dirty and unkempt skivvy, utterly unlike her smart Warsaw self. Not only did they have to do everything on their own land, but they also had to work off the loan of a horse and tools from some rich farmer; and the manor, the last in the vicinity, would often hire her for a job of work. She was a good needlewoman (she used to make her pretty frocks in Warsaw), so she used her evenings to sew for the whole village, even for the men, for whom she tailored with the aid of the sewing machine, a wedding gift from her employers. In the third year of their married misery came the war, and everyone knows what that was like. They lost two baby sons in those war years; only Susie, who was born in a beautiful Warsaw hospital, and Jadwiga, their youngest, had lived to see better days and grown up healthy.

After the war, life began to change with lightning speed. New laws came and new customs, which were not so easy to understand, let alone get used to. And there came new fears; people did not sleep peacefully for weeks on end; their hands shook at work because of the tales that were being told. And life meanwhile continued on its own course, always different from what one expected it to be. The village was only about thirty miles from Warsaw; but it was far from the railway, dismal, lost amidst forests, coppices, groves. And here, all of a sudden, in the neighboring towns factories began to go up, a new railway line was being laid, and a very few miles from Pawlowice a huge new brick kiln was erected to supply the builders of Warsaw. Easy, good money could be earned. Stephen became a new man, for he liked variety. Thus for a year or two he worked on the railway, then at the brick kiln. Presently they bought a horse out of the money, and that horse helped him to earn still more money, what with those industries and all the building going on.

Even Susie had earned enough at the brick kiln to buy herself clothes last year. And lastly, they inherited the Pawoniaks' farmstead. What if there were small shares to be paid off? A new life had after all begun, a true life well worth working for. And their marital harmony improved, for one improved with the other. Margaret had a grateful heart and was of a serene disposition; she knew how to value her good fate. Why, then, couldn't she sleep? Why did she sigh and struggle with her thoughts as if not Susie but she herself were preparing for that important change in life?

"Now, about this wedding," her thoughts kept nagging. "One might say happiness. Only God knows how Susie will fare with Czesiek. He's a bit too fond of vodka. A man who drinks is sure to beat her. But does Susie have any understanding? Haven't I warned her enough of what life was like when Stephen got drunk? It's no use. Susie won't let an unkind word be spoken against her daddy. She says a man must drink. Pity about her first fiancé. Much better-looking than Czesiek and he never touched vodka. They both cried when she broke off her engagement because they had taken to him as if to their own son, but what could they do? They couldn't interfere with their own child in her choice, and their child chose Czesiek. The first one was too short, it appeared. Czesiek's considerable height won her over. And he, what was he after? The land? And since Susie had only one sister, there wouldn't be many shares to pay off and only a few divisions. Oh, dear, there's not much love between them, that I can see, only goodness knows what . . ." She was sad . . .

"And now this worry" — her thoughts chased one another — "if only this wedding reception will pass off without a brawl. If only it could pass off decently." A shiver ran down Margaret's spine when she recalled the varied incidents that disgraced many a wedding. There was blood spilt or even worse. The year before at a wedding somewhere, not in Pawlowice, drunken men outraged a twelve-year-old girl, an orphan from the village. "And Michael, now" — her thoughts wandered — "he was all for a registry marriage and for those co-ops. He must have been talked into that newfangled notion. So many guests, all that work to be done, I'd had no time to talk anything over properly with him. Nor with Angelica. Perhaps they'd have told me things, them two — they're clever. But my head is just too mixed up. It's been so hard, this life of ours; we've no sooner got ourself a stake, so what happens? They say it was bad. Who the devil invented those co-ops to poison people's lives? One grew to an age, got a bit of sense, and what happened to make one walk about in one's old age like someone with the staggers, not knowing what's right or what's wrong? We never wanted to do anything wicked and just look — they say everything about us is wrong. Are we gone daft, or is the world gone mad? Who knows what we'll see yet. Susie and Czesiek may yet tell us we're wicked, stupid, or perhaps they'll give everything into that community of theirs. They may be just biding their time siding with us parents; once they get together with the young'uns it'll be a different kettle of fish.

"What's the matter with Stephen?" Her thoughts were angry. "Why does he bluff and say he was not approached? They did come, and he refused to listen, only saying it should be as his old woman said. Should I be responsible for everything? What do I know? Or would he rather I agreed? And this wedding, now. A pile of money . . . Will the guests collect for the bride, without the capping? But they won't collect even half the expenses. With money like that the cottage and the outbuildings could be nicely done up. And there could be a fence so the winds wouldn't blow one's head off here, and there could be flowers sown and planted — I'm mad about flowers . . . and a third cow could be bought . . . For heaven's sake, I forgot to milk the cows this evening . . . A new room should be built on for the young couple. But everyone says don't do anything, don't put yourself out; even so, they'll take it all away from you; and if not that, they'll tax you out of existence, squeeze life out of you, 'cause they'll say you're rich and your cottage is well tended, so you can pay up. And it's only because of this talk that all the money will be spent on food and drink or spent on clothes; but clothes are for the young; the young will be forgiven everything, even dirty tricks; the old ones are ashamed to dress up, for they'll say, 'the rich dandies.'

"And those co-operative productive farms" — her thoughts were a torment — "even the name is so inhuman that it gives you goose flesh. But maybe there's some good in them co-ops. The things one can't help hearing about the electric light in the new houses that are to go up, about the bathrooms, gardens; only the land is to be in common. Would I have such communal land? And if it's all so fine, why does Pauline now walk about so fed up and say things are looking bad? I forgot to say my prayers, that's why my thoughts are tormenting me. In the name of the Father, the Son and the Holy Ghost, Amen. Our Father which art in heaven, hallowed be Thy name, Thy Kingdom come, Thy will be done on earth as it is in heaven . . . on earth . . . But this couldn't be happening without the will of God . . . Give us this day our daily bread . . ."

Here Margaret was overpowered by a short but deep sleep.

2

MICHAEL BOGUSKI did not sleep nearly as much as he had promised himself, either. Jack returned well past midnight, yet at five in the morning he was already up and was going to see the Jasnotas.

"I have to see to the wedding posset," he explained to his wife, who was irritated lest he waken the children.

"Lots of time yet. Can't you get the posset ready here?" she droned on sleepily.

"Do it here?" Jack mocked her in a pained voice, and with that he left.

Michael still enjoyed the sleep of the young but not so young that nothing could disturb him. He was therefore awakened by noises in the night. Now he got up early, silently slipped through the kitchen, where all had again fallen asleep, and as day broke he set out for the cottage where the wedding was to be celebrated. The air was bracing, without frost or wind. A clear sky, honey-gold streaks in the East, and a whitish mist over the distant brook betokened, despite yesterday's fears, a serene, warm and pleasant day. And the surrounding world was attired in its October colors. Against the gray-green of the pine forest, birch groves gleamed golden, pine trunks were reddened, and birch trunks stood silver-white. Young oaks glistened purple, russet and brown; the chestnuts, of which there were many near the cottages, glowed like copper. Here and there on the small, nearly nude fruit trees a dew-drenched leaf sparkled, pink, yellow or gray. Here and there leafless mountain ash stood resplendent with scarlet, already frozen berries, and the plateau, gently undulant beneath those autumn colors, stretched its blackish, flaxen, grayish plowed land and glaring green winter wheat. Here and there still flowering, fragrant yellow lupines.

The Jasnotas' cottage looked poor indeed among all those gilded autumnal spangles. The cottage stood on a well-trodden patch of land, its gable facing the village road from which it was separated by the remnants of a fence, a few broken and toppling stakes. The cottage, having under its roof the main room, the hall and the byre, was built of hollow bricks, not even plastered, just barely whitewashed. Only two tall poplars, shedding their yellowing leaves on the dark, moss-grown thatch and on the shingled roof of the barn, graced the unattractive homestead. People were bustling about the cottage; from the Rucinskis' the bridegroom's fleet-footed mother could be seen advancing as if flying on her walking stick. She burst into the cottage together with Michael.

"Morning, one an' all," she exclaimed in a hoarse but powerful voice. "What was I going to say? Oh, yes. The band's here! They'll be here in a minute to play the guests in, to greet everyone. Now I've told you and I'm off. That's me way."

Before anyone had time to reply, she was already tearing off along the boundary strip; anyway, everyone was busy with something or other. Stephen, swinging the chain, hallooed at the cows to get them to go and graze in the meadow. There was no point in keeping the animals in on a day like this. Margaret, her eyes still saddened by her nocturnal thoughts, stood in the doorway.

"Stephen! Them cows haven't been milked yet. Not last night nor this morning. Turn them back, do," she expostulated in wrathful despair. Stephen set off at a run and quickly headed for home the one that hadn't gone beyond the fruit trees; the other one, making off at a fast trot, was far away down the road. But even that one looked back, stopped, and then reluctantly returned.

"Jadwiga. Call Susie to milk them cows!" Margaret smiled guiltily at Michael. "We're always at sixes and sevens," she said plaintively. "I'm one tablecloth short, Michael, p'r'aps you could go to the Marzaleks. They're sure to lend us one."

"Why not? Of course, I'll go. Marzalek, that'll be by the road near the wood?"

"That's right, then you know them. Jadwiga! Go along with Uncle and bring me the cloth."

"With a fair maiden I'll go to the ends of the earth," laughed the uncle, "but I'll get the cloth for you myself."

"No, it don't seem right to have a guest go alone. But if I send the child alone they might take offense. She'll take you across the park and show you where they have that co-op farm, she'll tell you."

And so the two went, the early sun on the horizon behind them. Boguski's eyes, not dazzled by sunshine, took in the blades of the winter wheat standing straight in the field like the teeth of a fine-tooth comb.

"You've got it all beautifully done," he voiced approval. "It hadn't been this way before. Looks like machine plowing and sowing." Here he reflected on what a child like Jadwiga could know about all that; the right topic for her would be games and school.

But Jadwiga's piercing voice gravely replied, "Yes, it's machine-sown. And for the potatoes we had the digging machine; only it leaves a lot in the ground, and not everybody knows how to use a thing like that."

"And where does the machinery come from?"

"From the manor. The rural council also borrows some from the Machine and Tractor Stations. Here," she added, "all this is Mr. Dabek's, and over there Mr. Guzek's."

"How on earth did you acquire so many misters?" joked Boguski.

Jadwiga did not reply; she had not understood what it was all about. Politely and quietly she continued to explain. "But from here, on either side of the road everything now belongs to the co-op. Right down to the fish ponds."

"I know. It belonged to the manor once. When things were difficult, we used to come here with your mother, to work. Before she went to Warsaw."

"I've been to Warsaw too. The air is bad in town, but it's so good in the countryside, isn't it? And in spring, when I go to school, the larks sing so, I often leave for school early on purpose and walk ever so slowly, and they sing so, oh, how they sing! Is it true, Uncle, that the lark always comes down to the very same place it flew away from?"

The uncle must have been thinking of something else because he inquired abruptly, "And those co-op people, where do they live?"

"At the manor. They used to live here in this house," said Jadwiga, as they passed a ramshackle building standing by the road in a desolation of dung. "Only now, since the co-op's been set up, they live at the manor house."

"And how long is it since they've set up the co-op?"

"Not long. This year."

"People lived in this for nearly ten years?"

"Well, if they hadn't joined the co-op, they would still be there. But they did sign up, so they live at the manor now."

"Wouldn't they like to have their own houses?"

"They're to have them. In Piaski they are already built. It's nearly three years since they started their co-op. They haven't built any here yet. Let's go this way, Uncle, by the manor. It's nice there."

They walked into an old unfenced park, now very neglected but glowing with colors so rich that they dazzled the eyes. Among the lindens, fir trees, beeches, chestnuts, elms and copper-leaved maples, the soaring white poplar — tallest of the trees, and covered with leaves yellow on top and snowy-white on the underside — rose against the dark blue of the sky like a creamy fountain. Boguski reflected that, as a boy, he had often gone to the manor to work but had never been to the park; he had merely seen it through iron fencing; and now peasant children walked in the park. But it was no longer a park. It was rather like a forest wilderness; much water would flow under the bridges before the country folk would learn to cultivate parks for their beauty.

"And here is the manor." Jadwiga's words called him back from his reveries.

It was not the original, ancient structure but a modern building erected in its stead, showy enough — a ground and first floor, with a terrace, balconies, a verandah, everything hideously dilapidated. And all around it silence and desolation. Two sickly children suddenly ran out from the so-called manor, a girl and a boy, both in cotton cardigans and little berets; they dashed off to a dried-up pond full of fallen leaves, and jumped into those leaves, sinking up to their armpits and rowing about with their hands.

On their way back with the borrowed tablecloth, Jadwiga told her uncle that they had slept little during the night, but that they had dozed off when day had almost dawned.

"And did you sleep well?"

"Well, I feared we'd never get to bed, and what would I've looked like today if I hadn't slept the night through? If I don't have enough sleep, I'm not fit for anything. I get so moody, so irritable." Then she added, excitedly, "All the lights will be on."

"Where? In church?"

"Of course. Susie and Mr. Rucinski paid for the wedding service yesterday and for all the lights to be on. And the chandeliers too. And there'll be a taxi for the bride and groom."

Before they reached the Jasnotas' cottage it became so warm that Michael took off his coat. People were swarming around the cottage; the band was playing "welcome" to ever new guests. Michael still remembered village custom, and while passing the players he put a suitable tip into the pocket of the man in front. The player in the front row was Adam Rucinski, the bridegroom's uncle, who had been the railway worker in Warsaw and a member of the railway workers' accordion players. He was a man small of stature but of most dignified bearing. His face was swarthy, very handsome, and even his bald pate seemed to lend him an air of neat smartness in contrast with the bushy manes of the boy and girls. His features were finely chiseled, the expression of his brown eyes and his smile were full of a refined courtesy, and, although he was well past fifty, the gleam of his white teeth when he smiled made him look pleasantly young. And he had all his own teeth, or were they dentures? In this village a good set of teeth was a rare enough thing, and old men possessing beautiful teeth were known only from hearsay.

On entering the room Michael asked Margaret, "Where on earth did you find such a lord to play the accordion?"

Margaret blushed crimson.

"Yes, isn't it?" she asked in turn, and added in conspiratorial whisper, "He's always been like that, so gentlemanly. It's Adam Rucinski. Don't you remember him? He used to call on me in Warsaw. Dear me, did I like him! I did so want to marry a musician. Of all men, I only liked him and none other. When he got himself married I even cried a lot and . . . but I wouldn't tell this to anyone but you, Michael."

She gazed brightly at her brother, but suddenly clutched at her head. "Here I'm rattling on about nothing, and just look, we ain't even got anything ready. We're only now making the wedding posset, and there's the breakfast to be served before the guests leave for church! Jack's cross because he got up before daybreak to make the posset, and we had all the pots boiling, and we ran out of butter so we had to hunt up some in the village. For Chrissakes, Mike, we've got nearly a hundred people here for Susie's wedding!"

The room was like a beehive. Susie, still in her housedress and assisted by Aunt Pauline, was arranging meats, bread, cake and doughnuts on the tables. Stephen and Czesiek were wiping the drinking and wine glasses. Margaret was brewing tea and making barley coffee. At the stove Leocadia Boguska was stirring with a ladle the contents of a huge pot, into which her son Jack poured sugar, added butter, crushed mace, and poured liter bottles of vodka. Although young, Jack had quite a name in the neighboring villages as the best brewer of the wedding posset.

Now Michael Boguski appeared in the doorway and announced, "If you please, breakfast is ready, posset is ready. Come along! He is better who comes first, but he is best who comes last. The young ones are to stand; the seats are for the grownups."

The guests fell into a file and in a jiffy took their places at the horseshoe table. The elderly and those with children sat down; the younger guests crowded into the middle of the room, reached over the heads of those seated at the table to help themselves to tidbits — some with bread, some without — which they popped into their mouths; others used plates if they could get hold of any; there were enough forks. Everyone, however, made sure of a glass for the steaming, spicy wedding posset.

The guests somehow had to crowd still closer when the band came into the room; but they had to come in, for it is unseemly to do anything at a wedding without music. There were three musicians. Besides the accordionist there was a violinist and a drummer; but the latter had to leave his drum outside, for it was quite an affair. It stood, huge, on the floor, a bar with a padded head fixed to the pedal which the drummer pressed with his foot. At the upper rim two oblong pieces of hollow wood were affixed; these the drummer would strike to produce the dry sound of a tom-tom or of Spanish castanets when the drummer really went to it and beat an intricate tattoo. Attached to a metal bar over the drum was a brass plate which the artist would pound when he wanted to produce a brassy sound to stir his audience. The drummer came from Pawlowice and was on familiar terms with most of the young men present. He had been an urbanite for a long time now, brassily drumming and castanetting at dances and popular affairs in Warsaw — both indoors and in the open air. His mug looked somewhat like a circus clown's; the mouth stretched from ear to ear, the features irregular. But those impish eyes, with a merry twinkle, made his whole bearing so likable and infectiously gay that when he laughed all eyes were upon him and everyone had to follow suit. They called him Tolek. Besides his triple-voiced drum, Tolek possessed an inner instrument — he was a first-class singer. So he entered the room and straightaway began to sing in his steely baritone the latest hit; and although he usually excelled in ribald ditties and humorous songs, since these were unsuited to a wedding, he chose to display his skill in a tender song about a young girl. Rucinski worthily accompanied him in his small tenor voice and on the accordion.

But everyone gazed at the violinist. No one knew him here; the two from Warsaw had discovered him. Outdoors no one had noticed him properly, but now in the low room it could clearly be seen how tall he was. Ridiculously tall. And his legs, well, he seemed mostly to consist of legs and head with a smallish body between them — in one word, a stork. His face was narrow and hollow-cheeked, you could say made up of side views and always visible only in profile, so that even the eyes were in the sides, like a bird's. Because the violinist's head was inclined and his nose was exceedingly long, it seemed as though he were resting his nose on his rounded chest, the way storks do. Someone shouted, "Look at papa stork!" Someone else exclaimed, "Hey, diddle, diddle," and that was how they nicknamed him among themselves: "Mr. Diddle." "Mr. Diddle," said some; "stork" insisted others. And the violinist began to play. He drew forth a note so plaintive, so passionate, that it pierced all hearts and even dampened the festive hubbub. The violinist glanced with his yellow eyes — just like a bird — to the left, to the right; his hair was russet-yellow too. And he played on. And now the women placed a small table in front of the cottage, arranged refreshments on it, and asked the musicians to come out for a drink of posset.

The hubbub inside the cottage defied description; everyone had something important to say to someone farthest away, so they all kept up a shouting contest. But Catherine Gadek outshouted the tumult when, with little Bernadette clasped to her bosom, she sang in a piercing shriek, like a whole hundred lapwings over meadows:

> How good was the vodka, and how good was the punch,
> But better yet the maiden to be wed after lunch!

And without waiting for encouragement, Catherine, ably supported by Grandmother Jasnota, again drowned out the noise with another verse:

> In the glade by forest path the nightingales are singing,
> And on my wedding day bird music is ringing!

There were guffaws of laughter, mostly among the youth; some of them tried to outdo Granny, and sang a new song from town, here unknown:

> Marinica, Marinica does not even open her eyes!

One of the guests, said to be Rucinski's son-in-law — he was called "the intellectual" — wanted to do honor to the two Old World singers. "Sing like this, madam," he called to Granny. "Always like this. You have ennobled this assembly, madam, this feast! You have given us heart. That is our beautiful folk song, the tradition of People's Poland. Long life, madam, a very long life to you! Noble, madam . . . I drink to your health, madam . . . This posset . . ." Here the charmed guest gulped down his third glass of the wedding posset.

Grandmother Jasnota did not hear the eulogy; and although the guest addressed her across the table and wanted her to drink with him and offered his glass, she saw nothing, for in her great emotion her eyes were closed as she sang at the top of her voice, opening her toothless mouth wide until one could almost see her uvula.

Stephen's brother, Joseph Jasnota — and the brothers were like an apple cleft in two, except that Joseph's eyes were bigger, clear and glassy, shining feverishly and his chest even more hollow — Joseph then stood up in the doorway and called, "Time to get ready, everybody! Time for church!" There was a turmoil as everyone rose. The bride and groom had disappeared long before to dress for the ceremony.

Susie was being dressed in neighbor Popiolek's cottage. Angelica

Pawoniak directed the ceremony — she knew what was nice. She herself looked nice that day, in a black skirt, a bright yellow silk blouse with a black lace-edged collar pinned with a shining black brooch.

Margaret, still in the rags of a maid-of-all-work, called at the Popioleks' and, glancing at her own daughter, gaped at Angelica. "What taste she has. How smart," Margaret thought, and added aloud, "My late-lamented mistress looked like this in her portrait. She was painted like this before she grew old. And she also had a cream-yellow blouse with a black brooch."

"Well, and how d'you like Susie?" Angelica smiled patronizingly. "Not like this," she admonished the bridesmaids. "We'll arrange the veil differently. Must have more asparagus fern."

"Jadwiga, run home and get the asparagus fern," said Margaret. Jadwiga, at last taking her eyes off her elder sister, dashed out and soon came back carrying in her arms huge pots of asparagus fern, the same pots they had so carefully decorated with white and pink tissue paper only the day before.

The hostess, holding the tulle veil and shedding a tear, said, "How different everything is now. In the old days the bride had to grow myrtle or rue for her wedding coronet. Nowadays, with the new government, they must have asparagus fern, oh, my God!"

Susie submitted to the dressing-the-bride ceremony obediently and silently. Her eyes were wide open, dry, and her stare fixed. She looked prettier than yesterday because she had powdered over the spots on her forehead and chin, put a touch of rouge on the pale cheeks and a suspicion of lipstick on her lips. Czesiek liked a woman to be made up town-fashion.

Outside the cottage the guests began to get impatient because the young couple did not appear. The service should already have begun; the taxi had come from town and was waiting with its motor idling. Carts kept arriving from the farthest corners of Pawlowice; from the neighboring villages came maternal and paternal cousins, once, twice or however many times removed; young people on foot came from all directions, among them two soldiers, now doing army service, who were courting the daughters of Luke Boguski and Pauline Szatkowska. The band played "welcome" over and over again, but at last it stopped. Adam Rucinski, with his accordion, stood in the village path watching for someone.

"Looking for someone, sir?" asked Michael Boguski.

"I'm expecting an important guest," replied the accordion player gravely, "the squire."

"The squire?" Boguski did not understand. "What squire?"

"We call him squire because he's the most important man around here now," the accordion player explained, in a dignified sort of way. "The director of the state farm, of those fisheries."

Michael Boguski said nothing to that, but seeing Margaret run out into the road at the back of the cottage, as if she were expecting someone, he went up to her.

"What, are you, too, watching for him, Meg?" he asked. "They're waiting for the 'squire.' The director of the state farm," he explained, in answer to her frightened glance.

"Ah-h-h," nodded Margaret. "Must be Mr. Stepien. A relation of the Rucinskis. They say he's been asked to the wedding. But you wouldn't be likely to see him in our place. He won't come. No, I'm waiting for Stephen. Just waiting and waiting," she sighed, and her voice was tired.

"And where's he got to?" Boguski inquired. "Come to think of it, I haven't seen him around quite a while."

" 'Cause he's gone to meet Rucinski's sister and her husband who are to come by bus. She's something wrong with her feet and can't walk. He's softhearted, Stephen is, so he just up and went. He says to me, 'I won't have an elderly, sick woman come on foot to any wedding in my family.' I ain't complaining, but what's to be done now? And the bus gets in late sometimes. When are the young people going to get to church? After all, Susie can't go without her dad's blessing. And there's just no sign of Stephen."

"He'll come all right. And the priest will wait with High Mass. He's been paid anyway," Michael consoled Margaret.

"But the guests are waiting, so many of them," complained Margaret. "It don't matter that much to me, only Stephen; he's worked himself to death to prepare for this wedding, and now he's not even here to bless the bride. And for him this blessing means so much, like I don't know what."

The two young people meanwhile joined the crowd of guests. Along the rubbish-strewn path from the Popioleks' cottage Susie advanced stiffly, in her long white dress, like the statues carried in processions.

From the opposite direction came Czesiek Rucinski in a navy-blue suit, a white bow adorned with a sprig of Susie's asparagus fern. Both are surrounded by girls and young men. On a cloth-covered table placed in front of the cottage are a cross and two candles; and the air is so still and warm that the candles burn evenly, their yellowish flames barely visible in the bright light of day.

People began to get impatient. "Where are the bride's parents?" they asked. "What, no father?" "Went off to meet the bus?" "When will he turn up, then?" "Couldn't someone else have gone instead?"

Margaret kept running out into the road; suddenly she noticed Adam Rucinski standing next to her and staring fixedly in front of him.

"No sign of the man," said Margaret shyly. "Can't see Stephen," she added recalling that Rucinski was expecting Stepien.

The accordion player glanced at her, bowed, shook hands with her.

"So you are the hostess, the bride's mother?" he greeted her civilly. "You look thinner now than when I used to call on you in Emilia Plater Street; I remember it, but those days are over now."

Suddenly Margaret forgot everything; she only knew that she was standing in her kitchen-stained clothes, before that smart Varsovian, who had been dear to her heart in those days long ago. And here she was unable even to dress up, or to attend her own daughter's wedding, because there was the washing up to be done and the wedding reception to be seen to. She wanted to say something to this accordion player, but words failed her. Fortunately people called her away now; it was impossible to wait about any longer. Let the mother alone bless the children.

The young couple, pushed forward by someone, knelt on a rug that Joseph Jasnota had thrown down for them; Angelica handed Margaret the sprinkler, but Margaret did not see it. Shaking all over, she embraced Susie and cried, "My daughter, my dear children, God bless . . ." And she could say no more, for the tears flooded her words. And even those she uttered went unheard in the din; the clamor did not subside. Suddenly everybody realized that Margaret was not there at the table. The bridegroom's lively mother had whisked her away like a feather and herself delivered a speech which held everyone present spellbound. Mother Rucinska did not look at her son, but on the crowd of guests as if to bless them; she spoke solemnly and gaily and in rhymes all the time. It was a lengthy oration which ended with:

And I bless my handsome son,
For whom the last hour but one
Of bachelorhood has come.

Many were now wiping their eyes. No one noticed that the bridegroom's father was also absent from the blessing ceremony. When it came to setting out and the couple had got into the taxi, Susie suddenly declared that get in she might, but she was not going to be married without her daddy. So the waiting began all over again. Some sneered: what a careless man, so important in the ceremony and yet he had gone to meet the bus as if he had no one to send instead. Others were arranging themselves in the carts. There were shouts of "The band!" And answering quips, "What, to beat a tattoo in church?" "The band stays here, only the violin goes to the service," someone resolved. "The violin goes." The news was passed from one to another. "Mr. Stork; get in with us." "Mr. L. here!" "He don't need to get in the cart, his legs are so long, the cart will drive under him!" someone joked. The red-haired violinist, manifesting no particular joy at the honor, got up into the cart pointed out to him, his violin case clasped to his side. And his astonished yellow eyes blinked at his fellow passengers. Next to him sat Granny Jasnota, who despite her years would not be left behind for anything. Her eyes were closed — she was probably seeing visions of groomsmen, dressed up to kill, on horseback, beribboned bridesmaids wearing beads and glittering headdresses. She shouted in a rusty voice:

When they drove her to her wedding she kept
wailing oh, and how;
Do not let them, Mother, dear, do not
let them take me now.

"Mother," reproved Catherine Gadek, "no singing now. Leave off, Mother. These ain't those times . . . different people."

Margaret waited; she was on tenterhooks, thinking of nothing but that Stephen should arrive in time, that he shouldn't fail to take leave of Susan-the-maid, that he should get here even the very last minute. That much joy was due him — there had been so little gladness in his life.

The guests were also waiting; bored, irritable, they got off the carts, stood about on the road, climbed into the carts again. They didn't know how to hasten the arrival of that irresponsible father. "He's coming!"

someone shouted at last. The bridal party stopped moving, and the only sound that could be heard was the purring of the bridal taxi's engine now being warmed up for the third time. From behind a gentle rise in the road there appeared first a horse's head, then the cart, as if sprung up from somewhere underground, the horse galloping toward the spectators.

"Father! Father's coming!" The cry went up from nearly all lips, and probably never before was Stephen Jasnota's paternity so honored, although he had no idea of it, since he did not hear the shout. He drew in the reins until the horse reared. He was alone in the cart. Obviously the expected guests had not arrived. Stephen did not just get off the cart; it seemed as if some force lifted him out of it. Jostling people right and left, he ran to the taxi shouting, "Susie, me darling daughter!"

Susie jumped out of the taxi as if she had been catapulted and threw herself on her father's neck. No one saw anything after that; everything was seething. "Get on, off we go. Taxi first. Keep to your places," could be heard on all sides. The bridal party was about to start. Margaret dashed out of the cottage with a pair of her husband's shoes — that lunatic had gone to the bus in his working boots. Stephen threw the reins to one of the many men who were going in his cart; and he put the shoes on while the cart rolled on.

There were nine carts, all belonging to the family; some had only borrowed a second horse, because it was unseemly to drive to a wedding in a one-horse cart. Only Stephen, poor fellow, had not time to harness the mare borrowed from the Popioleks. They were driving at a good pace following the taxi that led the procession at a discreet speed so that the horses would not have to gallop to keep up. The carts were of the solid, regulation type: the boards painted yellow, gray or brown, rubber tires on the wheels, on every cart a plate fixed to the side, with the owner's name and address printed on it in black paint. They were altogether modern carts, and so was the road, much of it being paved. Only the clear weather above the silent procession, only the earth aflame with autumnal colors, were ancient and had been time out of mind.

— *translated by* RACHEL KURAHO

(From *A Village Wedding and Other Stories.* Published in English by Polonia Publishing House, Warsaw, 1957.)

Sweet Flag

BY JAROSLAW IWASZKIEWICZ

JAROSLAW IWASZKIEWICZ, born in 1894 in Kalnik (Ukraine), is a poet, novelist and essayist, and received a law degree from Kiev University in 1918. Because of territorial and political changes after World War I, he moved with his family to Warsaw. There he joined the then very influential group of poets associated with the literary magazine *Skamander,* of which he was a cofounder. His first book of poems, *The Octaves,* appear in 1919, and since then his literary production has continued to grow. In recent years, Iwaszkiewicz's poetry has been collected in two important volumes: *Poems from Different Epochs* and *Autumn's Tresses and Other Verse.* A versatile writer, he is also one of the best novelists of his generation, with a wide field of interests which spans both the historical and contemporary scenes. He writes music criticism, having been professionally trained in the field, and is also a playwright. As president of the Polish Writers' Association and chief editor of *Tworczosc,* a literary monthly, he is a prominent figure in the literary world. His major works are *The Moon is Up,* a novel (1925), *The Girls from Wilko Manor,* short stories (1933); *The Red Shields,* a historical novel (1934); *The Mill on Utrata; Italian Short Stories; Fame and Glory,* a voluminous novel depicting Polish society from 1913 to the present time (1955); *Sweet Flag,* short stories (1960), one of which follows. His plays include *A Summer at Nohant,* about Chopin and Georges Sand (1936); *The Wedding of Monsieur Balzac* (1950). His biographies are *Chopin; Johann Sebastian Bach; Karol Szymanowski.* In 1959 he published "A Flight," written in answer to Camus's *La Chute.* Mr. Iwaszkiewicz lives in Warsaw.

SWEET FLAG, which in some parts of Poland is also called the Tartar weed, has two smells. If you rub its long green leaves between your fingers, you will release the gentle scent of "waters shadowed by willows," slightly reminiscent of Oriental nard. But when you tear open a strip of sweet flag and put your nose to the seam lined with a kind of woolly fluff, you will sense, along with the musky scent, the smell of marshy loam, of rotting fish scales, of mud.

Since my earliest days the smell has been associated with the idea of sudden death. In my childhood, the floors of the entrance hall and the balconies at home were covered with sweet flag during the warm, gay days of Whitsuntide. But the weed also reminds me of the death of my first true friend, who bore the odd name of Gratian and who drowned at the age of thirteen.

This was long ago. But even now this ambiguous scent fills me with somber thoughts. Every end has a mysterious connection with the beginning; sounds, colors and smells echo from one pole of life to the other. The scents of childhood find their way to those of old age, and youth is reflected in the dusty mirror of maturity.

People tend to be surprised that in order to escape from the bustle of cities and the fatigue of travel, I detach myself from tiresome and sterile tasks and am in the habit of spending part of the summer, or more accurately of late spring, in Z., a small town on the banks of a large river. Apart from the river and the meadows through which it runs, the rushes along the riverbanks, and the slender bridge, there is literally nothing beautiful in the town. A dusty market square, a few houses, a few cottages — ah, yes, there are also the fine orchards and gardens to adorn the place. But the greatest lure for me is the fact that I can stay there in a rest home without giving my address to anyone, unworried by telephone calls and telegrams, receiving only a daily letter from my wife.

There is one more thing which attracts me there: my friendship with Mrs. M. It is a perfect friendship since we see each other only once a year for two or three weeks; we never write letters and have no overweening curiosity about one another's secrets. This accounts for the frankness of our conversations, and has a beneficial influence on our characters. Throughout the twenty-five years of that relationship we have never ceased to be somewhat "special" for one another.

Mrs. M. — Martha — a doctor's wife, lost her two sons during the Occupation and is now very lonely. Her husband is grossly overworked. Apart from his work in the hospital, he has an enormous private practice around the little town. In the past, I used to see him on peasants' carts, traveling ten or fifteen miles to see his patients. Now that he has a car he can visit a great many more people in a day. This reflects financially the life of the household. In spite of this established affluence, Martha feels her loneliness keenly. The few weeks in a year when I am staying in town cannot make her forget the emptiness of her daily routine. I must add that Martha never complains, never speaks of her feelings. She runs the house efficiently, answers the telephone, takes messages from patients; and her overtired husband, when returning home, finds order, peace and harmony there.

The doctor's house is an old-fashioned "town-residence," of which there are a few in the little town. The awkward design of the several large rooms makes a subdivision of living space impossible, so the couple have the whole house to themselves. The boys' room is locked, and no one ever enters it. And the other rooms, low-ceilinged but bright, are filled with antique furniture.

Martha usually receives me in the drawing room, where there is a set of nineteenth-century mahogany chairs, covered with royal-blue velvet, and on the walls a few prints and Martha's portrait by a local artist, who must at one time have sniffed the air of Paris. In the black jardinieres there live clusters of exotic plants, looking as if they were made of silk and tin. An enormous grand piano which has not been touched for ages stands in a corner. The floor is covered with a reddish carpet, its center a woven picture of a woman carrying two buckets of water on a yoke.

It is not an ideal room for intimate talk. And yet it was here that Martha told me the story of her life. It was here too that a short while ago, after she had learned that she had an incurable disease, she told me the story which follows. Of course, I made some notes — all writers do — later supplementing them and giving rein to my imagination and even trying to look into the hearts of the principal characters. Perhaps I have overdramatized the whole thing. Basically, it is quite an ordinary story; hundreds like it must happen daily in our towns and villages.

Martha never goes to the "boathouse," which is the name given in the town to a fairly large wooden building, some distance from the river. It consists of two large rooms, in one of which there is a counter where cigarettes, beer and the excellent local fruit juice (the mainstay of this fruit-growing area's economy) are sold. There is also a large veranda with a wooden floor on which people dance. The whole ramshackle structure is perched on a high cement foundation, which prevents it from being swept away in time of flood.

The veranda is the greatest "draw" in the little town. The young people come to dance and meet there when they get bored with the monotony of work or study in a place remote from the centers of culture. It is most crowded on Saturdays and Sundays. On Saturdays, the boys wear informal clothes, brightly checked shirts and slacks, their hair tousled "beatnik" style. On Sundays, however, their hair is meticulously neat, their shirts are white and their jackets dark. Whatever their style of dress, the boys drink only fruit juice, and in spite of what people say about drunkenness in Poland, they never bring vodka with them: they are too poor to buy it. They also play bridge for a hundredth of a cent a point. Not many girls are to be seen in the "boathouse," and they, for the most part, come with their partners to dance.

Where could Martha take out a woman friend who has come from the capital to stay with her? What was she to show her in the little town, ruined by the war? Of course, she had to take her to the "boathouse."

The river glistened in the moonlight. From time to time a wave would break against the bank with a loud splash. But no one looked at the river. Couples were dancing on the veranda, as the loudspeaker croaked mercilessly. Inside the "boathouse" almost all the tables were taken. Some young men were playing bridge.

The two ladies sat at a small table at the side of the room, looking around them. In the corner, behind the counter, a friendly blonde was selling soda water and that fruit juice, the pride of the soft-drink factory. You had to fetch the bottles yourself.

Martha went up to the counter and took two bottles of apple juice. Returning to her table, she passed a group of card players. One of the youths, banging his card on the table, lifted his hand too high and knocked it against the bottle which Martha was carrying. The bottle very nearly slipped from her hands, and the boy looked up from his game and apologized politely.

Martha sat down at her table and was silent for a while. Then she poured out the drink, which had a ripe, lovely color, and again sat still. She glanced toward the table where the card players were installed. The young man who had nearly knocked the bottle out of her hand was sitting sideways to her, showing his irregular profile, with its flat, rather squashed boxer's nose. He had a fine head of hair which he wore combed up. His hands were beautiful, with long well-shaped fingers.

They were in distinct contrast to the broken nose, the fairly large, solid head and the heavy neck, showing above the collar of his red shirt.

Martha soon realized that she had very little to say to her friend. They had some common memories from their youth, but Martha had come to the conclusion that for some time now she did not much care for reminiscing. It made her feel old — and reminded her of so much that had turned to ashes. And Martha still had some obscure hopes for the present. So she listened to her friend, who had four children, scattered all over the globe, who received letters and parcels from them, and now thought it polite to tell Martha all about them in great detail. Martha tried to hide her lack of interest, from time to time asking a question, and out of boredom continued to watch the card-playing boys.

At a certain moment she noticed a girl briskly enter the room. Going to the card players' table, the girl laid her hand on the arm of the boy. He turned around, and Martha saw him for the first time full face. As sometimes happens, his face did not match his profile. It was a broad face, with prominent cheekbones, but there was an expression and a light in the eyes which Martha found most attractive.

The boy said a few words to the girl, then turned back to his cards. The girl remained standing by him for a moment, as if at a loss what to do. Then she slowly walked away.

She was wearing a black sweater and a colored skirt. Her hair was pinned up in a fashionable "pony tail" — yet she impressed one as rather untidy and poorly groomed; there was a certain languor of movement, a disenchantment in her whole appearance. The tight sweater showed plainly the lovely lines of her body, and she moved like a cat. She looked like an interesting girl.

The boy now interrupted the game and, to the indignation of the other players, followed the girl. His place was immediately taken by a short, thin, crafty-looking youth who had been obviously waiting for such an opportunity to arise.

Soon afterwards, Martha left the "boathouse" with her friend.

The next day, the two women went for a walk along the embankment which ran beside the river for miles on end. As I said, the only thing of any character in the town was that river. Its beauty compensated for the dust, dirt and dullness of the streets and made one forget not only the indifferent houses but also their inhabitants. Wide and majestic, it flowed in a broad bed, bordered on both sides by thickly growing reeds. At the very start of the summer, sandbanks emerged from the grayish waters like the oblong backs of monsters, but in midstream the current remained swift and powerful, and after rain, the waters would rise, swirling with form, and quickly cover the sandbanks again.

The sight of the river was too primeval, too inhuman, for Martha's liking. On her walks she preferred to stroll along the embankment, away from the main stream, and to look at the green meadows spreading from under the reeds and willows like another, gentler stretch of water. Along the embankment grew whole clumps of willow trees and, here and there, a few tall, extremely old, silver poplars which, even on apparently windless days, trembled with a strange musical whisper, continuous and soft, unlike the dry rustle of palm leaves. It was a music which Martha loved above all country sounds.

When she climbed with her friend onto the embankment, there was brilliant May sunshine, the sky remained cloudless, the willows never stirred, only the leaves of the white poplars whispered.

They walked peacefully along. On their left, a slope, blue with forget-me-nots, fell gently toward the meadows; on their right, market gardeners' huts stood among orchards in bloom, and the glass of the hothouses glinted in the sun. Martha listened indifferently to the tales of her old friend.

At a certain point she saw a couple sitting on the edge of the embankment. It was the same couple that she had seen in the "boathouse." The girl was wearing a light dress, the boy a khaki shirt. The girl was talking animatedly; the boy was sucking a blade of grass and turning his head toward the river, which at this spot shimmered blue through the thick reeds.

Martha saw them from some distance. When the two women drew level with them the young people stopped talking; when they came back from their walk, the couple had gone. Martha remembered where they had sat and observed some crushed clover and forget-me-nots.

A few days later, her friend left; one of her children was due to arrive from America. Martha was alone again.

And so, one afternoon, she once more went for a walk along the river. She felt she would again meet the young couple who had fascinated her by their beauty and youth. Presently, she did meet the young man, sitting in almost the same spot as before, but without the girl. Martha had already learned his name and what he did; he was Bolek K. and, although only twenty-five, had been employed for quite a long time, as a surveyor in the offices of the Water Board. Bolek was very popular in the town; everybody knew him. Martha was also well known. As she passed the boy, he blushed and greeted her. She stopped.

"So you are alone today?"

He blushed even deeper, making as if to rise.

"Don't get up. Don't get up, please," said Martha. "I'll sit down too. This is a beautiful spot."

She sat down on the grass and looked around. In front of her grew a tall spreading silver poplar; the wind lifted its leaves to show their white lining.

"Are you alone?" she repeated.

"Halina's gone away," Bolek muttered halfheartedly.

Martha noted with satisfaction that his voice was low and pleasant.

As it was hot he was wearing no jacket over his sports shirt. He had broad straight shoulders — but his face with its flat nose seemed, from close up, rather ugly and wild. Martha watched him intently.

"Who is Halina?" she asked.

"Oh, a girl," said Bolek in his charming voice, smiling.

Despite the difference in their ages, sitting next to him, Martha had to think of her body. Would he find any pleasure in her fully blown — perhaps overblown — charms? She felt suddenly conscious — although she had not been for a long time — of her hips, her thighs; she thought of her breasts. "He does not even notice what I look like." Yet she was pleased now that her habit of daily exercise had allowed her to preserve until middle age elastic muscles and an unwrinkled skin. She had always had small breasts; she moved quickly and gracefully. Would this be enough to attract him?

She grew ashamed of herself; there was silence between them for a moment.

"She is a student," said Bolek suddenly, not looking at Martha, "and she's rather clever. And I am only a simple boy . . ."

There was real grief in his voice. Martha was not in a mood to listen to his confidences.

"Are your parents alive?" she asked.

"No," he answered, "they were killed in the Warsaw Uprising. I was brought up by Granny."

"She has brought up a fine-looking boy," said Martha, and stopped herself at once. "What makes me say such stupid things?" she thought.

"Where did you study?" she asked soberly, in order to erase her last silly words.

Bolek looked at her with momentary distaste, as if he were thinking: "This is not an examination, by God!"

"At Elblong," he said. "I trained to be a water supply engineer."

"Wouldn't you like to have done something different?"

"Here you go," said Bolek impatiently, "just like Halina. I shall never be anything else, can't you see? Never. I was born to work for the Water Board — a water surveyor, that's me!"

"And what would she like you to be?" Martha inquired, pleased with the boy's sharp reply. He obviously had not noticed her previous idiocy.

"Well, she wants me to read books and take her for walks along the river on moonlight nights."

"And you prefer to play bridge?"

"Of course."

"I saw you that night in the 'boathouse.' "

"Yes, I know."

Down below, under the embankment, people were driving cows. Replete, with udders green from the high grasses, they walked slowly, heedless of the drovers, who frequently called: "Come on!" One of the cows held a bunch of forget-me-nots in her mouth and did not swallow it.

Martha put her hand on Bolek's hand.

"I also would like you to study, to read books."

Bolek did not withdraw his hand; a midge had settled on his bare forearm; Martha killed it, and a drop of blood appeared on the beautiful bulge of his muscle.

"I sometimes do some reading," said Bolek in a deep bass, "but I cannot get any books. I cannot afford to buy them. I must support my grandmother," he added, as an explanation.

"You could borrow books from me," Martha said, rather to her own surprise. "We have quite a few books. My husband has them sent or buys them in the local bookshop, but he has little time for reading. They mostly lie about unopened."

"Thank you," said Bolek with embarrassment, as he was not really very keen on reading.

"When will you come?" asked Martha.

He did not answer. He sat gloomily, chewing his blade of grass. Martha touched his forearm. He did not notice it, thinking his own thoughts. Suddenly he exploded:

"She imagines God knows what. She wants to be a professor at the university and says she would be ashamed of an ignoramus like me. Maybe I am uneducated. I, myself, don't hanker after any philosophy. I am all right as I am. If she wants to marry me, all right, and if she doesn't — I shall manage too."

Martha was astonished.

"But surely you are too young for marriage."

Bolek looked at her with irritation.

"Too young, too young. That's what she says, too. I shall never be different."

"Come and see me tomorrow," said Martha rather firmly, and got up. Bolek also got to his feet. "Do you know where we live? By the Krakow Gate."

She extended her hand. In the opening of his shirt, she saw the quivering of the skin on his breast.

"Do you swim?" she asked.

"I do, of course," he answered, and kissed her hand.

"Then perhaps we shall meet one day on the river?"

He did not answer. He seemed surprised, but not uneasy.

Martha was in a fairly good mood during supper. The doctor looked tired, but he unbent a little. They talked of daily affairs with an animation which had long been lacking at their board.

Their life together had lost all purpose a considerable time before. Martha, in a sense, fulfilled the duties of a good housewife, but the kitchen was the domain of old Sophia, who had brought up the boys, and arranging flowers and answering the telephone were not too absorbing tasks. Martha realized the futility of her occupations, but did not know what to do about it. From time to time she invited an old friend from the capital to stay, but often the visitor escaped after only a few days. One of them commented on her return to Warsaw that the atmosphere in the house was like that in an Ibsen play, and this made the others reluctant to accept Martha's invitations. The doctor was not very demanding: he liked good food, and on Sundays read newspapers and medical magazines. He almost never engaged in conversation with his wife, as he was so stultified by overwork and making money. In the evenings he had no strength left to talk at all.

That night, however, something between them seemed changed. This momentary animation was a surprise to them both — and sitting at the table, facing each other, they saw themselves afresh. The doctor was intrigued. He saw Martha lift both her arms to her head and smooth down her hair at the back. It was the long-forgotten gesture of her younger days.

The doctor sighed, turned his eyes away, and again looked at his plate. The food was excellent that night — crayfish with creamed rice, and *crème brûlée* for dessert. After supper, Martha suddenly got up and took a key from the drawer of a small table next to the piano. Her husband looked at her, amazed. Quickly, although she tried to slow down her steps (thinking of Bolek's graceful gait), she walked up to the door of the boys' room, unlocked it, and went in. She switched on the light. The room was dead and empty, with nothing of its old atmosphere remaining. Martha sat at the table where her boys used to study. A few years before, she used to spend a few hours a day sitting at that table, but for a long time now she had not entered the room.

In the dining room the doctor was drinking tea, apparently unperturbed. The door to the boys' room was facing him, and he could see his wife. After a moment, she covered her face with her hands and stayed so, her elbows propped on the table. When the doctor had finished his tea, he got up with an effort and went in to Martha.

"Come now," he said, putting his hand on her shoulder. "Don't sit there."

Martha started. She turned her face to him.

"Don't you feel ashamed," she asked, "don't you ever feel ashamed to be alive?"

He shrugged his shoulders.

"I feel ashamed at being alive when so many are dead," said Martha. She got up and started pacing up and down in the large, empty room. "I'm ashamed before all who are dead, let alone our own boys."

The doctor stood helpless in the middle of his sons' study, his arms hanging heavily, as if they were made of stone.

"Only think: there is such a crowd of young people," said Martha, "and our boys are not among them."

"They would not be so very young either by now," sighed the old doctor.

"What d'you think? Would they be married now?" asked Martha.

"Oh, I am sure they would. We would have, besides them, some young women in the house."

"That would be terrible." She shivered. "I hate young women—they are so conceited."

The doctor again came over to her. He took her by the arm.

"Well, let's get out of here," he said. "You'll only upset yourself."

Martha gave in to his coaxing.

"I am always overcome by terrible shame when I see a young life. Youth is so shameless, don't you think?" she said, going with her husband to their room.

But the doctor shook his head in denial.

"You seem to forget one thing," he said, "namely, that life can so easily become death."

The next day Bolek called. Martha was quite bewildered. Only after a while did she realize what he wanted of her: he had taken literally all she had told him about the books. He wanted to borrow something to read, but did not know what. He said rather oddly: some Polish literature. Martha guessed that he wished to read something connected with Halina's study of the humanities.

Obviously, he never read anything now, and did not even remember the titles of the few volumes he had read when at school. He would accept any old book thrust into his hand, yet Martha insistently tried to drag an admission of a literary preference out of him. She was unable to do so.

They sat for a time in the drawing room with the royal-blue chairs. The weather was beautiful, and again there was a fine sunset. In front of the house, enormous syringa bushes were growing. They were in full bloom and obstructed the light with their greenish-white waxen clusters.

"Have you seen our syringas?" asked Martha. "They are real syringa trees."

This was one of her favorite remarks, the saying of her youth. At that time the syringas were not so tall. But even then she called them "syringa trees."

Bolek did not seem to know which bushes or trees Martha meant. Like many very masculine men, he was unable to remember the names of flowers and trees. He did not have a clear idea what syringas were. He only knew what lilacs looked like — and that, because he had heard at his college a silly story about them.

"So they are," he said, and looked at Martha with a blank expression.

"You are terribly young," said Martha unexpectedly. "How old are you?"

"I told you — twenty-five."

Martha thought that it was pleasant to be with someone who said he was twenty-five. The very sound of these words cheered her. So did the fact that there was somebody in the world who had such a strange, such a beautiful number of years.

For a moment she felt like saying this to Bolek, but, realizing he would not understand her, she gave up the idea.

Still there were other subjects of conversation. Again they spoke about swimming and the floods which had recently occurred in the locality. The conversation flowed more easily than the day before. They also mentioned the embankment.

"Do you often go there?" asked Martha.

"There is nobody to go with," said Bolek, and blushed.

"Why?" Martha wondered.

Bolek drew a breath and shot quickly:

"Unless you want to come for a walk with me."

Martha was taken aback.

"Gladly," she said, and then added, "Has Halina gone away for good?"

"She has gone to stay with her aunt. She did not even say good-bye to me," Bolek told her in a childish voice. This was a completely new tone for him, and Martha looked at him with warmth.

"Well then," she said. "Are you free tomorrow at noon? Let's meet on the beach, under the bridge. We can go for a swim together."

Bolek accepted readily. Soon afterwards he went. And in the end he did not borrow any book.

The next day Martha received a letter. It was a folded sheet of paper, without an envelope, brought by a boy from the Water Board.

DEAR MRS. M.,

I was so confused yesterday that I made the appointment to meet you at noon, although it is a working day and I shan't be free until about four. Can you meet me at that time, in the same place? With respectful good wishes,

BOLEK K.

The letter was written (copied perhaps?) in a careful, childish hand, was faultless. "Did a girl friend write it?" wondered Martha.

So around four o'clock she went to the beach under the bridge. It was not large, and completely empty at that time of day. No sign of Bolek. Martha undressed in the bushes — as everybody did whatever their age or social position — and got into her bathing suit. The strength of the current was so great that there was no question of swimming against it. You had to swim with the current for a time, then you landed, and walked back to the beach, across the fields. Martha made a couple of such excursions. She did not want to admit that Bolek's absence was a great disappointment to her.

When she went in for the third time, she swam a little farther, and walking back, she saw on the bridge the well-known silhouette. Bolek was there with Halina — obviously she had not gone to stay with her aunt yet. They were walking toward the station, talking excitedly.

Martha returned to the spot where she had left her clothes under a large blackberry bush, next to a thicket of willows. Shattered, she sat down, unable to regain her composure. She suddenly realized the character of her feelings for Bolek, and that realization was like a hammer blow on her head. She shook as if in high fever.

For so many years sadness and resignation had reigned in her heart. And now, as she felt the germ of a mortal illness grow in herself, the figure (what else?) of a young boy, younger than her sons, had played havoc with her soul. She wanted to curse Bolek. Yet she kept repeating, "But is it his fault?"

She sat there for a long time. Various people passed by the beach, soldiers bathing in their underpants, children. Small boys walked by carrying bunches of sweet flag plucked in the meadows over the little pools of water, the remains of those chronic floods. It was Whitsun the next day, and sweet flag was used for decorating the houses.

Martha sat for a long time. "And will I have to live on after this?" she thought. "It's horrible; it would be better to die at once."

Suddenly she heard a voice overhead:

"Mrs. M., Mrs. M.!"

She looked up. Bolek, smiling brightly, stood on the bridge.

"I am sorry I am so late," he called to her, leaning over the parapet. "I'll come down at once. We must pick some sweet flag."

Martha waved to him. She picked up a green strip of the water plant, which a passing child had dropped. She smelled the odorous leaf. She adored the smell.

Then she got up and walked in the direction from which Bolek would come. She waited a little, until he appeared from among the osiers. He was undressed and walked towards her with his dancing step, completely naked except for a pair of tiny lemon-colored bathing trunks. He was not at all sunburned; instead, his body was white and soft like silk. Again she was struck by his exceptional beauty. The lines of his chest and thighs were so harmonious, so perfect. Martha remained quite speechless. In silence she put out her hand to him, but he did not kiss it this time. He looked straight into her eyes. His plain head fixed on this glorious body had acquired a different expression. "If only he does not talk," thought Martha.

But he was talking.

"I am sorry I have come so late. I had to see Halina off to the station."

"Did she go away?"

"She did not have enough money for her ticket. I had to lend her what I had, and now I'm completely broke."

He smiled so radiant a smile that his face was transfigured. The smile seemed to extend to the whole body.

"I shall lend you some money," said Martha.

"Really?" Bolek was overjoyed.

It was terrible.

Martha wanted to wipe away as quickly as possible that vulgar, awful conversation. She wanted to separate him and herself from the world. She wanted to cover him with a green tent of leaves. And she wanted him not to talk. The beach, the bridge, the children calling to each other, the bathing soldiers became intolerable. She did not want to look at the houses that could be seen from where they were standing.

Somewhere downstream, a yellow thrush was calling. One could see the glimmer of its golden feathers on the silver poplar, not far from the bridge. Martha was holding Bolek's hand.

"Come, let's pluck some sweet flags for tomorrow," she said, and pulled him toward the meadows. On the flats, between the overgrown banks and the level stretches of grass now covered with a thick net of daisies, blinked larger and smaller "eyes" of stagnant water. They were the remains of the rivulets, which had disappeared under the mud, or else holes which were filled by the swelling waves of innumerable floods. Among those "eyes" some were like real lakes — picturesque, overgrown with sweet flag, covered with the fanlike leaves of water lilies and kingcups. In their green waters were reflected the clumps of osier, the tall, clipped willows and the white cumuli calmly floating high above. Martha and Bolek passed them in silence.

She was now heading for one of the larger pools, one she especially liked. At one end of the long, dark and probably very deep water a small accumulation of white sand formed a kind of beach. There they threw down their clothes which they had taken with them, and stayed in their bathing suits. It was quite late — about six o'clock, but the air was warm.

Bolek, wearing his lemon-colored trunks, lat flat on the sand, looking at the clouds as they appeared over the pool. Martha glanced from time to time at his perfect body, in such contrast to his face of a barbarian slave, with its small upturned nose. In other, more distant pools frogs were croaking madly. In the osiers, nightingales were already screaming with pathos. Martha and Bolek were silent.

"What are you thinking about?" asked Martha.

"Nothing," answered Bolek, with unpleasant haste.

"About Halina?"

"Yes, Halina." He sat up.

"Your back is covered with sand. Let me brush it off." And she at once started to do so.

"I shall wash in a moment," he said impatiently.

She did not listen but carefully continued to wipe the boy's back. Then she put her cheek against it.

"What are you doing?" Bolek cried out. He turned toward her. Martha leaned back. For a moment they looked into one another's eyes, then he pulled her head toward him and kissed Martha on the mouth. The kiss lasted a long time.

When they at last drew apart, she said, "What have you done, Bolek?"

He smiled and said lightly, "You are so kind."

She blushed. She was very angry when she said, "A man should never tell a woman that she is kind . . ."

"And what should he say?" he asked naïvely, but with some petulance.

"Nothing," she hissed through her teeth, and turned away.

They sat side by side, in complete silence.

At last he sighed. "We had better pluck those weeds," he said.

He got to his feet and jumped into the pool. The water was very deep. He dived, emerged in the middle, and after a little while got to the other end, where the aromatic plants were growing.

Martha remained on the bank, her heart heavy with despair. There is nothing left for me but to commit suicide, she thought. Everything was lost. When Bolek reappeared before her with a bunch of sweet flag she stared at him as at a strange, unknown being.

"One of us must die," she thought. And she imagined at once what infinite relief she would feel if that boy should cease to exist. There would be no one on earth to know of her secret then. The burning torture and the burning shame would be wiped out.

"Hold these," cried Bolek gaily, not in the least disturbed by what had happened. "I shall get some more."

He threw a mass of long crisp leaves at Martha's feet.

"He must be used to doing such things," thought Martha bitterly, not wishing to look at him. Instead she looked at the sheaf of verdure lying on the sand.

"This will probably be enough," she said.

"No, certainly not, I don't want you to complain that I was lazy," laughed Bolek, and put his hand around her neck, brushing her lips lightly. Martha wanted to hold him.

"Wait a minute," he said meaningfully. "Let me fetch some more of this rubbish first."

He slipped away from her and ran into the dark water. He dived and did not emerge for a long time. At last she saw his head in the very center of the pool. He was moving along slowly, as if not quite sure of himself.

"What's the matter with him?" she wondered.

Bolek swam to the other side of the "eye." His arms rose rhythmically from the water, his hands elegantly stroked the surface, and small splashes flew from under his fingers. She saw him reach the ground at the far end and stand next to the clump of sweet flag pulling at the long strips. When he turned back he had some difficulty in swimming with the heavy sheaf. He could navigate with one arm only, and his progress was slow.

"What can be the matter with him?" thought Martha again.

Then suddenly, in the middle of the pool, he disappeared under the surface.

"Why is he diving?" she thought in alarm.

Bolek's head emerged for a moment from the deep. He was some distance away, but Martha caught something like fear in his eyes. She leaped to her feet.

He disappeared again. And when he re-emerged, he made a few desperate gestures; he was drowning.

Now Martha jumped into the water and swam toward him. There was nothing on the surface. In the center of the lake, she dived into the deep cold well. Opening her eyes, she saw that green opaque light one usually sees when diving. She flapped her hands here and there, trying to find the body of the drowning man; she could not find it.

She went down deeper. She could not stay long under water and was just beginning to swim up with eyes closed, when her body was touched by Bolek's blindly groping hands. She turned around and grabbed him. At that very moment two strong arms clasped her neck. She tried to swim to the surface, tugging him, but his arms were heavy, pressing her and dragging her down, down, to the bottom. She lost her breath and in another second would have started swallowing water.

With a violent jerk of her head, she freed her neck from the choking embrace and, lightly pushing herself upwards, broke the surface. She was near the bank. She could not remember how she reached the sand. She looked back at the pool; in the middle of the dark waters, something was gurgling, bubbles of air appeared and vanished. She covered her eyes with her hand. When she put it down, the surface was smooth.

She climbed onto the embankment and ran along it, shouting:

"Help! Help!"

From behind the willows, two boys rushed out who had been mowing the meadow. She shouted to them, pointing to the lake.

"Quick, quick! Bolek is drowning! There, under this tall tree," she yelled.

The boys were quicker than she was, and when she caught up with them, they had stripped. They started diving, systematically searching the bottom. Emerging, they called to one another.

"In the center, in the center," Martha urged them.

The boys searched the whole "eye" to the very end, and then turned back to search again. Suddenly the older of them exclaimed:

"I've got him!"

"Pull him by the hair, pull!" cried the other.

Both dived in together and surfaced in the same place, then swam toward Martha, tugging a great weight under water. They reached the bank and pulled Bolek out, heaving him laboriously, with great effort, on the sand. It all took at least half an hour.

They began artificial respiration.

Water poured from the mouth of the drowned man, but he gave no sign of life.

"Wait here," said the older boy. "I'll run and fetch the others; we'll have to swing him."

"I'm coming with you," his friend cried, eyeing the body uncertainly. He must have realized that their exertions were in vain. Bolek had had a wonderful reputation as a swimmer. This must have been a heart attack. And so the "swinging" would be of no avail.

"You had better stay here," he said to Martha.

They put their clothes on their wet bodies and ran off. Martha could hear their voices for a while, and the slap of their bare feet on the hard earth of the embankment.

Then a deathly silence spread over the water. Bolek's body lay on the sand, just as the rescuers had left it, next to the sheaf of sweet flag which he had plucked. His arms were spread wide, and large green drops of water shone on the hair under the armpits. The open eyes were blank and dull, like the eyes of antique statues. From the wide-open mouth a thin stream of water or perhaps mucus was seeping.

Crouching next to the body, Martha looked at it intensely, as if wanting to preserve forever the memory of its rare beauty. The figure of the drowned boy was being veiled, as with cellophane, with a film of stiffness and foreignness; it was ceasing to be human.

In the bright light of the May sunset, Bolek's bathing trunks shone garishly, their yellow color only slightly obscured by the green sediment of stagnant water.

"Why didn't I drown with him?" thought Martha, leaning over his body. "Do I wish to live? Go on living? What for?"

Over and over again she relived the moment when with a sudden jerk she had freed her neck from Bolek's choking embrace.

"To live?" she repeated. "To live?"

She delicately touched Bolek's breast. The skin of the drowned man was drying fast, although the sun was low in the sky. Under her fingers she felt something infinitely cold, like marble. The jutting muscles, perfect in their harmony, were straining the skin. Martha placed her lips on the spot where a delicate down grew, between the breasts. It was already dry.

She gradually moved her lips below the breasts, then with a mulish passion, began to kiss the diaphragm, the stomach, the navel; in the violence of the kisses showered on the dead boy, she descended lower and lower. The whole sculptured body smelled of sweet flag.

When under her lips she felt the edge of the yellow trunks, the smell of marshy loam, of rotting fish scales, of mud, reached her nostrils — the aroma of death which very soon was to catch up with her.

— *translated by* CELINA WIENIEWSKA

(From *Tatarak,* short stories. Published by "Czytelnik," Warsaw, 1960.)

Jokes

BY MAGDA LEJA

MAGDA LEJA, at twenty-six, is one of the youngest women writers in Poland. She graduated from Warsaw University with a history of arts degree, but now works as a press reporter. Her debut as a fiction writer came in 1957 with the publication of a volume of short stories, *The Art of Screaming.* This was followed by a novel in 1959, *The Neurotic.* In 1960 she published a book for teen-agers entitled *Letters to My Boy.* Also in 1960 she took a long and – as she says – "strictly private" trip to India, which she considers a major event in her life.

ALTHOUGH they all lived nearby, on the only street of this community, or suburb, she walked home alone, a young woman in a light blue raincoat which rustled dully and had cracked on the surface into a multitude of darker lines, like a too loose celluloid wrapping. The unsteady beam of streetlights above, among the luxuriant tree branches, illumined her face again and again, a face soft, helpless and tense, as if the woman were attempting to concentrate on something, knowing in advance she could not and that maybe it wasn't even necessary; arrested in a vague effort, she was so completely absorbed in it that an observant passer-by would wonder how she could walk in such a brisk way, not forgetting to rearrange, from time to time, the parcels she carried in a white plastic basket. But the evening was late, and the cool wind had also played its role — no one came from the direction of the one-story houses standing by the road, and the people coming from the factory, if they looked at the blue coat at all, had no thought of looking at the girl's face. She heard the gates creak as they said their good-byes, one after the other, almost without words, going into their apartments, which they would leave in the morning to creak an even shorter greeting, as they joined their friends. In the lights of the streetlamps she saw the peeling remnants of bright paint which had been permitted to age, not so much because the people were careless, as poor. Two men dissolved into the darkness of a yard, and a moment later a rectangle of light outlined neatly arranged plants on a flower bed, growing low — the wind in passing did not even touch them — so fragile and two-dimensional. There was no one in front of her now, and from behind the wind brought sounds of last returning steps; but she knew they would neither catch up with her nor pass her, because there was no reason for it, and she walked rather quickly, though not hurriedly, since she had no premonition and always walked that way. She thought, *Two roads, no, one road, going this way and back, this way and back. It shouldn't be, it shouldn't be as if nothing else existed* — realizing at the same time that such thinking brought her neither nearer to nor farther away from the truth because she would not have been able to say what, in her opinion, should exist besides these houses in their yards (some of them contained shops and one a movie theater) and these factories; she did not even know how to ask herself this question — she only felt it was very close, very plausible and very important. She had once been taught something, and although she did not attach much importance to it, she remembered how it should be: twisted ropes with everyone pulling according to his strength and in his direction; they had even taught her the names of the groups united in that common effort of pulling, each for itself, and anyway she had read about them in the newspapers. But now she thought, *It shouldn't be,* because just about an hour ago her strength had not proved enough. She thought also, *If I don't find anything, if there is nothing besides this road, then I can only await defeat. But that's impossible.* She thought, *Impossible,* just as if she had thought, *I?* — she understood nothing, she made nothing on her own, except her own fate, and that was determined by her dignity, a good fate. She put the basket on the steps and, drawing toward her with her left hand the door carelessly hinged in its frame, searched for the key. *It's begun, and that means it is. Nothing can change that, and if I myself stick by it, well, no . . .* A radio played in the house, but she was still much too preoccupied to be surprised. Only when she had taken off her coat and had begun arranging on the table the things she had bought before the meeting did she take any notice of the music, and even then she first told herself, *The Kubiks bought a radio,* in a tone of indifferent approval, before she heard the song which had greeted her at the door and was just now coming to an end:

This table is
Veronica's table,
this corner is
Veronica's corner,
this gesture is
exactly her gesture.

Straight and stiff, she sat down on the bed, holding in her hands a bag of sugar and an empty stringbean jar; she sat like that for quite some time — without a thought, without a smile. Afterwards she returned to the objects strewn across the table. *Isn't my name Veronica?*

She heard, one after the other, muffled bangs on the wall. The radio fell silent, and the Kubiks embarked on an indistinct quarrel. Suddenly:

"The hell with him!" Mrs. Kubik yelled, and the radio once again roared into a tune. But only for a short while; Veronica did not need to listen to know that the Kubiks were scuffling in front of the newly bought radio. Something fell to the floor with a piercing, metallic sound, and the other neighbor, Potelski, or maybe his wife, again banged on the wall. Mrs. Kubik was now enumerating all the excellent matches she could have made if to her own undoing she hadn't fallen in love with Mr. Kubik. Potelski was Kubik's foreman; that too Veronica did not have to bother about. She was eating her supper, sitting sideways at a table littered with old magazines, and darkness wedged into the windowpanes reflected her thoughtful face, paler and smaller than in reality. Unseen, trees rustled at the edge of the only street. She did not look at her reflection, just as she did not listen to the growing music of the trees, but it was within her now as she tried to remember the song, those few bars, few words, on the radio which she had managed to catch, but which eluded her as if they could exist only in this way, at arm's length, a step away. *If that is a song he wrote for me,* she thought, and everything stopped within her in a sudden reflex of self-preservation; and then it came from a nook in her memory: "I listen for steps — maybe it's you; if I'm out, the key is downstairs. Take it and come." That other song *was* for her — and right away, *So something else does exist. So I'm not alone,* and beneath it all the thought, *I knew, I knew I was right,* as faltering as the efforts of the first bird at dawn. Slowly, she drew out the many pins in her hair, and black strands fell on her bare shoulders; now she was looking at her reflection. She looked, taking more time than she needed to prepare for bed. Suddenly trembling seized her; she ran barefoot toward the switch, put out the light, and jumped into bed.

Through the murmur of trees filling the room — perhaps it was a dream, dark, turbulent water — late at night she had time to think one more thought, *Now I'll wait for the song,* and to smile before she slept soundly.

After that she smiled all the time; and under the street clock these smiles looked like shining leaves strewn the length of that single, twice-daily-traversed road. At two in the afternoon she was buying *Trybuna* at the newsstand near the factory gate, and — involuntarily slowing her steps — she studied the radio programs. Then she looked ahead of her, above the news page — and the workers shifted their gaze in embarrassment. Everyone, of course, knew who she was and about that meeting the other night, and perhaps they associated these facts with some other, earlier ones, if indeed, similar situations had occurred; *They must have occurred,* she thought, and, *They thought me stupid when I smiled.* She chuckled, and a young man sitting on a bench nearby winked at her invitingly, but she paid no attention. *And yet, I was right. I'm going to Lutek now, to Warsaw. To smile was simply the best way of living through it. Because, finally, I knew how little I hold in my hands.* Some sort of protest welled up in her: *I knew?* — but she stilled it; it wasn't important any more, how much had been awareness and how much instinct. Loudspeakers on all the stations were blaring away Lutek's song, and she preferred to reminisce rather than think.

Bent over the reagent-smeared laboratory table, her hands doing work known well enough not to require her entire attention, but sufficiently interesting to provide satisfaction, she had smiled defiantly, mockingly, as if she had escaped from the ominous circle of desks, through an unseen crack, into freedom, freedom of action. Only her work was checked each day, personally, by the directress; only she was reprimanded, although none of the other girls in the laboratory wore head coverings either; she had always answered respectfully, with a bright, stubborn smile, which she could not chase away even if she wanted to, and the supervisors had turned away their eyes with something other than embarrassment. *How long did it last? I don't know myself; I'd have to count.* Automatically, she took a step forward and moved the small oilcloth valise — the move brought a strand of hair across her face — to look at the clock. A breathless woman, holding a baby, rushed out of the tunnel, looked around the platform in panic, and wiped the perspiration off her brow after putting down the child. The train was late. The young man was eating plums, spitting the pits in front of him and looking stubbornly at Veronica all the while. She patted her hair, *Ah, no, it's not for you I'm smiling,* and it was a very pleasant, sad thought — much-encompassing and short-lived.

She had listened to the radio at the Kubiks'. Mrs. Kubik was not surprised at the sudden interest and, hinging her hands on her formless belly, had said in tones of unconvincing self-pity:

"One thousand eight hundred zlotys it cost us."

"But you won't have to sing to the baby now," Veronica had answered prettily, which immediately brought about a long monologue, full of pauses, exclamation points and confidential mouth-to-ear whispers. *And it still happened that I half smiled, as if through mist, as if I were going numb — that was when I thought of Lutek. Poor Mrs. Kubik had said, "You're not even listening to me," and I. . . .* Veronica felt even now the warm upsurge of the scene: Lutek raises his head suddenly looking straight into her eyes; she could reconstruct his every movement (there exists a special calculus of reminiscence), but she didn't care to; never before did she have so much fun, and what was now totally absorbing the girl with the oilcloth valise, standing on the railway platform, was nearer to a repeat performance of past reality than an echo of it, a new reality more easily defined in words pertaining to abstraction than in any other words, if ever there should be a need for oral definitions. Since she could reconstruct that gesture and that gaze in her mind, there was no need to do it, why should she? As in years before, she knew their meaning and felt the same poignant faith in the right course of events, spanned as they were by his serene gaze.

"Rail workers! Improve your qualifications," suggested the P.A. system, and without so much as a pause the overdue Warsaw train was coming into the station.

The platform became alive with agitated persons. The young man crushed his paper bag, now empty of plums, and tossed it under the wheels of the locomotive. Veronica picked up her valise, someone pushed her, the child yelled, and the act of boarding was recorded on her calf by a dark oblong mark, which she did not see at the time.

After a rainy day, dusk had muddied the chaotic panorama of little houses, and for one fleeting moment the baskets of geraniums hanging from the lampposts swayed in relief against the lights, which had burst into bloom no one knew when, until the train leaped out of the embrace of roofs straight into open fields.

On that other station, where they said good-bye three years ago, one of the two white handkerchiefs quickly became soaked with tears. The warm dampness of that tightly clutched handkerchief had stayed alive, *as if it were the very heart of what I felt,* thought Veronica in amazement.

"I know you from somewhere."

"Could be."

And that voice in the loudspeaker with its singsong accent . . . After that she had not cried any more and had thought about Lutek but rarely, she had flirted with boys, nearly married one, seeing no discrepancy between her behavior and the certainty of going, one day, back to Lutek — a certainty so whole that it needed no thought, no reassuring memories. It was as if by its very nature her union with Lutek could never end, not even through separation; it could be suspended at the most — a super fact that suffers no obstacle, difficult as this was to put into words.

"How far are you going?"

"Warsaw."

"And are you going to stand all night? As long as we're talking time goes by quickly, but I get off soon, three stops."

In Biale Konskie an extravagantly dressed group of travelers rushed into the car, and windows were thrown open with a bang.

"Heniek, give me the bag! Here, here we are!"

"Let me go, Bunny; Frank, hold me; after all, I have to tell him something. Oh, oh, it's moving. . . ."

Some character, fat as a tank, rolled through the aisle, to and fro, waking passengers who had been asleep in their seats.

"It's scandalous," he declared. "Two compartments. All the rest reserved. Scandalous!"

"Are these two full? Let's see."

"Packed."

"It really is scandalous," said the young man to Veronica, the one who was getting off at the third stop. Just then a thin thirteen-year-old boy came out of one of the reserved compartments, looked around, and moved toward the washroom. Sighing, a huge blonde shifted her bulk to let him pass. Veronica did not join the conversation. *They don't know anything either, they don't know about me,* she thought, but she felt no more festive or unusual than if she were traveling to the main office to replenish the laboratory's chemical supplies. Lutek asked that she return, and she was returning; to her this was a normal development, the only possible sequence, and no one is surprised when life goes on normally. At least not she; in her opinion she was doing only normal things; even that other evening, when speaking publicly at the meeting about the results of the analysis at the factory laboratory being faked, she was not motivated by despair, or some secret ambition, no; and although no one else seemed to act in this way, that belief of hers in the complete naturalness of her acts was perhaps the reason why a wall of security surrounded her.

"Unfortunately, I must get off now," said the young man. They shook hands. The attention-compelling party had simmered down a little but was still, in an imperceptible way, underscoring its separateness from the meek other passengers. The blonde sat down on her valise, and one of the men bent over and whispered something into her ear, pointing toward Veronica with his eyes, but the blonde shook her head. The fat man said, "And the children are asleep. Just imagine, that's not even hygienic."

In the compartment, under the dimmed greenish lights, children swayed helplessly on the benches.

My valise is too flimsy to sit on, thought Veronica, *I didn't stuff it enough,* and with slight apprehension, she listed in her mind the things she had taken with her; there weren't many: towel, soap, white blouse, nightgown, tortoise shell hair pins, of which she was very proud because they cost two thirds of her salary and she never wore them. *Maybe I should have taken the raspberry-colored dress? But I didn't, so. . . .* She shifted her position to free her left shoulder, which had gone to sleep from leaning against the wall. Some sort of light rushed by outside the window. *Mrs. Kubik said she was afraid her time might come at night. Is Kubik working the night shift today? Krystyna is on duty in the laboratory. The directress is an old louse, but no one will mumble a word to her face* — the outlines of thoughts rose chaotically and then ebbed, separated by long pauses filled with the clatter of wheels, monotonous and compelling. *Lutek liked to recite this poem: "And in every city there are at least two hundred of you, my sisters, the streets. . . ." I don't remember any more. "My sisters, the streets. . . ." Anyway, the point is not that there's only one street. It's just that interests vary, and there should be strength to support them; where is that strength?* Vaguely, she felt something akin to triumph. *I must remember that sentence; after all, I'll be telling Lutek all about it.*

The compartments resounded with mountainous snores; soiled dawn sketched wrinkles on the face of the sleeping blonde. *It's not far now.* Veronica sat on her haunches, and opening her valise, she noticed the black smudge on her calf. She rubbed it hard until the skin reddened and the soot on the handkerchief formed a pattern of breaks. She put the pins in her hair.

2

THE STAIRCASE in the house where Lutek lived was poorly lit and melancholy. The light seeping from the wire-covered bulbs deepened the impression that long ago someone had left and forgotten this unfinished and uncleaned building. Veronica passed dark windows each of which displayed a fragment of the elevator shaft, a scenic decor highlighted from behind by the ever more distant street; finally, she stopped and with a jerk of the head tossed back the strands of hair falling across her face, and knocked on the door. It was evening already; she had spent all day looking for the address.

"Maybe you're Veronica," said a red-haired girl, without letting go the knob on the half-opened door, as if the arrival could still turn back; her delicate, childish face flickered uncertainly between mockery and amazed sympathy; Veronica put down her valise next to a coat-filled rack and started taking off her own coat. A hubbub of voices came from the apartment; the redhead moved suddenly, and with high heels clicking against the floor, like small agile hoofs, she announced: "Veronica!"

Bottle in hand, Lutek stiffened, bent forward, and the others also remained immobile in their places, but she passed the redhead and walked across the room without any embarrassment, with only a slight blush on her cheeks. And then she greeted them, in turn, smiling in turn—a good and gracious hostess—Stefan, Olek, Marzena, Kosooki, Gerard and Basia standing in the door. It lasted enough time for Lutek to think of something, anything.

"In the first place," he said, "Veronica must catch up on the drinks."

"Pour a whole glass, if she's going to catch up with us," pointed out Marzena.

"Don't be a fool." Gerard got up from his chair. "I would like to propose a toast in your honor, madame, who has graced . . . And for the success of the meeting . . . In the name of the importunate but lucky witnesses. Because it's not every day that . . . Hey, Lutek, I have no more vodka!"

"Let's drink to love. . . ."

"Ah! How tactless you are. . . . 'I listen for steps — maybe it's you; if I'm out the key is downstairs.' . . ."

Basia burst out laughing and ran out of the room, mouth covered with hands.

"Olek, go and keep that idiot quiet," said Stefan sharply. "And where did you come from?"

"I . . ."

Lutek cruised around the room pouring vodka — *a big boy dressed like a grown man,* thought Veronica. Marzena arched her eyebrows and with a comical seriousness whispered something into his ear; he blushed and looked around sheepishly.

"You want to watch TV?" but they shouted him down, and as he stood there, uncertain, his hand on the knob, half-turned, Veronica felt she would burst into tears at any moment and quickly took out her handkerchief. It was dirty, and naturally everyone had noticed it, since their eyes traveled from her to Lutek and back again. Thinking about it later, she could not find a reason for the tears, except for the fact that she had a dirty handkerchief. And anyway, the whole evening was turning out very strangely. Lutek sat next to her and was saying nice and pleasant words; following his gaze, she saw her ankles, swollen after the past night and day when she had sat down only once in a milk bar; she saw her feet overflowing the rims of her black patent leather high-heeled shoes; Lutek's look was not kind, but she only thought, *Why did I put on those pins?* and *They're very beautiful, these girls, Marzena, Basia; I like them.* Lutek, however, appeared oblivious of the rest of the company; they whispered and giggled in the corners, until Gerard, offended, knelt in front of the couch. "We want to drink to the lady's health, and you won't give us any vodka, Lutek."

But Veronica's glass was always full, and she looked at Lutek, because everything else was changing more and more into a blurred photograph. Lutek would lift the glass to her lips, and she felt as if she had been here all the time, without any in-between, in the only proper place for her, surrendering to the soft wave of torpor. Lying in Lutek's lap, she still heard one of the men say:

"Well, Lutek, when are you going to collect your winnings?"

And Marzena, with inexplicable but easily detected spitefulness, said, "I don't know whether it still counts."

"Quit it, she's not so bad looking, the poor thing."

"So, when?"

"Things aren't yet so bad that I have to depend on your vodka. And you know what you can do with your opinions."

"Stefan, look at that expression on the pining lover's face."

"It's all flattered conceit."

"But I still think he deserves that vodka."

"Still . . ."

The object of the argument, some kind of bet made previously, did not interest Veronica. *They're talking quietly not to wake me,* she thought; *I must tell them they don't have to, I'm not asleep.* But at that moment sleep claimed her completely.

She was wakened by a cloudy feeling of something lacking; her outstretched hand touched a pillow. She lifted her head hesitantly: Lutek was asleep on a cot on the other side of the sunny smudge which, after having squeezed in between the window curtains, divided the room into two halves.

"Come here," said Veronica, holding back laughter. "For three years I never once woke up with such a feeling, and now . . . come, Lutek."

But he still slept, so she ran across the sunny screen and bent over him; she kept bending lower and lower with that kind of joyous trepidation which — more than anything — hallows love and, before she touched him, his eyes opened.

Veronica lay on the cot now, hands under her head, free and easy, gazing at the crumbs of light swirling in the air. Returning from the bathroom, Lutek walked into them and stopped, the sun highlighting the shadow of his summer tan. He said:

"What stupid friends I have. You are beautiful. You look now like a sculpture; really, Vera, your looks have improved immensely. How long is it since we saw each other? Three years! You've become more feminine. It's a shame they can't see you now. You should always be naked, my 'Venus Awakened from Sleep' — I don't know how that would be in Greek — every dress distorts you."

Veronica felt compelled to explain her appearance of the evening before, and propping herself up with an elbow, she said, "I'll tell you, I simply don't have any nice dresses — that is, I have one, raspberry-colored, but I didn't bring it with me. I . . . Where I live people have different tastes from here in Warsaw and I . . . after all, I belong there now."

"Oh," laughed Lutek, and his laughter was as before, disarming and contagious — it suited him so well — "you belong there! We'll change that in a matter of minutes."

"What do you mean?"

"We'll simply go shopping. 'Fashionable Wife,' IWUPE. . . .* You came at the right time: I happen to have some money. I made a pile on that song I wrote for you. You should get a percentage, don't you think? You brought me luck." He sat down on the cot and repeated almost inaudibly, "You brought me luck. . . ."

But these were cares rather than happiness or, to be more exact, a somewhat careworn happiness — a happiness all the same surprising, she thought. She thought so at the moments when the confusion of Lutek's life swept her aside by the sheer force of its obscure laws, unknown to her — laws which ignored her reinstatement. But automatically, effortlessly, she discarded these — she thought — misunderstandings, sitting alone in a room on the fourth floor of a new, still-unplastered apartment house; she turned on the radio, the melody "I look at my room in the evening, I listen for steps," resounded frequently and convincingly, and Veronica suddenly realized she was searching her mind for something to confirm the logic of events, then, irritated, she turned the dial. "And so, my dears, ink and fruit stains," said Mrs. Koc on another wave length, and Veronica slipped into the bathroom to clean the stains on Lutek's suit.

That same day — that is, the day after her arrival in Warsaw — they went on a long shopping spree; taxed by the cold eyes of the salesgirls, Veronica lowered hers and mangled a handkerchief in the pocket of her cheap light blue coat.

"Don't you like it?" asked Lutek, surprised.

"No, no . . . it's too expensive," she whispered into his ear.

"But you like it. After all, Veronica, I can't decide, it's you, the woman . . ."

But all she wanted was to return as quickly as possible to the turbulent street, be one of the many, unnoticed, and if the purchased finery were to make her resemble Marzena or Basia, he had to be the one to decide. He chose badly, or maybe making her resemble them was simply impossible? They bought a gray blouse made out of something

---

* Warsaw stores.

resembling soft suède, a narrow-pleated pink skirt and seamless stockings; at the Hotel Bristol, Veronica heard Lutek's friends say to one another:

"I never would have believed it, but she looks like a teacher from an uplifting movie."

To them I'm a teacher from an uplifting movie, she thought. *What does it really mean?* and the effort to understand why they wanted her to be like the other girls interrupted her account of the faked analyses, the only thing she could talk about and to which they even listened with some interest, interrupting at times with the effective commentary:

"Shitty country!"

They didn't even notice when she stopped in mid-sentence, the facts she was recounting were so exotic to them; they were so much in a hurry to return to their gloomy denunciations of the world, to that rebellion which tormented them, ready to explode at the slightest provocation. She understood this about them, she realized it quickly; ignored amidst their exclamations, she sat there in her nice dress which proved inappropriate, and only Gerard looked into her bewildered eyes — but she paid no notice. At night she said to Lutek:

"You know, where I was, there is only one solitary street. Not symbolically, really. And facing everyone who does not want to run away, there is only one possibility, one duty, one force. After a while it seems that there is nothing else. Nowhere in the world. But I fought back; I didn't believe it for a moment. And, of course, I heard that song. . . ."

"Poor little thing. . . . But tell me, didn't I surprise you just a little bit?"

"No. Only now, maybe country life's dulled me, but you know, Lutek, I can't find that point where they meet. . . ."

"What meets what?"

"Oh, you know, that life there, that street, and all of you . . . you and your friends, your conversations, what you do. Because if they don't meet, Lutek, then it has no value for me! It's just as if it didn't exist!"

"But you can see that they do meet. Your being here is the best proof." The momentarily brighter glow of his cigarette pinpointed Lutek's thin dark lips, smiling at some unspoken footnote. "Veronica, why do you want to waste time? Come closer."

The new apartment had in it the old table, "Veronica's table," with its black scar, burned in by an iron they had forgotten about while kissing; it was covered by a tablecloth, but Veronica felt with her fingers the small bulletlike indentation. She was talking all the time about the same thing, the faked analyses, her eyes lowered under her straight eyebrows.

"It really is disgusting," Lutek said.

Little white crosses shimmered on the tablecloth; she did not raise her eyes to see his smile wisely confirming nothing. After a while he got up, and she heard him pacing the room and the creak of floorboards blending with the sounds of a childish scuffle next door.

"Damned brats. And you, too, what is it to you whether they cheat or not at the laboratory? . . ."

But I come from there, Veronica wanted to say, but she didn't, stopped by fear and the sudden realization that neither he nor she knew what to do to connect these two worlds, connect them with something more than rails, and if he didn't know then it was probably impossible — *impossible? rather, undesired.*

"If you want," said Lutek, "I can get Gerard; he's a good journalist, he used to be interested in this sort of thing a while back. Try it, talk to him. . . . He's sweet on you. . . . He was the only one of my friends who defended you. You didn't make much of a hit, I can tell you that."

"And so, you see," Veronica was telling Gerard, "the measurement results are lowered to norm level; there is such a norm, and if it's exceeded . . . Because those gases are very injurious to health."

"If it's exceeded, then work should be stopped."

"I don't know."

"They will fire you sooner or later, ma'am. People will always find fault where there is none. No one backed you up at the meeting?"

"No, no one."

"Perhaps it would be best not to wait but find you a job here, in Warsaw, right away? You're a chemistry graduate, aren't you?"

"Yes. But I . . . thank you very much . . . I don't . . ."

Gerard moved his chair to where their knees touched.

"Why not? You really don't want to live in Warsaw, do you?"

"Of course I do." She felt as if delivered into the cool ruthless hands of a surgeon; she could not explain to him, perhaps to no one, why she should remain with what had been begun, whatever the chances; she did not know how to say it, because up to now verbal descriptions of clear-cut matters had not been necessary — she never did it, she only did what she had to, about which there was no doubt — and now this necessity found her unprepared, stammering like a little girl.

"You wouldn't stay, Lutek or not?" Gerard asked.

Flying skirts swept across the little table, knocking an ashtray to the floor; Veronica's rise from her chair had been too panicky. She poured cognac, saying, "It's excellent, from Georgia. It won't take a second to clean. It's nothing, broken glass brings luck," while at the same time thinking several instantaneous sentences which mounted, jostled, and did not end: *Lutek says Gerard's a drunk. He goes for me. He knows something more than I, more than Lutek. He knows something that's loaded, something that hasn't happened yet. That's what he's looking at with those crossed, unmoving eyes of a badly stuffed bird. He knows . . .* A few mixed sentences hardened into a petrified landscape never to be entered.

3

She was returning home alone, a young woman in a light blue raincoat with a plaster-taped elbow, along the only street of this community, or suburb; leaves shrouded the cracked pavement of the sidewalk, and on the driveway children ran after chestnuts, calling to one another in low, throaty voices. Wind blew strands of hair into the woman's face drawn with an effort to understand and a reluctance born, perhaps, of knowledge of the futility of effort in general, and not because she couldn't make it, although she probably couldn't. Gerard left after having had several talks. He had no intention of writing about a matter which had no backing; she knew the matter had no backing, and whatever he said, she did not hold it against him; he came and went, his was a completely different province. She also believed him when he said that Lutek had placed a bet with his friends on her love, ready to come running at the slightest sign from him. If the song expressed truth, he did not want to know it — he was not strong enough for that truth. The "Bristol" evening had been a celebration of Lutek's victory, *Ah, yes,* she repeated, *Ah, yes,* and Gerard's graceless overtures could not pierce the amazement beneath which she stood, as if under a high wall; this amazement still lasted, a dulling background for the question, *What next?* and anyway, she also didn't know which was the background and which the leading motif, and if anyone were to look at her face, he would wonder how this girl could walk so briskly in her black over thin-heeled shoes, avoiding so unerringly the ruts in the road. But it was not the hour of work's beginning—which to others is its end—no one walked the street in either direction, only kids chased around in the road, and near the fence a cat, elongated in flight, leaped over the shadow of a bird. Mrs. Kubik was hanging out diapers on a line stretched between window and rickety cherry tree. Turning, she said:

"I can't play the radio. The Potelskis keep unscrewing the fuses." Her hand, sunk in a bowlful of white rags, remained motionless. "You tell me what else is there I can enjoy. . . ."

Veronica stopped and began painstakingly to unbutton her coat at the neck, because she suddenly felt stifling hot, and her strength had left her.

– *translated by* EWA MARKOWSKA

(From *Nowa Kultura*, a weekly. Published in Warsaw, February 28, 1960.)

Strength

BY JULIAN KAWALEC

JULIAN KAWALEC was born in a village near Sandomierz in central Poland in 1916. The son of a smallholder, he was the only child in the family who went to school and graduated at the University of Krakow, having majored in Polish philology. After the war, he took up journalism and at the same time contributed to literary periodicals. His first book, a volume of short stories, *Paths Within Streets,* appeared in 1954; the next, *Scars,* was published in 1960, and the vignette that follows was chosen from the latter.

Another story by the same author appears in the section of this book entitled "Their Humor."

THE MEADOW stretches in a long strip from small, yellowish houses to a line of ancient willows. The willows are enormous and beautiful, for they have grown without human aid. They have stout branches, each of which could easily be a separate large tree. Their boughs touch one another from tree to tree; they gleam with leaves like little silvery green fish, and rustle quietly. Birds take shelter in the boughs. For them every willow is a whole world, a good and secure world.

The meadow is level and luxuriant; all kinds of flowers grow in it, most of them yellow in color. Perfumes and insects hover over the meadow. Beyond the line of old willows and beyond a deep ditch is a great railway siding where iron is unloaded. Life has never exposed so many hard edges and sharp corners to man as are found in such places. In these sidings iron doesn't have many colors. There are only many shades of rust. The various objects, the people, the trucks and the ground are all rusty. You can hear the hissing of locomotives, curses, the rattle of cranes and the sound of metal banging against metal. It is the sound given out by broken mandolins when they fall off a table onto the floor.

A little while ago a long freight train arrived. The first cars were low, and had large wheels. These cars carried the enormous, brightly rusty girders which are the most important element in the construction of factories. Further cars carried a load of darkly rusted tanks, belted around with the brows of large bolts. Beyond these were freight cars with sharp-angled bars, rods, shafts, and thick sheets of iron. Cranes that looked like greatly enlarged and reinforced gallows were slowly driven up to the cars carrying the girders. A movement set in around the cars loaded with the stout iron sheets. A bald-headed, bandy-legged little man said that an automobile was due to arrive, and the sheets were to have been loaded by the cranes straight from the train, but for the time being its arrival was held up by rolls of wire. The sheet iron would have to be held up by rolls of wire. The sheet iron would have to be unloaded by hand.

The workmen began to object, to swear, to take off their shirts, to split up into little groups, to tighten their belts. The work of unloading began. Some of them jumped onto the freight cars to shift the sheets down to the hands of their comrades on the ground. Those below were split up into twos. Two men took each sheet and carried it to the spot assigned to automobiles by the road. The sheets were stacked in piles, one on top of another. Soon a large truck with a small crane was to arrive for them.

The men who were stronger worked on the ground. It was heavy work taking the sheet iron from the train and carrying it to the piles at the roadside. Two of the strongest were working with the last car. The thickest sheets of iron had been packed there. A huge, small-nosed, freckled, ginger-haired man was teamed up with a small, thickset one, who was overgrown with hair like a monkey. The ginger-haired man was nicknamed "the Little Pike." He knew innumerable swear words drawn from many national vocabularies. When he flew into a temper he could go on swearing for a long time without taking breath. At such times the others all kept away from him.

The short hairy fellow was called "Cabbage" by his workmates, because he often ate cabbage and peas. Apart from that, he was taciturn, grumpy. "Pike" and "Cabbage" were the strongest of all the workmen on the siding where the iron was being unloaded. Though the sheets they carried were the thickest and heaviest, they worked more swiftly than the rest.

They had already carried thirty-seven sheets from the car to the pile and set them down. Now they were carrying the thirty-eighth. Once more they had to swing the sheet onto the pile.

But Pike looked at the pile and swore.

"See that?" he said to Cabbage, and swore again.

"I see it," the other answered grumpily.

"What has it settled there for, the son of a bitch?" Pike snorted.

"Hm!" Cabbage muttered helplessly.

"All that would be left of the son of a bitch would be blue dust."

"Hm . . . Blow on it, and there'd be nothing . . ."

"Like after an atom bomb, eh?"

The ginger man and the stocky, hairy man, the two strongest workmen on that siding for unloading iron, sweated holding the large iron sheet in their hands. Stout veins stood out on the ginger man's neck, and dirty drops rolled from the hairy one's forehead into his eyes.

But on top of the pile a little azure butterfly, like a tiny, airy fragment, was resting blissfully.

— *translated by* HARRY STEVENS

(From *Blizny,* short stories. Published by "Wydawnictwo Literackie," Krakow, 1960.)

The Gold Fox

BY JERZY ANDRZEJEWSKI

JERZY ANDRZEJEWSKI was born in 1909. When his first novel, *The Order of the Heart,* was published in 1938, he was hailed as a young Polish Mauriac. His next book, *The Night,* did not appear until 1946. This volume, a collection of short stories, tells of the horrors of the German Occupation, and the novel *Ashes and Diamonds,* which followed in 1948, dealt with postwar frustration of the younger generation. A film was made from this book, under the same title, and was shown in this country. During the Stalinist period, Andrzejewski was active mainly as a publicist, doing work far removed from his Catholic beginnings. However, in 1955 came "The Gold Fox" and "The Great Lament of a Paperhead," both of which are expressive of the author's reawakened sense of individualism. *Like a Wood,* another volume of stories, was published in 1959. This was followed by *The Gates of Paradise* (1960), an interesting experiment in style. His *Inquisitors* was published here by Knopf in 1960. The author lives in Warsaw.

THE FOX ARRIVED quite unexpectedly one October evening, when Lucas was at home alone. All of a sudden the door squeaked, and he walked in. At first he stopped by the door and glanced around curiously with bright-shining eyes, his pointed little snout slightly raised; then, without the slightest trace of fright, his paws stepping along softly, he moved toward the center of the room.

Despite the darkness, Lucas noticed right away that his guest was extremely beautiful. First of all, he was a very large fox, but at the same time slender and dainty, wonderfully built, with eyes that glittered in the dark, with a big bushy tail and, most amazing of all, he was gold, with a goldness that appeared soft and silky and glowed in the darkness with a mysterious light.

Lucas, although only five years old, was a prudent little boy, and had no intention whatever of showing his great delight right away. But, even though he tried, he couldn't contain himself, and suddenly a short but loud "Ah!" resounded in the quiet of the night.

As he heard his own voice, Lucas stiffened with horror. "This is the end," he thought desperately. And, afraid he would see the fox's retreat, he shut his eyes tight, and whispered to himself, "Oh, my dearest fox, my beautiful fox, please don't run away from me, please! Stay here, and I promise that I will love you very much and will always see to it that you have everything you need, only don't go . . ."

Not the faintest sound broke the silence, and all Lucas could hear was the wild thumping of his own heart. When at last he gathered enough courage to open his eyes, for a moment he couldn't believe his own luck: the fox was still standing in the middle of the room. Only his head was now turned toward Lucas; hence his eyes appeared still larger and more fiery.

Lucas couldn't control himself any longer. He sat up.

"Oh, fox!" he whispered.

Hearing this, the fox greeted him by nodding his head, almost smiling; then he slowly walked in the direction of the wardrobe, his bushy golden tail swaying majestically behind him. Lifting himself on his front paws, he opened the wardrobe door and soundlessly slipped inside. For an instant the golden glow illuminated the wardrobe; then the door closed as softly as it had opened, and again the room was dark.

Lucas wasn't quite sure how long he had lain awake that evening, listening to the excited ticktock of his own heart, but he was not yet asleep when Gregory came into the room making much noise with his heavy sport boots. As he turned on the top light, he noticed instantly that Lucas wasn't sleeping.

"You're awake?" he asked. "Why? It's after ten."

Lucas quickly shut his eyes. "I'm asleep," he muttered.

Gregory began unlacing his boots. "What d'you mean, you're asleep? D'you think I can't tell you're not asleep? Why must you lie? Mother!" he called. The mother put her head inside the door.

"What's the matter?"

"Lucas is awake," explained Gregory. "He must run a temperature. Look how red his ears are."

The mother leaned over Lucas's bed and fixed the blanket which had fallen to the floor. "Are you ill, my little boy?" Lucas shook his head. "Go to sleep, son, it's late." She kissed his forehead and then said to Gregory, "Turn off the top light. Lucas will sleep now." Without waiting for Gregory, she put on the little night lamp by his bed. "Hurry up, Gregory," she called, already at the door. "Tomorrow morning again you'll complain about having to get up. And don't forget to wash!"

"What'm I going to sleep in?"

"What do you mean?"

"You took my pajamas to the laundry."

She shook her head impatiently. "Don't you know that there are clean ones in the wardrobe?"

Lucas's heart began to beat faster. How could he have forgotten that Gregory's things too were kept in the wardrobe? And now what? What will happen if Gregory sees the fox hidden inside? Naturally, he's going to raise the roof, and the fox will get frightened and run away. Perhaps he should warn him?

But in the meantime Gregory went to the bathroom and vanished there. It seemed to Lucas he was gone for ages. "What's he doing in there?" he thought. "Surely he's not washing his ears . . ."

Finally Gregory returned. He walked up to the wardrobe. For a moment he stood facing it, pondering over something; then he opened the door and started looking through the top shelf in search of his pajamas. Lucas stopped breathing. However, the fox didn't get frightened and didn't jump out of the wardrobe. What's more, Gregory seemed completely unaware of the presence of their guest hidden right beside him. The search for the pajamas lasted a long time. Lucas knew they were on the second shelf from the top, but, just as he wanted to speak up, he was suddenly overcome by a violent shiver and felt a quick flame flash through him. The interior of the wardrobe clearly lit up with the familiar, golden, delicate, strangely mysterious glow. It was so very beautiful that Lucas completely forgot all his anxieties and felt such unspeakable happiness, such overwhelming delight, that it seemed as though he himself had now begun to glow with that strange light.

All at once he felt an urgent need to share at least a part of his happiness with another person. So he lifted his head off the pillow and called in a half whisper, "Gregory!"

The bed squeaked as Gregory jumped onto it. "Aren't you asleep yet?" Gregory's voice sounded not at all friendly. But Lucas didn't care.

"Gregory, tell me . . . Did you ever see a gold fox?"

Gregory sat up. "Are you crazy? There aren't any gold foxes."

"Yes, there are."

"Where? Somebody must have filled you with some fancy tales.

Foxes are red, like our ordinary foxes, or silver and blue, but their fur is that way only in the summer, and in the winter they turn white."

Lucas smiled to himself tolerantly in the dark. "And I saw a gold one. Completely gold, with a golden tail."

"You're lying!" Gregory got angry. "You couldn't have seen a gold fox."

"Yes, I could."

"Listen," hissed Gregory through clenched teeth. "If you don't shut up this instant and go to sleep . . ."

"Well, what?" shouted Lucas.

"I'll spank you, you little devil! Understand?"

There was silence. And then in the silence came Lucas's voice, not very loud but quite deliberately clear. "You never saw a gold fox? Well, I did." In an instant Gregory was up on his feet; a pillow flew through the air. There was a moment of turmoil and tumble. And then the door opened, and the light from the hall cut through the darkness of the room. Their father was standing in the doorway.

"What's going on in here?" he asked.

Gregory, his hair tangled, his face very red, blinked in confusion. "Lucas won't let me sleep. He's been telling me some nonsense about seeing a gold fox."

"And so you beat him up?"

"I did not! I just wanted to explain to him that there are no gold foxes."

"Don't shout so loud," said the father. "You'll wake up the whole house."

"But why does he have to lie that he saw a gold fox?"

Lucas's curly head popped out from under the blanket. "I didn't lie!"

"Quiet," said the father. He sat down at the edge of Lucas's bed and stroked the boy's blond head. "Have you been dreaming?"

"No."

"Well, then, what's this about a fox?"

"I saw him."

There came a stir from Gregory's bed. "You see! He says he's not lying. Tell him that there aren't any gold foxes, because he won't believe me."

The father bent over Lucas. "And where did you see this gold fox?"

"Everywhere," Lucas whispered.

"What do you mean, everywhere?"

Lucas snuggled up to his father and put his arms around his neck. "Tell me," he pleaded softly, "are there gold foxes?"

The father smiled. "In fairy tales, my son."

"But not for real?"

"There are many kinds: red ones, blue, silver, but there are no gold foxes."

"And you never saw a gold one?"

"Never. Well, it's time to go to sleep." The father tucked him in, kissed his forehead, and left the room, closing the door behind him quietly.

After a moment, in the silence came Gregory's voice: "And have you ever seen a green cow?"

Lucas did not answer. He lay back, his eyes wide open. When he became accustomed to the dark, the room again began to fill with familiar outlines of the walls, objects and furniture. Particularly, the wardrobe seemed to stand out sharply from among the shadows. But how lifeless it was now! There it stood against the wall, massive and straight. It was hard to believe that only a short while before it had been filled with the most beautiful golden glow. And then Lucas began to feel a vague doubt as to whether the fox was still inside the wardrobe. Could he have overheard Gregory's mocking remarks and run away unnoticed, his feelings badly hurt?

"Oh, my fox, dearest fox," whispered Lucas soundlessly. "You didn't run away, you haven't left me without saying good-bye?" But the more he tried to hold on to his hope, the more painful was the anguish that filled him. Unable to endure the uncertainty any longer, he threw off his covers, sat up, listened carefully for a moment, and convinced that Gregory was asleep, started tiptoeing toward the wardrobe. The immense silence of the night folded around him, as if profound sleep had embraced the entire earth and universe, up to the distant skies. Lucas listened to the silence, and an increasing fear filled his heart. What if the gold fox had really gone away? And when he imagined that the wardrobe might now be empty, he felt terribly lonely and sad.

He reached it at last. It now looked like a huge dark mountain towering over him in the darkness. Carefully he put out his hand, but as it touched the door he hesitated. Suddenly it seemed to him that very close, inside the wardrobe, something stirred with a rustling sound. Afraid that it might be only an illusion, he came closer and, pressing himself against the door, held his breath. Yes, he had not been mistaken. The wardrobe was alive with barely audible, delicate sounds and vibrated with a kind of heart-touching warmth.

With trembling fingers Lucas turned the key and stood in a transport of delight; through a crack in the door, no wider than his index finger, came a stream of the familiar golden glow. At first he did not dare move. But after a moment, gathering courage, he kneeled down and, bringing his lips up to the miraculous glow, whispered, "I have come, my golden fox. This is Lucas. Are you asleep?" The fox did not answer, but his regular breath could be heard distinctly. "He's sleeping," thought Lucas. So he whispered, his voice overflowing with affection, "Good night, my dearest fox, good night."

Then he shut the door slowly, but as he did it, it occurred to him that perhaps, just in case, he ought to take the key along to bed with him for the rest of the night. How could he be sure if Gregory, having guessed the whole affair, wasn't waiting for the moment when Lucas would fall asleep to chase the fox away? Quietly he drew the key from the lock. Even when he was already back in bed he continued to hold it tightly in his fist.

Next morning he overslept and didn't hear the alarm clock go off. A different noise, equally shrill, woke him up. As soon as he opened his eyes he saw, to his horror, that Gregory was desperately trying to get into the wardrobe. His face flushed with anger, he banged and kicked with such might that it seemed as though in a minute the wardrobe would break into pieces.

All this ado brought their mother. "Gregory!" she called. "What's the matter with you? Why are you ruining the wardrobe?"

"Can I help it if the key is gone?" he shouted furiously. "How can I get in when the key is gone?"

"And where has it gone to? It couldn't have walked away."

Before she could finish, the missing key slipped down off Lucas's bed and dropped to the floor with a loud clang. Silence fell in the room. And then, in one leap, Gregory rushed toward Lucas. "You see who took it? And you scold me right away . . ."

"Lucas," spoke the mother, "will you tell us why you were hiding the key?"

"Oh, my dear fox," thought Lucas bitterly, "why won't anyone understand me?" He sat up and answered, "Because!"

Gregory's eyes became completely round with amazement. Then he turned away from Lucas and said to the mother, "Did you hear that? One day that child will grow up to be a hooligan, you'll see! Last night he lied that he saw a gold fox, and now he sleeps with the key. Tell him there are no gold foxes, because he didn't believe it even when Dad told him." Since it was getting late, the mother decided not to go any farther into the mysterious affair of the fox or the key episode.

After the previous night's stormy weather, the morning was overcast, though it was not raining. The dew still glittered along the green slopes below St. Ann's Church, and a fragile mist hovered in the air. Perhaps, because of that mist, the statue of King Sigismund, solitary against the far-stretching sky, the walls of the church, and the old town houses behind it, appeared to be more distant and higher than usual. Even the bridge seemed farther away, with the trolleys trudging over it slowly; they looked like enormous red June bugs. It all made an impression as though the entire scenery had struggled to leap up, but was suddenly stopped in the attempt, suspended in mid-air.

Despite the unpleasantness of the key episode, Lucas was full of exuberant joy. He hadn't any doubt now that Gregory was the only person at home with a skeptical attitude toward the golden fox.

At the corner of Sowia Street, under the mosaic clock, he caught up with his best friend, a classmate from kindergarten. Her name was Emily, and she was the daughter of a metal worker at the Zeran factory.

"D'you know, Lucas," she began straight away, "my daddy is going to Moscow for the Revolution Day."

"My daddy has already been to Moscow," said Lucas. "Now he is planning a trip to Paris to be in some conference."

Emily thought for a moment. "Paris — is it far away?"

"Awfully far away."

"But Paris is littler than Moscow, isn't it? Moscow is the biggest and the prettiest."

Lucas was swinging his shoe bag back and forth. "No, the biggest and prettiest city is called Colorado."

"And where is it?"

"Oh, it's at the very end of the world. On a huge island. And, do you know, there are mountains there that reach up to the clouds. And lakes. And forests, but terribly tall. And the houses are made only of marble, all white . . ."

"Not huger than our Palace of Culture?"

"Oh, yes, much huger. They reach to the clouds."

"You said that the mountains reach to the clouds."

"Mountains too. But the houses are even huger. Would you like to live in a house like that? Nothing but clouds all around. And at night the stars are right next to you. Would you like that?"

Emily shook her head. "No, because if the elevator broke down, Mummy would get awfully tired walking upstairs with groceries."

"Over there elevators don't break down."

Emily stuck out her lower lip in a characteristic fashion. "There are no such houses, or such a city. Moscow is the biggest city of all."

Lucas swung his bag with increased energy. "If you don't believe me, I won't tell you my secret."

Engrossed in their conversation, they didn't notice that they had passed the kindergarten and were already turning into Bednarska Street, toward the river. Emily shrugged her shoulders. "You can tell me."

"Come over after school, and then I'll show you. Just you alone. Will you come?"

"I don't know. Mummy said that after school she'd take me to buy a new dress."

"So come afterwards. We'll be alone, and I can show you my secret."

"Couldn't you tell me about it?"

"No."

"But you made it all up about the city and the houses? Moscow is the biggest."

Lucas hesitated for a moment. "But my secret is for real."

"And the other was just make-believe?"

"Just make-believe."

"Then I'll tell you a make-believe story too. Do you want me to?"

Lucas beamed. "Let's go over by the river — you can tell it there."

All around, autumn was already very much in evidence. The air felt crisp that October morning and smelled of dying leaves, which blanketed the entire boulevard. The chestnut trees along the riverbank stood in a bluish mist, motionless and straight, looking somewhat like an artificial flower arrangement in red, bright yellow, and fading green. They sat down on a bench.

"Go on," said Lucas.

"Wait, first I must remember."

She was silent for a while, concentrating. Finally, she threw back her blond braid. "I've remembered now. So — it was long, long ago, all the way back, before we were born . . ."

"During the war?"

"No, longer ago. Before the war."

"What happened then?"

"Then, there lived a dog."

"What breed?"

"Just a plain dog."

"A mut?"

"A mut."

"What was his name?"

Emily thought for a minute. "Brownie."

Lucas seemed a bit disappointed. "Sapphire or Sparky would be prettier."

"I like Brownie better."

"So what happened to him?"

"Wait. So — Brownie lived with some rich people, you know, with capitalists."

"I know."

"They had a factory. And they were terribly mean to him."

"They beat him?"

"They didn't give him anything to eat, and he had to work for them."

Lucas's eyes flashed. "I wouldn't work for them!"

"And what would you do?"

"I'd run away."

"You think you're so smart! Brownie didn't have any place to run away to, because only capitalists lived on that street."

"Then I'd run farther away."

"Farther away there were also capitalists."

"Then I'd tie wings to my arms and fly off."

Emily became annoyed. "I'm speaking for real, and you're just kidding. He couldn't fly off."

"So, what did he do?"

"He tried to run away, but they caught him and they were even meaner to him afterwards. And then . . ."

"The capitalists were thrown out?"

Emily shook her head. "Not yet. And then Brownie got old."

"And he died?"

"Wait, not yet. When he got old and wasn't able to work any longer, the capitalists threw him out on the street. He was unemployed and could find no work."

"Did he have children?"

"He did."

"And they threw him out together with his children?"

"Yup!"

"And what happened to them?"

"Brownie died."

"And the children?"

For a long while Emily said nothing, only kept swinging her leg up and down, lost in thought. "The children are still alive," she answered at last, staring into the distant sky over Praga.

"Where are they?"

"Different places. One's coming to live with me. Daddy promised to give me a puppy for my birthday."

"Brownie's son? Please call him Sparky, Emily . . ."

She shook her head. "Wait a minute, I'll call him. . . . His name will be Brownie."

Lucas saw a falling leaf and quickly caught it in mid-air.

"If I asked my father," he said, "he'd give me a dog too. But I have something better."

"What?"

"When you come over, I'll show you."

"Is it alive?"

"Come, and you'll see. Will you come?"

"I don't know," answered Emily. "If I have time . . ."

When Lucas got home, Elza, their part-time "domestic help," a tall, bony woman, opened the door for him. "Is Mummy home?" he asked.

"She is," answered Elza.

Unfortunately, it turned out that his mother was very busy correcting her pupils' homework. "Don't bother me, Lucas," she said.

"Are you working?"

"Can't you see for yourself?"

"But will you read me a story tonight?"

"I don't know, Lucas. If I finish my work, I'll read to you." Lucas left her with a heavy heart.

Gregory wasn't alone in their room. His friend Christopher, a fair-haired boy, rather tall for his age, was with him. He grinned and put out his hand in a friendly gesture. "Hi, Lucas. I hear you've been seeing a gold fox." Lucas blushed, but Christopher did not seem to notice it. "Was he pretty? How many legs did he have? Four, or more? Or maybe just one?"

"Better leave the stinking brat alone," muttered Gregory, shutting his satchel. "Come on, let's get going . . . I have no patience for this brat and his gold fox." Then he left the room.

"Well, that's that," said Christopher. "So long, Lucas. Give my regards to the gold fox." With one swift movement, he stuck out his foot and tripped Lucas. "Hey, pal," he laughed, when Lucas sprawled on the floor, "you seem to be a bit weak in the legs. Must be out of form."

Although Lucas hurt his elbow badly, he didn't call out, nor did he start to cry. He stood up. All was quiet in the house. Only now it occurred to him that until dinner he had almost three hours entirely to himself. And all at once a feeling of love and adoration for his fox hidden inside the wardrobe overcame him with such an intensity of mixed joy and pain that it seemed to him as though two huge wings had suddenly grown from his shoulders and were lifting him up into the air, very far and high, but in two opposite directions.

This experience was so strange that he stood dumfounded for a long time. Everything inside him was in a state of turmoil. He thought, rather vaguely, that he probably should let the fox know that he had come back, but something else told him to postpone the visit until later. In the course of these doubts, he realized he had become very sleepy. "Oh, my dear fox," he murmured. Groggily he walked over to the wardrobe, opened the door and slipped inside, as though it were a sheltered cave. There was little room between the hanging garments, but the space down below proved big enough to curl up in comfortably. And then he found himself surrounded from all sides by the golden glow, and next to his body he felt the fluffy warm fur of the fox.

"I love you," he whispered, throwing his arms around the fox's neck. Sighing deeply, he fell asleep.

When he woke up, dusk had already fallen, and the room was in darkness. But Lucas knew instantly that he was not alone. And sure enough, he heard Emily's voice, hushed and somewhat hesitant. "Lucas, where are you?" As he crawled out of the wardrobe, her eyes opened wide with surprise. But she composed herself instantly. "I've come," she said curtly but with much dignity. "Mummy let me, but only for one hour."

Lucas let out a yawn so deep that his eyes filled up with tears. Emily scrutinized him critically and asked, "Is your secret in this room?"

He nodded, feeling quite wide-awake now. She looked around, examining the familiar room. "You're kidding. I don't see any secret around here."

"Just wait," said Lucas. "You'll see in a minute. First I must make it dark." With the shades drawn, the room became pitch-black.

"Turn on the light," cried Emily.

"Are you scared?"

Emily's voice began to tremble a little. "Where are you?"

"Over here," he answered, right next to her in the darkness.

"I can't see a thing . . ."

"Don't be afraid. Give me your hand. Come on." She resisted weakly, but he pulled her in the direction of the wardrobe. And there, as he had expected, shone in all its splendor the lovely golden glow.

"Do you see?" he whispered.

"I don't see anything," she whimpered. "Turn on the light!"

Now Lucas became really annoyed. "Don't yell, silly! Why can't you see? Go inside and look." He began to stuff her into the wardrobe by force.

"Let me go!" shrieked Emily. "Mummy!" Lucas seized her around the waist and packed her inside. Then he slammed the door and turned the key.

"Now d'you see?" he called. There was no answer. All he could hear inside the wardrobe was Emily's loud, though somewhat muffled, bellowing.

"Let me ooout!" she screamed desperately. "Let me ooout!"

His mother rushed into the room. Quickly she pulled Emily out of the wardrobe. "Home, I want to go home!" Emily kept calling, at the top of her voice.

Lucas knew perfectly well that after what happened, a long talk with his mother was in the making. For an instant he even thought it might be a good idea to pretend he didn't hear her. Apparently, however, his mother also anticipated such a possibility, because she opened the door to the hall before she called to him. Lucas quickly whispered to the fox, "Don't worry about a thing," and left the room.

His mother was seated at her desk. As soon as Lucas came in she asked, "Lucas, can you tell me what is the meaning of all this? Why did you lock Emily inside the wardrobe? Was it supposed to be a game? How would you feel if someone locked you up like that?"

Lucas shrugged his shoulders. "I could."

"You could what?"

"Stay inside the wardrobe."

"Well, if you like being locked in a wardrobe, that's your own affair. But it seems that Emily didn't ask at all that you lock her in."

"Because she's silly."

His mother looked at him for a minute in silence. "Come over here, Lucas." She drew him closer. "Emily said you wanted to show her some secret. What is your secret? Can you tell me?"

"I can," he whispered.

"I have a . . ."

"A what?"

"A gold fox."

Afraid that he might discover disbelief in his mother's face, he fixed his gaze on a little hole in his shoe. But he didn't detect the slightest mistrust in her voice.

"Where is he?" she asked.

Lucas sighed. "In the wardrobe."

There was a short silence. Finally, he gathered enough courage to look up at her. "You don't believe me?"

"Why shouldn't I believe you? Is that what you wanted to show Emily?"

"Yes, I wanted to, but she's silly and she doesn't see anything."

"But think for a moment, Lucas. Was it nice to try and force someone else to see your gold fox? You just frightened the girl, and maybe the fox felt hurt that you wanted to show him in such a naughty way."

"You think so?" worried Lucas. "I'll tell him I am sorry."

"And Emily?"

"I'll tell her, too, I'm sorry," he decided. "But you, don't you want to see the gold fox?"

The mother patted his head tenderly. "You see, Lucas, the fox came to visit *you* . . ."

"And you too."

"Maybe. But he's your guest, and you must see to it that your guest is happy here. Do you think he would enjoy being looked at by everyone all the time?"

"Not all the time. But you can."

"Of course I can, but let's make a deal that for today we shall leave him in peace. All right?"

Unfortunately, the next day, as well as the following days, everything turned out so that his mother couldn't visit the gold fox. Lucas did not ask her again, but a few times he tried to remind her about her promise by a meaningful glance. He had a feeling, however, that she decided not to understand what he meant. Everybody in the household, it seemed to him, including Elza, behaved as if they knew quite well of the golden fox's presence, but preferred not to talk about it.

Lucas couldn't understand why everyone had suddenly become tongue-tied. Was it possible that the gold fox didn't really interest them? Weren't they curious to know what he looked like and how splendidly he glistened in the dark?

Meanwhile, his own relationship with the guest developed nicely, although their meetings were somewhat haphazard, since they had to be adjusted to the situation at home. And so, for example, all the evenings were lost; Gregory had a habit of reading in bed and, naturally, until he turned off the light and fell asleep, a visit with the fox was out of the question. Then again, in the afternoons Gregory did his homework. And the mornings? Ah, how useless to even mention the mornings; there was so little time then that he barely had a minute for a short "Hi, fox!" And so slowly Lucas began to realize how very bitter, how unsatisfactory even the most beautiful emotion can be if one cannot share it with others. He learned that a secret not only contains the thrill of mystery, but can also be a source of such sadness that at times it's difficult to measure which is greater: the happiness or the pain. It also became clear to him that people, even his own family, could be cruel and difficult to understand.

Despite this, Lucas never ceased to hope that the silence surrounding the fox would one day be broken, and the decisive step taken by his mother.

But, as several days passed and nothing happened, he began to worry in earnest. He lost his appetite, he looked pale, and finally one evening, right after dinner, his father, who was a doctor, led him to his office for a physical examination.

Lucas didn't say one word during the entire treatment. Obediently he took deep breaths, quick breaths, coughed, raised his arms over his head or stretched them forward, while his father put the cold stethoscope against his chest. At one point, his mother looked into the room.

"Well?" she asked.

The father straightened up. "Everything is fine."

But Lucas felt sure it wasn't so. That very evening, knowing that for once his mother would be at home, he decided to act without further delay. Luckily Gregory turned off his light earlier than usual and fell asleep almost instantly. Lucas got out of bed, found his slippers in the dark, and quietly slipped out into the hall.

The light was still on in his mother's room as well as in his father's office. Lucas did not foresee, however, that his mother might not be alone; his father was in her room, and they were talking. Since the door into the hall had been left ajar, Lucas could hear every word clearly. His father was saying, "You know, I'm worried about Lucas. Doesn't it seem to you that there's something wrong with him?"

"I'm not sure," answered the mother hesitantly. "Sometimes I feel that we know so very little about our children. We never have enough time. Even though we live together, we actually all live our separate lives."

"Has he spoken to you again about that gold fox of his since the episode with Emily?"

The mother sounded surprised. "No, why? I suppose he's already forgotten about it. Such fantasies don't usually last long with children."

"I'm not so sure. I think it may not have been such a good idea that you played along with him in these fantasies. The boy is oversensitive, anyway."

They were silent for a moment.

"You know," spoke up the mother, "I've wondered about it myself. But do we have to deprive our children of the right to dream?"

"We must, I think," answered the father.

"Didn't we ourselves dream once?"

"With us it was different. Yes, we did have dreams, and not just in our childhood, but didn't we pay for them dearly? It's better not to give our past as an example for our children to follow. Nowadays they must learn from the beginning to think and feel as does the rest of their society. You know it yourself. What'll be the fate of a man who insists on thinking differently from the rest? Just because we ourselves got used to often saying what we don't think, will our children also have to lie?"

"You are tired?" she asked softly.

"I am. All of us are tired. But what of it? It's that much more reason to guard the minds of our children!"

"I'm not sure you aren't overrating the importance of all this," said the mother after a pause. "After all, the gold fox affair is really trifling. . . ."

"It may be trifling," agreed the father. "But certain traits of Lucas's character can't be taken lightly. I don't know, perhaps it's a capitulation on my part — or perhaps it's precisely because I understand our times — but it seems to me that it's best not to be different from others. And so I wouldn't want our son . . ."

Lucas was standing with his forehead pressed against the frame of the door. He didn't understand all he heard, but one thing became obvious: his mother had never seen the gold fox, and what's more — just like his father, like Gregory, like Emily, like everybody else — she did not believe in the fox's existence, and therefore she had cheated him, she had lied to him, she had treated him like a stupid child whom she kindly permitted to go on believing in his foolish fairy tale. And so his last hope had now failed him. They had all betrayed his fox; they crossed him off and threw him out of their lives. But why? What had he done to them? "Oh fox, my dear fox," he thought sadly. "Why don't they like you? Why does no one want to look at you? But you are here, you live, I can hear you and see you."

After that memorable night, there came an altogether new phase in Lucas's relationship with the fox — a phase without illusions and without hope that what was of such vital importance to them both would ever find approval from the rest of the family. If only he and his fox could be together somewhere in the desert or in a deep forest! Unfortunately, they had to stay among people, at all times encircled by their activities. How frail and perishable did his secret seem to him at times! Glowing with a lonely light, it flowed gently on through darkness in the surrounding indifference; but to what shores was it flowing, what would be its final destiny? Now it happened more and more often that when Lucas finally managed to visit the fox in the wardrobe, he could find no words to say to him except a short greeting, in which he tried to communicate all his mixed-up emotions. "Good morning!" the fox would answer. And then the two of them would be silent, cuddled close together, engulfed by the peace of the golden glow.

These were not happy days. Oh no! Lucas decided that in the presence of his parents and in front of Gregory he would behave as he always had: he would try to act relaxed and talkative. At times he succeeded, but the better and more natural was his pretending, the heavier his heart felt, and the more intense was the sadness that came upon him when at last he could be alone. But he did not complain to the fox, since he felt that the guest knew exactly as much as he himself. And, as he pondered about all this, he found inside him a fear which hadn't been there before. Then one day he could contain himself no longer, and putting his arms around the fox's neck, he called desperately, "You won't ever leave me, my fox, will you? You and I will never part!" And the fox murmured in his peculiar way, "Never."

Time rushed on further and further into October, and Lucas's birthday was drawing near. He knew that Elza was preparing a chocolate birthday cake, on which soon, during an afternoon party, *six* candles would be lighted.

On the eve of his birthday, before going to sleep, Lucas was so preoccupied with thinking of what the next day would bring that he forgot to say good night to his fox. Actually, he could have easily jumped out of bed to look inside the wardrobe, since Gregory was not in the room — but he felt awfully sleepy. So he just put out his hand in the dark and whispered, "Bye, bye!"

"Bye, bye," answered the fox from inside the wardrobe, like a faraway echo.

The next day was Sunday. When Lucas opened his eyes and sat up in bed, Gregory was already standing by the table, barefooted and still in his pajamas, examining the presents. "Come, Lucas, look at the grand new tractor you got . . . See that? It has a combine, a mower and all these other attachments. The 'Star' is from me. Pretty nifty, isn't it?"

"Yeah," whispered Lucas. It was true — over by the metal tractor, he could see a fair-sized wooden truck. And next to it stood a red box with building blocks. He peered inside curiously. Gregory too leaned over the open box.

"Pretty nifty! You can build an entire village with these. Look here!" Gregory became more and more excited. "You have ducks, too . . ."

"And a pond?" asked Lucas.

"No, there's no pond. But you can make that yourself."

"I know!" cried Lucas. "I'll put some water in a soap dish, and I'll have a pond."

"Or in a saucer," advised Gregory. "The water will be cleaner, so you'll have a pond already purified by a filter-bed system — you understand? Look, the tractor can be wound up!"

"Great!" agreed Lucas.

But the real playing didn't begin until after breakfast. It was a beautiful sunny day, without a single cloud in the sky.

"We'll build a collective village," decided Gregory. But, alas, he couldn't complete his building project, for at ten o'clock his class was to meet at a village outside Warsaw for some games. Lucas liked playing with his brother, but as soon as he was left alone he came to the conclusion that Gregory's construction plans weren't really too good. So he ripped down the symmetrically laid-out street, paused for a moment to examine the ruins with satisfaction, and then, after much consideration, started by first building the scenery. When the forest was up, when the pond on the other side glistened with a smooth surface, and when he ran a winding brook cut out of blue paper through the still-empty fields — only then did he proceed to build the village itself. His work took a long time, since he constantly kept discovering the need for new improvements in the open fields. But just as he started to throw a little bridge over the brook, he suddenly realized he had completely forgotten about his friend. He was about to get up, when it occurred to him that the cows herded along the stream should certainly be transferred to the pasture as soon as possible. He therefore finished building the bridge, and only after seeing to it that the cows were left safely in the care of a cowherd did he finally get up to say good morning to the fox.

But before going in, he realized for the first time that it wasn't really worthwhile to draw the shades for so short a visit. So, leaving the shades up, he walked over to the wardrobe, opened the door, and quickly slipped inside.

"Good morning, my dear fox," he said in his usual whisper, and put out his hand to embrace his friend. But he only touched Gregory's low-hanging ski pants. He moved a little further in. "Where are you?" he asked in a hushed tone. "Fox!" Suddenly he could feel heat rush to his face. Something was changed. It looked as though the fox were not there at all. He called louder, "Fox, where are you?" No one answered. There was dead silence. Lucas pulled the door shut behind him and found himself engulfed by total darkness. His eyes wide open, he looked around, holding his breath, but not even a tiniest flicker of the golden glow broke through the night surrounding him. He felt that his eyes were beginning to fill with tears.

"My fox, oh, my fox . . ." he whispered, and his heart was breaking with pain, because he understood that never again would the fox answer his call. He was gone. He had departed to find new people, new friends.

Lucas felt hot tears streaming down his cheeks, but at the same time it seemed as though the most difficult and painful moments were already behind him, as though after a laborious climb up a steep mountain he had now begun to descend a gentle slope. "Perhaps it's better that the fox has left," he thought. He wiped his moist cheek with his hand, blew his nose, and with a sigh scrambled out of the wardrobe.

It made him happy to see the room filled with sunlight. The section of the rug where he had built his colorful village with the forest, the brook and the pond was illuminated by the sun; the rest still remained in the shade. It all looked very beautiful, and once again Lucas thought that perhaps it was right that the gold fox went off into the world . . .

Afterwards he had no time to think about it any more. When Sunday dinner, to which Gregory had brought Christopher, was over, Emily came to call. She was wearing a new dress, a blue one with white polka dots and a white turned-up collar. Her blond little braids were tied with new bows. Her eyes shone brightly. She seemed very proud of her outfit as well as of the admiration which everyone showed for the present she had brought for Lucas — a tiny model of the car "Warszawa." As a matter of fact, the "Warszawa" gave rise to a row, since Gregory and

Christopher didn't want to let Lucas play with it. A scene was on the way, when Emily interfered.

"If you're going to quarrel," she said firmly, "I will take back my present." Luckily, the storm was averted, and Gregory went back to the morning's project of building a collective village.

"You're dumb," he said, when Lucas stubbornly insisted on his own construction scheme. "If you scatter the houses all around, how're you going to plan scientifically the economic development of the village?" So the village was erected in accordance with his wishes. Then came harvest time, all the machines were put to work, and a group of volunteers arrived from the city in the truck in order to participate in the harvest activities. At one point Lucas had an idea that a great thunderstorm should pass over the fields, but Gregory protested.

"No!" he said. "There'll be no rain; we can't lose the grain. Our collective village must be a leader in production." And so there was no rain, and in the afternoon they could proceed with collecting the quotas and buying up the grain.

"You know," said Christopher, "let's unmask a kulak."

"Okay!" agreed Gregory.

"But how are you going to unmask a kulak?" asked Lucas.

"It's simple," answered Gregory. "A kulak is fat and has a big belly."

"And an ugly snoot," put in Christopher. "You can recognize him right away."

Slowly dusk was beginning to fall. In the midst of their playing, after they had "unmasked the kulak," Christopher leaned toward Gregory and began to whisper something in his ear. Gregory shrugged his shoulders. "Leave him alone," he muttered.

"Why? I'm going to ask him."

Lucas leaned further over the truck, which he had just been loading up with sacks of flour.

"Hey, Lucas!" called Christopher. "What's new with the gold fox? Do you see him from time to time?"

Lucas straightened up and blushed. For a moment nobody said anything. Slowly Lucas placed another wooden block on the truck. "No," he muttered.

"Not at all?"

Lucas raised his head and looked at Gregory, who, however, pretended to be very busy.

"Well then, you never see the gold fox any more?"

"Certainly not!" muttered Lucas. "You know there aren't any gold foxes." Still blushing, he turned away and walked over to the window. The autumn day was coming to an end. The blue sky above the statue of King Sigismund was still bright, but down below the twilight had already set in, very clear and delicate.

"I never saw the gold fox," thought Lucas, gazing at the peaceful scenery outside the window. Then, all at once his heart began to beat violently. Over in the distance, in the dusk, among the rust-colored trees a gold fox scurried along the embankment. Yes, it was he, there could be no doubt about it! He was rushing toward the steps leading to the city. Would he find other friends? Lucas moved closer to the windowpane . . . But the fox wasn't there any more. "Maybe one day I will see him again," he thought. "Maybe he will come back sometime."

"Lucas!" called Gregory. "Come play with us!"

Lucas turned around and looked at the boys and at Emily seated on the carpet.

"Well, come on!" said Gregory, smiling. And that smile made Lucas feel very warm around the heart.

"I never saw a gold fox!" he cried triumphantly.

"Hurray!" shouted Gregory.

— *translated by* BARBARA VEDDER

(From *Zloty Lis*, short stories. Published by Panstwowy Instytut Wydawniczy, Warsaw, 1956.)

An Unfinished Examination

BY TADEUSZ ROZEWICZ

TADEUSZ ROZEWICZ, one of the leading Polish poets of the war generation, was born in Warsaw in 1921, and his first poems were published in 1939. During the German Occupation he worked in a factory and taught

am not Tadeusz." But he just stood there facing me, and waited, smiling. So, after a while, I gave in. Although the matter was not really as simple as that. I was, after all, an altogether different person now. But this would have taken too long to explain. I surrendered.

We walked into a bar.

First I started answering his second question, "What's new with you?"

"I am, you might say, a man of letters. Writing hurts me. My neighbors upstairs keep walking over my head. But I would like to come back to the subject of my examination. My brain is a live animal. Locked inside my head and encircled by bones, pressed hard from all sides, it squirms. The bristles and thorns that cover it are very painful. If only it could be released onto paper. If only it were allowed to leave its enclosure, then it would spread its wings, open up like an umbrella. The poor squirming brain would skip and fly all around the room and over the pages. It should be permitted to leave the head and go for walks, run through the fields and meadows. But, sadly enough, it is trapped inside its box of bone, locked up. In the mornings one feels he might be able to begin afresh. Yet it is always just a continuation. Thoughts are like little white mice. They race over the fat double chin of a golden Buddha, then jump onto the leg of a certain lady doctor and travel along the leg — farther and farther up. Right away, questions come from all sides: 'And how about sex life; what's the situation?' So again one must bring up and explain certain pictures from days long ago . . . I was lying in bed in the dark, the door ajar; in the next room the grownups played cards and talked. I huddled under the quilt, sweating profusely and shaking with fright. I could hear the voices.

" 'I'll bet you that he knows where children come from.'

" 'Really, how can you talk such silly nonsense, Henry!'

" 'All right, let's ask him.' I could feel the blood pounding inside my head and inside my heart. I did know that women carried children in their stomachs, but it was not quite clear to me how they got there or how and which way they emerged into the world.

" 'Are you asleep, Teddy?'

" 'No,' I answered timidly.

" 'Listen, Teddy, tell us where children come from.' I sweated under the quilt, my eyes shut tight, and I was probably very red, although no one could see it. I did not answer.

"Silence fell in the next room. And after a while they started to laugh."

" 'Leave the child alone, Henry!'

" 'Teddy, where do calves come from?'

" 'They come out of a cow's ear,' I answered, with a desperate certainty. It was a lie, of course, concocted for the benefit of the grown-ups, to make them think I did not know where calves came from. Again they started to laugh."

Obviously I had been trying to avoid giving an answer. All the quaint childhood reminiscing was just an excuse. Since, after all, the question was clear: "What's new with you?" The answer also could be clear and short: "Nothing much," or one could add: "Same old troubles," or something of that sort. Yet, just this once, I decided to be honest and tell him.

So there we were, seated at a small examination table in the café. Who knows, maybe the examiner really wanted to hear my answer. Maybe he was not pretending; maybe he did desire, with all his heart, to learn what was new with me. So I began:

"I suffer dreadfully, like a man condemned. I suffer so much that I can hardly stand it any longer. I shall stab myself with this knife right now, before your eyes." I seized the little dessert knife lying on the table. "My life has lost its meaning. I no longer believe in anything. Neither in mankind and its struggle nor in eternal salvation. Look at this piece of cake in front of me. If you only knew what profound hatred I feel for this piece of cake. I simply must express all my pain, and though I have always kept it to myself until now, I will tell it to you. . . . I will tell you everything.

"Would you believe it, I feel hatred toward my own excrement. Here you have something new! Nothing is new? Oh well . . .

"I love mankind, but I do not know why. And I love the common man, with a love as strong and selfless as he has for me. I also love a common cabinet minister and a common cardinal. Yet I can feel no love for myself. If you only knew what frightful ideas come to my head. Frightful from a socioethical, as well as esthetic and political, point of view.

"You wanted to find out what is new with me? All right then, I have admitted it — I write poetry. I feel like a mother. Each poem has a different father, but they all have the same mother — the poet. A poem's father is the dream, the scenery, the feeling, the thought. The father comes, plants his seed, and leaves. Now the poem grows inside the poet-mother. The mother carries the fruit. She must take care. The father-stimulus, often forgotten, faceless, runs away, sometimes forever. He is looking for a fertile place to sow more seed. A poet-mother may be fertilized by anyone and anything, any place and any time. The seed enters through the open wounds. When the wounds heal, the poet becomes barren and dies."

My examiner suddenly shrugged his shoulders. He had been sitting there, sad and dejected. He shrugged his shoulders again.

"Words, words . . . How utterly pointless! It may be good for children or senile old men. Me, I have not read a poem in twenty years, and I go on living. So? So nothing. In any case, do you think I have been listening to you for nothing? Nobody wants to listen to anybody else for nothing.

"You, as I have gathered from your story, detest people . . . You detest them; I love them. I love them infinitely. I would sacrifice anything for their sake. I love the human race above everything else, but I am not sure of the reason why. What am I to do with my tremendous love? Sometimes a kind of evil spirit whispers to me, 'Why do you have to love the human race? Is it not sufficient simply to do your duty?' Yes, an evil spirit. It sidles up to me and whispers. But then, what would be the point of our life without this agonizing love? Believe me, I wish I knew what to do with myself . . . And you? Surely you are not a Marxist, or a Catholic?" He observed me closely for a moment.

I shut my eyes in order to concentrate on an answer. But once they were shut, I no longer felt like opening them again. Engulfed by darkness, I remained alone with my thoughts. In the main restaurant a woman was singing; I could hear her clear young voice.

Again I started answering questions, more and more rapidly, more and more obscurely. Undoubtedly my examiner understood none of it. Later he began telling me about his own life, his own suffering.

"Do you know," he was saying, "I am the center of the universe. A most peculiar sensation. I should like to tell you how it all began. It began rather harmlessly. First I became the center of my own room, then of my family, then of a certain group, or our 'crowd.' After that it went fast. To tell you the truth, previously, when I was still one of you, life was easier. I used to dress, eat, vote, like millions of my fellow men. Occasionally I used to make a little speech at some meeting, and people listened to me as they would listen to anyone else: they yawned, and so on. And suddenly one day there came this transformation, which I want to describe to you. Now the eyes of all people, as well as animals, are turned upon me. Even cows seem to scrutinize me carefully. Everyone's eyes are fixed not only on what I do, on my achievements, but also on my tie, collar, on my trousers, hair, buttons — in other words, on every detail. How exhausting this is! I guard my voice, I guard my face. My own facial expressions must now be arranged precisely. Any specific glance, wink, tone of voice — they are all carefully watched by everyone. I will never know by what miracle people often see me at several places simultaneously. Some visiting Swedes and children from the elementary agricultural school in 'Little Hell' — they are all looking at me. Thus, as I sit here with you in the café, I know that our table is situated right in the very center of Warsaw, of Europe, of the universe. Furthermore, I am jealous. In the past, of course, I used to envy people many things, but now, now I can hardly understand it myself . . . I become furious at a film star, or at a favorite race horse; it irritates me when people admire a favorite horse. So, would you believe it, I instantly undergo a transformation — I become that horse. Someone pats me lovingly on the neck, someone gives me a lump of sugar, a blue ribbon is being pinned on my bridle; I walk, or rather gallop, in front of the grandstand and bow to people. But this thing with horses — that is not all. You know, I am jealous of the dead. One day, a certain eminent colleague of mine died. I took part in the funeral ceremony, having been appointed to play an important role in it. First I was in the guard of honor, then I carried the coffin, made a speech at the grave side, and I even wrote something about the deceased. They took my photograph, next to the coffin and elsewhere. Yet I felt angry and frustrated. I was the more important person, to be sure, since I was alive and he was lying there dead; for me there were still many opportunities left to prove myself, I could still accomplish anything I wanted. But the decorations they gave him were a bit too much. My head began to fill up with such thoughts that finally I replaced the deceased colleague on the catafalque. Now it was I lying there, medals and ribbons on my chest; it was I listening to the speeches made in my honor which I myself had composed.

"Frankly, I prefer not to describe to you the things that happened at the canary show, since you would not believe me anyway. In short, it made me jealous to see the canary attracting so much attention, so I began doing very foolish things. I even sang . . ."

He went on at length about his suffering, but then he noticed that I had stopped listening long ago. As a matter of fact, I did not listen at all to what he was saying, because actually I could not care less what anyone had to say about himself.

I always have to close my eyes in order to see anything; I have to close my eyes and all the entrances through which the world about me might come in. I drank wine with my eyes closed. I no longer wanted to look at the sea. Roses against a white stone wall, palm trees, sea gulls and a hazy mist. White ships. Someone was teasing me, someone held my hands.

Before I could finish answering the first question asked on the street by my old school acquaintance, already a new question had come from the wife of a good friend of mine. She knew that I had spent a few summer days on the shore of the Adriatic Sea and asked whether it had been delightful. My answer was short and plain:

"That trip finished me up thoroughly. What an utter fool I was. Instead of collecting beautiful pictures of the world for the album of my memories, I concocted the theory that in order to really see, one must keep one's eyes shut. Because all the great cities of Europe are nothing but one city. Public toilets. Neon ads. Great masters in art galleries; restaurants, automobiles, cinemas, various houses of worship. The white city was so hot from the sun it sizzled. Now I sit in a locked room inside a big city, instead of being on the beach. I could have stayed there for a month . . . But I escaped. I escaped because on the third day, as I waded into the emerald water, I came to the conclusion that all this makes no sense. 'All this?' The wading or swimming in the emerald sea. It was the dead man in me. However, I must explain this point more closely.

"The fact is, I have 'died' more than once. I have died many times, and it might be worthwhile to describe it to those who are still alive. A dead man is extremely sensitive. To hunger, to heat, to cold, to words and smiles. His corpse is the most important thing to him in all the universe. I will have to expound on it sometime in greater detail. I will have to find a free moment. If a dead man cannot get the nourishment he needs, he goes blind with rage; should someone give him the slightest shove — he jumps on him, foaming at the mouth, and bites. Objects become gods to a dead man, the body becomes god; life dies at a dead man's touch; even the least significant delegate of power is a god; an electric shaver, a young girl's bottom, a leg, the boss's mustache, a cabinet, a shoe in a store window — even they become god. The world of objects, the body — they are a blind and intolerant god who swallows, digests, and evacuates his faithful dead follower.

"A dead man is extremely absent-minded. Generally, his air of concentration is quite deceptive. The slightest sound, any trivial incident, is enough to distract him; he interrupts his work, drops it, and runs. Dead men are not attached to anything. They live in a state of constant irritation, and they never have time. But the future belongs to them. Their number is steadily increasing. Particularly in large cities, on the beach, and in the mountains. They enjoy looking at beautiful scenery, they admire the wonders of nature, they listen to light music. They eat not only with their mouths, but with their eyes and the entire surface of their skin. So far no one has written anything interesting about our dead men. Take a look at them sometime in shops, restaurants, trains. Mostly they are people in the prime of life. There are no children or madmen among them."

Wacek stirred in his chair impatiently. I could see that he wanted to leave. He was right. I had been talking a lot, lecturing him on some theories concerning the behavior of the living dead, while he was unable to get a word in edgewise.

"Look at that," he said, and stretched his hand toward me. On the fingers of his right hand the fingernails were missing. I realized immediately that he wished to startle me and then tell me all about his terrible experiences in the concentration camp. He had suffered a great deal, and now people no longer wanted to hear about it.

Get up now and leave. Get up and leave. You need not walk past that table. You can creep along the other wall and cover your face with the newspaper.

It is raining. A milky haze hangs over the lake. The gray, drowsy lake dozes in the rain. Drowsily. Hills and clouds slowly sway back and forth. Water drips from the parasols covering the red tables and white enamel chairs. The floor glitters. I drink cool red wine filled with the green of the mountains and the silver of the graying sky. Why am I so sad? I can no longer sort out the world. Several times it seemed that at last all the pieces fitted together. It looked like an altogether sensible and solid structure. And I — even I — was beginning to fit in. All the wooden blocks were arranged. At the top, with great delight, I placed Socrates, St. Francis of Assisi, Marx, Gandhi, Einstein, and then I looked at it — how pretty it all was in the bright sunlight. And when I had it all nicely set up in the center of the room, two girls from downstairs burst in. These girls are not quite grown up yet, but for a long time they have had soldiers dropping in.

The lover of these girls' mother is "perpetually" drunk. A slight, thin man, sick with tuberculosis. He eats dog meat and drinks liquid lard made from dog fat. In the back yard one can always find a little mongrel kept there for this purpose. Last month I often used to see a large white bitch. She was gentle, sad, and she never barked. She must have sensed her approaching death.

The two girls from downstairs, with breasts still undeveloped, burst in and destroyed my precious structure. In such cases, of course, one ought to act energetically and notify the proper authorities, but I must admit that at the time I was rather perplexed. Now sometimes I want to eat a piece of bread, but nobody is at home. I walk a bit in the corridor, hands in my pockets, but soon a sense of futility overcomes me; how irritable I am. I go back to my room. Outside my window the city is wet. Completely gray. If only a single sparrow would chirp, or a fly would buzz. I am weighed down with certain serious problems . . . problems that I will never confide to my neighbors or my family. Furthermore, I would like to write something inspiring in connection with the forthcoming New Year. I am preparing a momentous proclamation to all mankind. Right here, in my room. And nobody knows about it. I conceal myself perfectly. Not a single muscle moves in my face to disclose the truth. And yet I am one of the most rebellious minds in the world. In any case, not a single glass vibrates on the table, not one bottle rings against another while I am arranging an explosion of the entire globe, not to mention the Great Powers.

Yet when there is a burning in my stomach, then I no longer think about the world but only concentrate on my body.

Anyhow, all this will never have any significance, neither for me nor for my examiners. The late P. always used to take me for Sikora. He thought I was Sikora and spoke with me as if I were Sikora. All right then, what good is it to me that since early childhood I have tried to develop will power, character, and other good qualities? What good is it to me that I held my finger over a hot flame, gave my savings to the poor, or fed the birds? I have gone through hell, I have suffered much, and P. still takes me for somebody else. As a matter of fact, I could have spent my life killing birds in their nests, taking money out of blind beggars' hats, loafing in bed . . . P. would, in any case, have taken me for someone else. And this is how it always is. Hence, this time too it turned out that my alleged school friend had made a mistake. We had gone to schools in the opposite corners of Poland and, besides, he was ten years older than I. He nevertheless wanted to tell me about his marital sex life, but I excused myself on the pretext of urgent business. We parted with a strong masculine handshake.

I entered a narrow street. Here the passers-by resembled turned-off lamps. Only the women glowed — the young ones, of course — as if untouched by the many centuries of European history. Evidently they were born only this morning and had not as yet read the newspapers. I walked into a little café. People hovered over small tables, talking with great animation. Yes, animation. This must be stressed. Passing by, I could hear some words and sentences. They were familiar words. Very similar to those I had heard in this city ten years earlier. Several years had gone by, and again people were speaking the same sentences. They were, actually, the same people. A cross-eyed young man, his hair combed in a bang, was now circulating between the tables. He, at least, was new — young. Spring was already in the air, and women's flesh glowed with a quiet, warm light. Their hands held objects of everyday use; an air of calm hovered over their bodies.

— *translated by* BARBARA VEDDER

(From *Przevwany Egzamin.* Published by Pantowy Instytut Wydawniczy, Warsaw, 1960.)

Ladies and Gentlemen . . .

BY KAZIMIERZ BRANDYS

KAZIMIERZ BRANDYS, born in 1916 in Lodz, began his literary career after the war. His first two novels, *The Invincible City* and *The Wooden Horse* (1946), speak of the German Occupation. In 1948 the four-volume novel *Between the Two Wars* appeared. However, in the social-realistic style, his most important work is *The Citizens,* which was published in 1954. Further titles are *The Red Cap* (1956), *The Mother of Kings* (1958), *Letters to Mrs. Z.* (1956-1959). During the 1956 political crisis, he published "Defense of Granada," an apology for the writers and actors who toed the party line during the Stalinist period. (See the Introduction.) The following story is from *Romantic Moods,* published in 1960. Mr. Brandys lives in Warsaw.

LADIES AND GENTLEMEN, forty years ago when I first took the path which was to bring me here, I was a very imprecise person. Except for my background, I had virtually nothing. And my education consisted mainly in exercises in self-conspiracy. At home, I was taught self-consciousness, which in turn I taught myself to conceal. The first mistake that you made was that you accepted me as an equal partner. I became prematurely involved. Allow me here to hazard a guess. The mistake I have just mentioned is probably common to everybody. We fall victims to misuse; the demand for adults has for a long time exceeded the supply; yes, indeed, minors are used for hard labor. I believe the same thing applies to you — therefore I forgive you this mistake and beg your indulgence. . . . Excuse me a second, while I take a sip of water — I am very moved myself.

But first, please imagine a plump little woman of sixty-seven. I have undoubtedly hastened her death. It all started idyllically: she had a wonderful hat with ostrich feathers. On Sunday mornings, I used to come to her bedroom and beg her to put the hat on. I suspect that she did not love me. She was my first woman and my first disappointment. Please close your eyes. Imagine a large dark room full of old furniture and the two of us in bed, she in her feathered hat, laughing her head off. Only much later did I realize her age.

Do you remember my novel called *The Buried Cities*? It is the story of a childhood, in which we all three appear: myself, my grandmother and Max. In reality, however, things were slightly different: from aversion to my grandmother, I had tortured Max, and this caused her illness and death. I used to remove lumps of sugar from between the bars of his cage and eat them. Ladies and gentlemen, he was beside himself with rage. After a few weeks, his eyes became bloodshot whenever he saw me. An unknown force pushed my hand toward the sugar; Max would throw himself against the bars. His vulgar despair was rather distasteful. The end was inevitable: I had to finish him off. You will, I am sure, understand this: the victim becomes a witness, it is unavoidable. Moreover, a number of other factors come into play, such as loneliness, boredom and habit. I had lots of time and little freedom; besides, I had already started — this must be stressed — I had started and therefore had to finish my first self-portrait: that of a murderer.

Max died of a stroke. Now comes another scene: it is evening, the nursery, white furniture. She comes in flushed with grief, with Max on her palm; I am sitting at my small desk. She: "Maxie, Maxie . . ." I blench, ladies and gentlemen, and get to my feet without a word; what can one say at a moment like this? For the first time in my life I had done something on my own behalf and at once these Shakespearean consequences: a murderer, a corpse and an accusing widow. But believe me: in all the years since that day, I have never felt so authentically naked, so truly myself and no one else, so utterly unconventional, as then, in the presence of these two who knew of what I was capable.

I see some skeptical smiles. You are wrong, I am not dragging out the well-known theories about the part played by childhood experiences in the development of the unconscious. Today, when we are gathered here to pay tribute to my achievement, I can solemnly declare that I don't consider childhood to be something over and done with, something separate, which nevertheless radiates to other periods of life, nor to be a kind of gland secreting infantilism until mature years. No. Childhood is merely a great misfortune which befalls us very early and leads to the splitting of our personality. It's a drama of captivity and mental backwardness, therefore — of downfall, with appalling consequences.

One becomes adult only by concealing defeat. Shouldn't something be done about it?

You ask — how? By granting equal rights. It is said that the modern school of child psychology recommends that children be treated as the leading class of the community. All their wishes should be complied with, the adults being only the executive apparatus. You want to be an organ-grinder — good, here is an organ, grind it. You want to build a house — all right, here is a site and some building materials, nobody will disturb you. You want to play soldiers — here is some live ammunition; to be a policeman — here is a list of murders and rapes. There will be victims, ladies and gentlemen, but, on the credit side, a complete emancipation from complexes which undoubtedly check our development. You know yourselves what trouble we all have with the younger generation. We would not have any if the children assumed responsibility for the world. Nonsense? Hurrah! That's exactly it: one should begin with nonsense, instead of ending with it.

Your antipathy to me results from two of my characteristics. Firstly, I am still trustful; secondly, I conceal my depression. This means that I am at the same time both naïve and inscrutable, which tends to be disconcerting; you don't know what attitude to adopt. Somebody (who is, I think, not with us here tonight) once wrote about my volume *The Dog's Paw* that it lacked internal identity. A very fair remark! *The Dog's Paw* wants simultaneously to be an organ-grinder, a policeman and a regimental commander, and becomes each in turn. You, on the other hand, think that one should first decide on something and afterwards stick to this decision. Either organgrinding, or crime, or a military career. I have never been able to achieve this; I have been unable to define myself before an audience, just as I have been unable to define myself before myself; I had (and, ladies and gentlemen, this is a real worry) too many internal possibilities.

And this is perhaps why I did not achieve that minimum of pride which is a condition of our existence. I have always suffered because of this, both as a human being and as an artist. I, too, would like to appear carrying the banner of my personality. I have often wondered why you should have this gift of which I am deprived, this capacity for projecting yourselves and choosing your subject, this ability to see yourselves from the stalls . . . It is so admirable.

Ladies and gentlemen, there are definitely too many subjects to which one can devote oneself. For instance: our city and its heroism, our city and its absurdity, our city and its depravity. A street in our city: love, murder, business and opportunism. A house in our street: twenty-four flats, several sets of opinions (each substantiated by facts) and several kinds of morality. Finally, my own home and myself. My honesty, my hypocrisy, my social optimism, my fears. All these are interlaced, on the move, in flux. A multitude of intonations and styles. Sociology, statistics and religion try to discipline it all, but what is an artist to do? Everything he tries to achieve will be pretense, an imitation of action. You were therefore quite right in your choice. One must, first of all, create one's own drama. Afterwards, the drama will take over. The boards — the stage boards — are the most important part of our accommodation. I realize that I am boring you, but I shall presently pass on to more interesting things. I should not like to abuse your patience.

The question of autobiography — I have thought about it too, for everyone is tempted. One might perhaps write it in the third person singular. Let us assume that Caspar was brought up by his grandparents in a bailiff's house in the country. First sexual experiences, relations with the local peasants, poppy-seed cake, Zola's *Nana* swallowed up in one session in the summer house, attachment to a goat. Then college. One must be careful from then on. Winters change into summers, it is white and green, women appear, he must shave every day, it is green and white (work, work, work!), and here is Caspar with his children, thinking, "What the use?" — but now it is too late, it is white and green, and white, white, blindingly so toward the end. Finally, the last thoughts.

Ladies and gentlemen, I gave this as an example, as one of the possibilities. There are others. If you don't want to buy Caspar, I could think of something else. Let's consider, for instance, sleep, the foundation of life. There is a theory that sleep is the natural condition of mankind. So I sleep. Isn't it strange that for years I have been dreaming about a man in a hood? Something similar to the one Erasmus of Rotterdam wore on his head. This man stares at me through a peephole in the door; but it is not I, it is he who is locked up, in a sort of shed. I enter, sit on a trunk, and wait for the face he will make. I am a wandering commercial traveler, and the story of the faces he makes is my moral biography. I say to him, "Boss, again no good?" And I know it is no good. This has gone on for years and years. It is clear that he is also myself. Ladies and gentlemen, what despair, what monologues! Such an autobiographical volume could be published under the title of *Trial.*

And what about sexual tortures? I must apologize: the times have played on my flute, too.

In short, no. And not only because of truthfulness or the lack of it. My dear listeners — in all three instances I would feel stale. It would not be me, believe me. I would not feel like myself, so please don't urge a style on me, as even the grammar itself is fundamentally at variance with my existence. No, no and no!

But instead I could provide biographical material. Certainly. There are my letters. Besides, some of my classmates are still alive. Apparently, while in the fifth form, I stole a pencil case; and what about my subsequent passion for the wife of Colonel S.? This was notorious, as you will recall. With all that, characteristically, I spoke very little, only a few words on exceptional occasions — I had a reputation of being taciturn. So you now have an outline of a person. A little intuition (for instance, I don't find her at home, I force the door in complete silence, and naked, wait for her on a divan, while making notes for *The Dog's Paw,* which, incidentally, I consider to be my masterpiece), a little understanding and sympathy, the ingenious linking of some contradictory facts and, most important, the background — and you will have a whole. This is how history is made; the rest is carried away to the grave. In mute amazement, precisely.

The Colonel's wife. She did not notice me quite, she was rather too preoccupied with herself. This is exactly what is wanted in such cases. This played on my vanity; I alternated between Heaven and Hell. Would you believe me if I told you that I had hired detectives? It was at a time when secret agents could be hired by jealous lovers. Yes, hidden in me was an Othello who categorically demanded his Desdemona. That woman was like fuel for my jealousy. An ash blonde; and you will surely be interested to learn that, apart from the Moor, I was hiding somebody else within myself, a kind of fair-haired lover, something decidedly European and sophisticated, a kind of Venetian princeling who had to kindle, in turn, a truly African passion. I therefore was at the same time Desdemona to a certain brunette.

Ladies and gentlemen, this was the situation. I was torturing the Colonel's lady, creating imaginary lovers for her, saying, "You are killing me!" while she was saying, "You always want more than I can give." Finally, I started to break up the furniture. The next day, an identical text: the other, dark-haired one, my internal Othello, tormented me for an hour, crying, "You are killing me!" — to which I replied, "You always want more than I can give" — and as a result she started breaking some glasses. Not to mention the fact that I was being followed. I was spying, while being followed myself — the strangler being strangled in his turn. I was Desdemona to one, and Othello to the other. The difficulty is to resolve who I really was.

I don't know if you have ever considered the exceedingly narrow repertory of texts. One speaks almost always the same lines, everything seems to be memorized, there is no room for individuality. It is either "Perish, you tyrant!" or *"Et tu, Brute."* You will understand that I am using a mental shorthand (my time is rather limited), but even these shorthand examples show the obvious impossibility of tracing one's self-portrait or making a self-analysis. How is it then? Could it perhaps be that we are falling out of the frame of the picture? That we consist only of a certain number of photographic plates — to risk a paradox — of an archivistic character? I sometimes cannot help feeling that culture has worked for us too long for us to be able to safeguard our private possibilities. Don't you feel this? A colossal heritage. We function like linked systems, and the main problem which I now pose is to what extent we can make free decisions and to what extent we are purely functional. This is the question, ladies and gentlemen — our modern "To be or not to be" . . . Allow me to take a sip of water again.

I mentioned my classmates. It is quite true that I still meet them from time to time. Some harmless reminiscing over a cup of tea, very rarely a drink — everything in an atmosphere of elderly cordiality. But there is one among them, Kulesza, with a withered arm. I hardly remember him from school, he was so colorless. During our get-togethers, ladies and gentlemen, I have come to feel that he has his own views about me. He never voices them, but I know. When our eyes meet, I can read in his: "Just you wait! One day I will tell you what you are!" This puts me off my stride a little, and I even prefer that my works should not be discussed in his presence, especially the *Stone Swan,* which contains some school reminiscences. We were once talking about that book, and they all laughed, "Well, old man, that book was really something!" while I explained that in my *oeuvre* it was rather a marginal item, when suddenly Kulesza made an odd gesture with his withered hand and said, "As far as I am concerned, you are shit." Later he sent me a letter of apology, but as you can see, he must have meant something. Kulesza lives in the suburbs, and a few weeks later I made my way there. Would you believe it? An autumn drizzle, and there I was, walking up and down in front of Kulesza's house. Please don't smile; I was quite sure that he must know it about me. You will ask — what? It. Just it. For unfortunately, I myself am constantly in a temporary, self-interested relationship to myself; apart from this, there is nothing, some nerves, a few unconnected scenes from the past, several daily rags of thought, and my clothes; but he, Kulesza, was in a position to know much more: he has always stood to one side, and moreover I had hardly ever noticed him, which means that I have always been exposed to him in the round.

Rain, taxis splashing mud on me, it was slowly getting dark, stray dogs rubbed against my knees — I had been standing there for an hour. At last, a small girl ran out from the house and handed me a note: "Go back home. I shan't tell you anything. Kulesza." Afterwards we met quite a number of times, but always in the company of other friends from our school days.

No, ladies and gentlemen, it is nothing to laugh about. Time is the greatest of human dramas and there comes a moment, horrifying in its sadness, when our own past becomes more mysterious to us than what the future holds in store. My life, as the Minister of Culture has said today, will be a model for future generations. Agreed, but what is there for me? Only the check? I should prefer an assurance that my life could not have been different. Unfortunately, Minister, I see that you are silent. And so are you, ladies and gentlemen. A pity. Well, I shall change the subject.

My hobbies? To lose my ambitions. You will be amused, but this is the only road of return to the community. A week ago my wife (yes, after the Colonel's death, she became my wife) told me in the morning, "You and your moods, your depressions. Who ever said that life must be better?" Please imagine: it is August, the sun is shining through the curtains, I lie in bed prostrated. And she continues, "You are eaten up by ambition. You always want more than you can achieve. Oh, if a deputation came to the house to ask you how you slept, you would leap from bed at once." And I say, "Haven't I been through enough? All the misfortunes described by Tolstoy. Not to speak of the death of one's relatives and the burning of one's city — this one can bear. But the nervous tension after the Armistice . . . Not a shot fired, only work and progress. No one has attempted to describe it. Not to mention, my dearest, that things have changed a lot since the Colonel's death, too: I had cooled down already during the funeral. So what is left to me apart from participation in history?" And she (rather hurt by the personal allusion) says, "Oh, you silly old man, you haven't been beaten enough. You still imagine you are the chosen one."

And there she hit the mark. I shall explain it to you in a minute. She knows me; she is the only one to know the extent of my tragic love for myself. I am shaving, let's say, and suddenly I am overcome with grief that you, ladies and gentlemen, don't love me as I love you. You don't know it, as I never appear before you unshaven, but she does. And the nights, the nights! I wake up, ignored by you, with a growth of beard, and sit at my desk to write, in order to attract your gaze. Meanwhile you, ladies and gentlemen, expect something quite different from me. Books, yes please, but in fact that is not what matters to you. Only by a true misfortune could I deserve your real attention. This is what you are waiting for. When reading my books, you are killing time until the moment when you can exclaim, "So there is no hope? What a great loss!" No, there is no hope — it has been fulfilled. But I shan't know about it.

This is the essence of your love. Without irony, love. Expectation and fear. How well I feel your lack of interest in my characters and situations. But if I should end up under a train, you would begin to quote my books by heart. Yes indeed, the ending is what one is waiting for. This is how I explain the size of my audience tonight. They did not come in great numbers, because they realize I am not moribund yet. If they knew that I would have a stroke tomorrow, there would be crowds here tonight.

And yet, I stand here surrounded by floral tributes and know that there is a bond between us. I exist rather in spite of you. You are oppressed by my unfulfilled span of life. My goodness, this is a lot. The relief I shall provide for you when I die will be my last accomplishment. When we depart, the world becomes a little simpler; we restore to the survivors a part of their freedom.

I should prefer you, however, to love me more simply. Take, for instance, my daily walk down the street in the afternoon. Of course, everybody should be discreet — no photographers crouching before me with their cameras — at most some soft whispers here and there. I would say, "Excuse me . . ." and pass; I could even be wearing an old tweed cap. Why then, by God, doesn't this ever happen? Such coolness on your part . . . And what is it that stands between us? Sometimes I too keep racking my brains to decide if I would invite a wanted man under my roof. At times the answer is yes, at other times — no. Of one thing I am, unfortunately, incapable: of deciding on a consistent course of behavior where wanted people are concerned.

Do you realize this? "A beast," you say about a man, "but a born organizer. And he will always help those in need." It is not so in my case. Sometimes I don't help those in need. It all depends on the hour and the day. I shall try to explain this.

Ladies and gentlemen, it is wartime; I am being followed. Deathly pale, I knock at my brother-in-law's door. He opens it at long last. I say, "Betrayal — I am being followed — could you . . . ?" At the word "betrayal," I see a gleam in my brother-in-law's eyes. Like, say, a gong striking: the start of his psychodrama. At "could you?" he is already performing a masterly shrug. The stage. The spotlights on him. Humanity in the stalls. Will he shrug his shoulders easily and well, saying, "What a question, my dear. My home is your home. Maria will lay the table." And this, ladies and gentlemen, is precisely what he says. He speaks a truly magnificent line and speaks it to perfection. A human being, my dears, a masterpiece of humanity. He has become almost handsome, and it does not matter that his voice is slightly hoarse — for every word he utters puts me one step further from execution. And you must remember that all the time he is terror-stricken at the thought that they will pursue me here with their dogs, and he is whispering to himself, "A disaster . . . but it can't be helped," and we, mankind, provide for him that drug: that line. A kind of injection, ladies and gentlemen, blocking his fear of death by fear of villainy. True despair, as Kulesza says, begins when there is no room left for lines.

So Maria pours out tea, and the clock starts ticking away the hours. Meanwhile, I play the part of Disaster. My brother-in-law is the man who has admitted a wanted man to his house, I — the wanted man admitted under his brother-in-law's roof. One thing must still be settled: for how long does my brother-in-law give shelter to those who are wanted? "How long . . ." These two words are not included in his, Maria's, or in my lines. But the clock struck these words. Do you understand? Everything has its deadline. My brother-in-law gave me shelter for a week.

The seventh day came. Morning, nine o'clock, and he appeared in the door. I saw at once that his form had gone; in fact, ladies and gentlemen, he could hardly creep over the threshold. It was obvious that the wanted man had become a lodger; sacrifice has become identified with service. He (thinking): "Maria and the children. How much longer?" I (thinking): "For me nothing has changed. Where else can I go?" And both together: "How disgusting is a human being!" But, ladies and gentlemen, man is disgusting only in his warren hole. Luckily, mankind is watching. For what happened? A gong! I suddenly straightened myself. And I heard my voice: "Of course, Maria's sister is coming to stay!" I am beautiful now, my spurs are tinkling. A second ago I was nondescript; now I stand in the floodlights. "Never mind, my dear fellow, I shall finish my cigarette and take myself off." He stands in the shadow and keeps silent. He would prefer me never to finish that cigarette, but this is not up to him. I shall smoke the cigarette for the sake of mankind.

A week, ladies and gentlemen. During that week, each of us increased his chance of salvation by offering the other the chance to die. And during that same week, each of us acted reversely. The difference was only in time.

Conclusions? Ladies, gentlemen, what conclusions can there be? We must pass judgment for external reasons (for instance "two years on probation" or "I shall never speak to him again"), but why here, among ourselves? It seems to me, Minister, that our psychological plurality should be dealt with by a special department. Since I read in a newspaper about a certain collaborator who rescued an old lady from the flames during the Occupation, I stopped bothering about ethics.

But I really wish to speak about us: you, ladies and gentlemen, and myself. There are various kinds of bribery. Are you afraid of the passage of time? Time — indeed — flows away. Are you afraid of being out of date, parochially *ancien régime?* Novelty rejuvenates, of course. Would you believe it: none of the characters in my books had a vacuum cleaner? The critics pointed it out to me. So what is there to talk about? I don't direct through my readers the current of modernity; I am not contemporary. Moreover, as I have mentioned bribery, I must also state that I don't open up. It is scandalous, I admit, but I have not done it so far. This has been pointed out to me. I have tried, but I did not succeed in opening up before you as you might have wished. But today, at this fortieth anniversary, with you, ladies and gentlemen, gathered here in this heat and you, Minister of Culture, I have decided to do so.

Why didn't I open up before? What were my motives or reasons? Don't let's go into them. Reasons are the first degree of servitude, and their disclosure does not mean freedom. Some time ago, I wrote a volume of intimate confessions. A complete internal monologue, consisting of one sentence on three hundred and ten pages. The title was concise: *Myself*. Please imagine the final reading of the proofs. I felt uneasy and wondered whether I really had the right to be so shameless. I shut myself up for a whole night. What a night, dear listeners! Truly face to face with myself. As a result, I transferred the action to the seventeenth century and made King Sigismund Vasa the main protagonist. The new title was *Vasa — Pole or Swede?*

Fragments, scattered bits and pieces. Things that had once been whole, but which have lost their meaning now. Dismantling. A lot of empty space with a protective coloring. Echoes, rags of creative ideas. Through this wasteland of broken forms we proceed, less and less identifiable. In the spreading whir of time, in the inexorable boredom of progress, we look for humor, love, tragedy. It is more and more difficult to find points of contact. Don't you all feel the weight of your heavy, parched lips? We argue with one another as in a dream, words swelling in our mouths. It's hot. I have nothing really to say to you, except to cast some nebulous doubts on myself and others. But there is little difference between myself and others. We intricately and painfully penetrate each other, don't you see? We are intermingled at random. Offensively at random. And despite this, things manage to move forward.

Of course — there is loneliness. Could I fail to mention it? With that small correction: our loneliness does not arise from being abandoned by people. Ladies and gentlemen, this is most important: We are lonely all together, communally, not so much in space as in time. Our loneliness is a realization that the world is experiencing something in which we cannot and will not participate.

Secondly — anonymity. Do you feel sufficiently individualized, ladies and gentlemen? I could not say as much for myself. My contours seem too fluid, I feel a certain aquosity, my edges merge with yours, although I don't experience any fraternal feelings. If I remember rightly, our parents did not suffer from this complaint. Am I a decent man? The old bookkeeper in my grandfather's office was certainly a decent man. I remember him distinctly: alpaca pull-on sleeves, pince-nez, a bald patch; he smelled of mint. Ladies and gentlemen, fifty years ago a decent man had a specific appearance, and even a specific smell. We at present are becoming a corporate body; our smell depends on the efficiency of urban transport. One refers to us as "men" without any adjectives, we are symptoms of the functioning of the species. More and more rarely — have you noticed it? — are our surnames known. Sociology, that's right. We are slowly being transformed into record cards, divided according to our reflexes and characteristics; we serve as material for the establishment of general laws. We — who formerly had made the laws . . . I am not stirring up trouble — I am simply stating the facts.

I have to mention, incidentally, that at night I feel much more separate than in the morning. The start is difficult. Despite the nagging of my spouse (she is indisposed, and to that we owe her absence tonight), it requires an effort to extricate myself not so much from bed as from the miasma of our mutual relations (and I refer to you and me, and not to my wife and myself), into which I sink between six and six-thirty in the morning. At that time you are with me, you oppress my chest. I wake up, as my wife nudges me. "You screamed." I did scream; it is hereditary. For thirty years, my father had been assaulted by bandits every night. He used to wake up shouting, "Where's my wallet?!" Here, a digression is necessary.

Ladies and gentlemen, imagine a fair-haired man with an aggressive nose, a pinkish-blue general coloring, a slight squint in the right eye. He exuded a pleasant aura of hair cream. I forgave him all his amorous affairs. One day he gave me a Baden-Powell hat as a present. It was a hot Sunday in August, rather like today; we went for a walk, he in a white Panama hat, I in my scout's hat. I put it on as scouts do: the brim up over the left ear, down over the right. Before we left home, he gave me the once-over. I felt I did not please him. I wanted to whisper, "Don't hurt me . . . ," but he had already taken hold of my hat with both hands and put it on my head straight as a basin. Do you understand? This is how I was to wear it. I was his property, I plus my hat.

Would you believe it, walking downstairs, I again lifted the brim over my left ear and pulled it down over the right? That's what I did. Father did not notice it at once. Halfway down, we had a rather heated exchange and he again set my hat straight. We went out into the street. After a few steps, I tilted the brim. Trembling with fear, I listened to his heavy breathing. When the same thing was repeated for the third time, he slapped my face. How I screamed! I shielded my eyes with my right hand while with my left I again tilted the brim of my hat as a boy scout should. Father jumped up to me with a strange moan, pulled the hat off my head, and put it on again, straight. Like a basin.

I did it the fourth time! Was it rebellion? My resistance was irrational. His own Panama hat askew, Father dragged me upstairs to our flat. He threw me on the couch — he, a heavy muscular man of forty, me, a boy of nine. His face was swollen with fury. Never before had he devoted so much attention to me, or stared at me so hard. We were joined together; I saw in his eyes a maniacal interest in myself, in my reactions and my body, and this interest appalled me. That is why I screamed, not from pain. Ladies and gentlemen, a climax. I almost ceased to feel the blows. I only knew that together we were performing an ambiguous act which would unite us for a long time to come. At last, he let go of me. He was breathing heavily; I looked to see if he was all right. I was again wearing a basin on my head; I loved him. He understood nothing, nothing at all! We went out again, he pushing me in front of him.

And now, ladies and gentlemen, comes the tragic denouement. In front of the house, in the green shade of trees, we met some boy scouts with collection tins. Father straightened up his back; I trotted along, shoulders hunched. The sun shone through my enormous crimson ears. And all of a sudden I heard, "How are you?" A new figure. Like Father, in a white Panama hat. An old friend, a judge. Two Panama hats, a double smell of hair cream, two colored bow ties. I, slightly behind, in my Baden-Powell hat. "Your boy?" I was introduced. "A real chip of the old block." "One tries one's best, Judge!"

Listen, ladies and gentlemen, my Baden-Powell hat again comes to the fore. I hear, "You have a lovely hat, my boy, but you are wearing it wrong. This is a boy scout hat and you must wear it as boy scouts do." Dear friends, I quiver. A strange hand lifts the brim of my hat over my left ear . . . Dear friends, I did not wish it! Father is silent. "As boy scouts do" . . . No, I could not stand it; I could not bear to look at him. Even now, the memory of it makes me shake . . . The Judge took his leave and walked on. We continued our walk; the heat was intense. Then a boy scout came up to me and whispered, "Be on guard!" A few steps later, I straightened the brim. Father did not comment when I slipped my hand into his warm, swollen palm. Ladies and gentlemen, great is the force of human sympathy, but does it always fill us at the right time?

Why had I felt so terribly sorry for my father? Not only because he had suffered defeat. Of course, he was bigger and stronger than I, and perhaps this is why I felt additional sympathy for him. But something else was at stake. The world had displayed before us one of its small, stupid, senseless scenes; a miserable episode with panting, instead of spoken lines. The casual, unimportant gesture of a stranger pricked the balloon, an idiocy blown up large through vanity and prestige-seeking. We were both ashamed, but father's shame was heavier by thirty years: he understood how very wrong he had been. We now walked along in silence. I let myself be guided, but in fact it was I who was leading him by the hand. I wanted to leave what had happened as far behind us as possible, to put a distance between us and that disgrace. To walk away. To move away from a defeat that had been disclosed. To apply isolation to ignominy. It is very much to be recommended. Yes — a certain discretion toward oneself, especially at moments of world revelations when the scandalous profile of our existence is unveiled. Universal thunderbolts, cloudbursts, metaphysical questionings in the flashes of lightning and so on. At such moments, ladies and gentlemen, the maximum of self-control is indicated. Don't stand on the site of defeat — walk away. Even if you can only manage half a step, still walk away, move slightly to one side, just as one does to avoid stepping in a puddle.

You, as far as I can see, like having your feet wet; yes, damp socks give you a certain satisfaction — the taste of downfall. I repeat: this is not to be recommended. The matter is much more complex; there always exists a second profile, and even if we consider truth only as a kind of self-awareness, there also exists a second truth, about which, I am sure, the Minister who is with us tonight is informed. What the world is like — well, this we won't learn here. Often, however, we experience the world in a disgusting manner, through a disgusting self-revelation. We are too preoccupied with ourselves as an effect, and not enough as a cause. And you still wonder why I don't give myself away to you? To disclose what? My despair and my feelings of futility? To reveal the bad smells? No, dear friends, I am nobody's guilt. I consider myself my own executioner. I don't wish to burden you, and I ask you please not to burden me. Discretion and distance, hygiene and aloofness. Nails well cared for in moments of failure. Discretion when facing the abyss. And again discretion.

Do I seem repulsive to you? A dead silence, although this was the moment for applause. No, dear friends, I stick to my guns: we should be deprived of our freedom. Freedom to know our worst instincts, our psychological rock-bottom. To deprive, to limit. Reach agreement as to the letter, decide on the duties, make a new list of necessary words and gestures. In short, repair the automatic machine and scrap the complaints. The world has always been an installation. One must educate the young so that they will know how it works. A minimum of illusions — a minimum of prejudices. I don't exclude hope; it is usually harmless.

A marginal remark, dear friends, in connection with the spanking I got from my father. In maltreating minors (which is inevitable in view of the number of their small villainies), one should use more elaborate implements than a strap or a whip. The people on the floor below our flat, Mr. and Mrs. Kogan, used to buy a hen in similar situations. Their heir was laid on the sofa, and his bare backside was covered with dried peas. The bird pecked at the peas, and that was his punishment. The family looked on from their chairs. The dignity of the adults was preserved, and complete calm reigned while justice was being administered. Afterwards, the hen was eaten for dinner.

So what is the meaning (I revert to essentials again) of an ideal? Or to use a more contemporary expression "a model"? Does it or doesn't it exist; is it possible or impossible to achieve? Let's take for instance the readiness to act shabbily. Every person has it in him. To seduce an orphan girl on the grave of her dead mother, well, this is a trifle compared with what Stawrogin did. But at the same time? . . . Huh, but if the orphan girl were also going blind, you would at once feel a characteristic thrill . . . To sacrifice oneself, to spend one's life with a blind girl, to serve as her guide dog . . . And do you know, ladies and gentlemen, there are always those who will do it. There is room for greatness among us. Therefore I am ashamed to go into detail how last year I had to get rid of a tapeworm. During that nasty performance, a stream of loose, quite interesting associations was flushed out of me, and if the thing had happened to anyone else in the literary world, you could now no doubt enjoy a true intellectual feast. But it was different with me. I insist on social situations, on gross facts and on accounting to other people. I am not always aware of my downfall, and I don't feel like talking to everybody who succeeds in uttering a moan.

But reverting to the Colonel's ex-wife. Ladies and gentlemen, for years we have slept on one divan bed. This provides an opportunity for countless conversations. My character, your character — your character, my character. Were it not for your faults, I would . . . were it not for my qualities, you would . . . Mutual conditioning, a dose of introspection, two existences joined like an eagle with two heads and — as she is fond of saying — two unexplored biographies. She comes from Eastern Poland; she has a rather simple approach to life. Please listen. A sleepless night and the following dialogue:

She: "So much vanity in you! If you were to save mankind as a fifth-grade civil servant, you would never agree to it. Why do you always have to preach then?"

I: "And what am I to do? There is vanity in every one of us. We only differ in the ways in which we satisfy it. I have chosen fairly harmless ones."

She: "You don't wish to be yourself."

I: "Be myself? Perhaps a plucky little man without illusions — with a fridge and a television set? No. One must play one's part to the end. I am not satisfied with stylization and a costume. You know very well that I am not young. I must act with dignity and sense."

At that she accuses me of not being genuine, of pretending. Act with dignity? Why don't I say "suffer"?

I try to explain. One can only suffer for biological reasons or because of ambition. The world, however, demands moral suffering as well. And one must give it that satisfaction. A certain amount of ham-acting is necessary for that, a drama of attitudes halfway between truth and lying. The world needs it urgently.

She: "What do you mean? Is everything to come down to acting? And you can talk about it so calmly?"

I (calmly, in fact): "When one is condemned to something, one must make it as pretty as possible. What is culture, darling, if not playacting by mankind forced to live? By playacting, I enrich mankind. My profession consists in diminishing the feeling of irrevocability."

And thus we go on, dear friends, night after night. And the years fly by. Sleeplessness. Both a little jaded, over our heads the skeletons of memories. Our bodies . . . well, don't let's talk about that. The city has also greatly changed. Do you also encounter fewer and fewer familiar faces? Young people are flushing us out — it is amazing. We are more and more *à deux;* my wishes have been fulfilled at last: no one turns his head after her now. And that frankness of hers: "You think perhaps," she says to me in darkness, "that you are in reality different from the person that people see? Then that is your sad mistake. The Colonel used to play Hamlet, too, and yet he was only what his obituary said he was: a good soldier and a loyal comrade. Remember this. You always hanker after fresh starts."

Touché. You can't imagine how accurately. Indeed, I had been tempted by every new opportunity. For instance, there was a time when I felt a reforming zeal and started preaching full tolerance. Listen, for example, to this quotation: "Treason would mean nothing, if everybody became a traitor. Only in that way can one wipe out jealousy, the basest of feelings — and lying, the malignant growth of modern times." As you will remember, at that time I supported the theory that those attacked should not resist, which, on the premise of universality, would liquidate the notion of an attacker. What a number of telephone calls this caused! . . . Soon, I had a bunch of followers and my own reserved table in the Literary Club. Yes, another inch, and it would have been a breakthrough. Unfortunately, war broke out, and I volunteered for the Armed Forces, and after my return had to spend three months in a sanitarium for nervous diseases: I had received anonymous letters about my first wife's little love affair.

And my sporting activity? I had really been an expert. You will remember no doubt how I handed out cups. I even began to walk with my right arm forward, always prepared to shake the hand of an athlete who had broken the tape. Only when Drake III broke his vaulting pole and impaled himself on it in my presence did I experience shock and disappointment. Apparently without reason.

Afterwards, I had a few other incarnations. I might have become every one of these men, but always at a given moment I stopped short for fear that I was not being myself, that I was beginning to imitate an image I had created. Therefore, I had to make a new start again. All this in order to capture something elusive. To get affirmation from the outside, to receive a proof of identity. Dear friends, inwardly I felt eaten up, deficient and void. I felt unable to be somebody new only for myself. For myself alone? Floodlights! I needed floodlights. Only their glare could warm me. But at the same time it showed me a path — and I trembled lest I be walking away from myself.

You, of course, have guessed all this fairly quickly. Is the author of the well-known lampoon entitled "The Elderly He-Star" here with us? Thank you, dear colleague; please sit down. I suffered a lot from you, until your wife called on me with flowers and admitted to me that you were suffering from me too. What a shock this was! I suddenly understood that all of us are eaten up. What then was I striving for? Whom was I striving for? I reached a turning point again, dear friends: and now began my Christian period, which found its expression in the famous two-act play *Pyrrhus's Army*. But again I brought upon myself general mistrust as a conjurer.

But I assure you that all this is closely connected. Goodness me, the times we live in. Yesterday, for instance, in the Literary Society Mr. Sabbath was crying because he had become so accustomed to keeping an eye on his colleagues for their possible deviations that he could not stop doing it now. They comforted him by saying that he would unlearn it if he was patient. A pathetic burlesque. There is a little of everything in each of us. Sentimentality and shrewdness. That spasm, that spasm of alarm and admiration which tightens my throat when I hear of a heroic deed. That joy and pain which I feel when learning about an act of pettiness. Why didn't I become a confessor? Oh, dear friends, my floodlights are of many colors. Blood-red lights on me! Would I be unable to condemn people to death? The rapture of signing a death warrant must be immense. Purple, purple — I used to be a good prelate and might still be one now — you all know the tone of voice I adopt when preaching of man's duties. Give me a pink light! Do you know, if I were a woman, I would be inclined to be flighty . . . Oh, temptation of my infinite possibilities! Oh, fear of the irrevocable . . . Ladies and gentlemen, this should be regulated; a person cannot always define himself — what? To define oneself once and for all? And what if the truth is completely different? Must one then die a phony? Pass away as part only of one's own, not a completely functioning whole? Why did my colleague Mr. Sabbath have to become Sabbath? My friends, I don't want to die like only one day of the week. Lights please! Lights on me! I should like to shimmer in all the colors of the rainbow, so that you should enjoy each of them together with me. I should like to be the fulfilled harmony of my unfulfilled fortunes . . . a collective biography of all the people I might have been. . . . I am nearly finished, I must only shortly mention Kulesza.

An empty large square, the sun aiming at the back of the cranium — noon. You know the place very well: the main square of our city. On the right the opera house, on the left a brass horse without its rider: the historical rider in a sitting position has been, as you know, transferred to the zoo, where something was needed with an outstretched arm to point the way to the bear enclosure. In the center of the square, Kulesza and I. Ladies and gentlemen, this happened earlier today. Well and good, but to meet Kulesza in the very center, in a place of the lowest attendance and on the day of my anniversary celebrations — well, dear friends, I may be mistaken, but the coincidence does seem rather strange.

In one word, we bumped into one another at the foot of the monument. Not a soul in sight — only the sun and we two. Even the dogs had hidden in the shade of the ancient arcades.

He is rather old, that Kulesza. And so dried up that he does not perspire even in the heat. He was wearing a black suit and a linen cap, and carried a briefcase secured with a strap. You will laugh, dear friends: he wanted to pass me by. At the last moment it seemed as if the sun had stopped him. I said softly, "Kulesza, it's me."

He (not looking at me): "I know it's you, but what are you doing here? At this time you should be preparing your speech."

Typical Kulesza. Ladies and gentlemen, I can understand that a man preparing his address of thanks (after forty years of literary successes) may be irritating to some people. Certain comparisons sound unpleasant: forest fires are breaking out in the country because of the heat and yet, at the same moment, a man may be sitting in a cool study and composing on a piece of paper a note of thanks for a medal. In my case this was not quite so, but the very tone of Kulesza's voice, his intention! And he also added something about a dinner jacket: that it was probably already hung out, freshly pressed. Saying this, he was of course looking at the horse, as if he wanted to say, "You are celebrating your anniversary; you don't care that the rider has been removed to the zoo."

And that, dear friends, attracted me. I said suddenly, "Let's go from here; that horse is so tragic. After so many years, they have unseated the rider. Such a sad sight." I assumed, when saying it, my special facial grimace of independence in my opinions. You know it no doubt: when we criticize the government, we seem to grow a goiter. It must be atavism.

We were walking back to the monument when Kulesza said, "Why do you show off so about that horse? Is it of any importance? Both the horse and the rider are made of brass — they can't feel. You are trying to ingratiate yourself with the community. On the quiet, which is worst."

I could not bear it any longer. "Kulesza," I exclaimed, "why do you keep on at me? Have you always hated me?"

Please try to visualize this: a completely empty, red-hot square, a horse rearing on its plinth and we two. Some distance away, burning forests. And under the monument this dialogue:

Kulesza (whom I hadn't seen for years): "You are mistaken. I have never hated you."

I (already hopeful): "And yet . . . don't you remember? I stood in front of your house once . . . in the rain . . ."

He (slightly embarrassed): "Well, if you bring that in . . . It was unimportant. You know, I was reading Dostoevski at the time, and you kept walking in front of the windows. I like my peace when I am reading. So you took it so much to heart?"

I (smiling): "Well, don't let's talk about it."

He (continuing): "You are very sensitive to what people think about you. That's bad. I noticed it already at school. You took to heart what people were saying about you. Do you remember that story about the pencil case?"

I had been, as a matter of fact, accused of pinching a pencil case. It was, I believe, in the fifth form. I can't quite remember, but my other friends mentioned it once or twice during one of the old boys' teas. A moment would come when they winked at me, and one of them would ask, "Now tell us, old man, how was it really with that pencil case? Did you pinch it or not?"

"It is I who pinched that case," said Kulesza now.

"Don't let's talk about it," I repeated.

"I pinched it specially to implicate you. You irritated me terribly by your faith in human nature. Later," — I quote Kulesza — "when you were walking home, I followed you on the other side of the street. I wanted to make sure that you had realized at last how much shit there is in the world. But you will never realize this. A detachment of soldiers came marching along the road, and you stopped on the pavement to wave."

"Was it so?" I was intrigued. "I can't remember it."

"But I do. Life did not change you. Show you a band, and you will wave your hat. And whatever did you write in your *Dog's Paw?*"

Can you understand — the morning of my fortieth anniversay. We are walking around the monument, a few steps toward the horse, a few steps toward the opera house. Kulesza is grilling me. He smiles crookedly and asks:

"Tell me frankly. How was it really with that camel? Did you travel on it in the desert, or was it just a stunt?"

"The camel?" I was completely at a loss. So he explained that a few years ago the *Globe* magazine published a photograph of me under the Pyramids. I was sitting on a camel, wearing a fez. Kulesza wanted to know the truth about this!

I explained: "The *Globe* sent me to Egypt, and it is customary there to have one's photograph taken on a camel near the Pyramids. The fez was also borrowed. And I traveled mostly by bus."

Kulesza: "Thank you. I might have guessed it."

Dear friends, what was he after?

"My dear Kulesza," I said, "what do you mean? I am what I am. Would you prefer me to be a real explorer?"

Then he: "You are not what you are. Even now you don't know how to appear at your anniversary celebrations. This is what irritates you. If you make a witty speech, you will regret not having spoken with pathos. That's how you are. And you keep thinking that life is slipping away from you. And I maintain that it all comes to the same thing in the end."

"Perhaps I have," I said, "some flaws in my character."

"Come off it! Character!" said Kulesza. "If you had a withered arm as I have, you would know to perfection who you are. When a man lacks something that others have, there is nothing he does not know about himself. Didn't you ever dream about being pushed in a bath chair?"

I nodded, ladies and gentlemen. He had guessed.

As we turned away from the horse, Kulesza kept talking:

"You write too often about dignity. And you attach such importance to the panache. And yet personally you are wet. Now, for instance, you are probably thinking that your collar is getting sweaty. You have never lain in shit—this is your infirmity. When one lies in shit, one thinks less about dignity, but one sees the world bloody clearly—and there is no room for doubt. You have not suffered enough. Without suffering, you are a nobody in this country. With us, whatever has been good has come from the guts. Once you stop the death rattle, you have had it. Even bastards are forgiven here: they too are unhappy. Look at our history: horses without riders and people without heads. The landscape, too, is not quite normal."

Silence. Then I spoke. I made a beautiful apologia for man. He is colorless I say, for everyday, and yet moments come when he reaches heights in spite of his real condition. That proud "and yet!" in spite of everything. "Haven't you noticed it?" I asked with amazement. And I went on: "Kulesza, our era is inhuman, because it has deprived man of the possibilities of heroism. Only sport remains now and an occasional saving of those who are drowning. No one knows how to behave any more."

Monument—opera house. Monument—horse. A heat, dear friends, beyond all imagining. Kulesza continues talking about unhappiness. For him, heroism contains some indecent reward of a sacrifice fulfilled.

"Listen," he says, "a really miserable man is naked and dumb. Didn't you ever experience this? Imagine a moment when you stop being the hub of the world and begin to feel like a speck. No one has ever described it. And anyway, it is not a subject for literature. One does not write about it; one wants to condemn to death for it. You can't imagine how many people I have executed for that arm of mine."

"Kulesza," I say, "you must be very unhappy."

And he: "I have abandoned the stage. I began to fight."

I: "I don't understand."

He: "It is quite simple. Happy people create a drama for themselves, unhappy ones — a drama for others. In the second instance, it is best to fight for a new era. You would never guess what I am carrying in this briefcase. It seems an ordinary briefcase with its strap, but it contains most important resolutions. When they are passed, you will have to do some explaining. If nothing worse . . ."

I became quite hot under the collar and said: "But Kulesza, I am . . ."

"What you are," interrupted Kulesza, "no one knows. One must first create a new era, and only then will we see what you were. The new era will assess you in retrospect. Only now do we know what the rider was; during his lifetime he was a question mark. The same applies to you, my dear. Everything you will say about yourself in today's speech will be phony. In a hundred years, history will judge you. There are no criterions in space — they exist only in time. Good day."

"It is not true!" I shouted. "It's a lie!"

Ladies and gentlemen, I reeled; the sun pressed on my head like a helmet. Kulesza was walking away, becoming smaller and smaller; he disappeared and still I was shouting beside the monument that I was myself and was becoming myself all the time, that I made choices in great uncertainty, that this was my great suffering in which I was slowly perfecting myself, and that each of us had his withered arm which he could not use as he would like.

Ladies and gentlemen, I don't wonder that there are so few of you left — it is very late. Time for summing up. We can't very well disperse without reaching any conclusions. To be frank, I have nothing more to say. Please think about me, dear friends. Perhaps I have forgotten something. I am sure I must have. But all the same, think about it, consider carefully who I am; handle with fairness that sum of truth about myself which I have presented here.

Well, this is the end. Full lights, please! The final presentation of all the principal participants in my personality. You will remember the hat with ostrich feathers? Yes, here she is: on her old, wrinkled palm rests Max with stiff legs and open beak. They stand on my right — on the side of the hand with which I stole the sugar from the cage. Next come three men. Do you recognize Caspar, the commercial traveler, and the man in the hood? It's I in a triple image, and none is true. Then comes the band with the music master, companies with standards flying; wrongly accused, I wave my school hat from the pavement (dear friends, one must always show sympathy to marching soldiers). And now, room please for my brother-in-law. A characteristic episode: as you will remember, he behaved like a hero; only a week later did he reveal himself as a coward. Who comes next? The familiar squeak of box-calf shoes reminds me of a near relation. Ah yes, here they are! A double smell of hair cream, two bow ties, two white Panama hats: my father and his friend; and between them, I in my boy scout's hat. Be on guard, friend! It might be tactful if you would repeat it in chorus . . . Alas — not a sound . . . Forgive me, I hear a whisper; thank you very much. Let's continue. You can see me now as Desdemona and as Othello. On either side of me, a blonde and a brunette: rather a frivolous scene, I'm afraid. I hope I have not disappointed you. Anyway, you should have seen these two in action. Now it's the turn of booksellers, carrying my works: yes, *The Dog's Paw* and *Buried Cities* . . . Please put them here before me with their spines toward the hall. Then *Vasa — Pole or Swede?, The Stone Swan* and other works. That, I think, is all.

One moment, though: there is Kulesza. Kulesza is always the trouble. Just imagine this: he has refused the invitation, which was natural, as I did not expect anything else of him. But he sent me a camel. Can you see the rider between the humps? In the fez askew I look quite interesting, suitably posed for *Globe* magazine, the outline of the Pyramids in the background. That, dear friends, is definitely all. It is time for a moment's silence.

Thank you. That's all. Ladies and gentlemen, a few more years will pass, but nothing more is likely to be added. In these few years which are left to me, I should like to complete my work. The work of becoming myself in spite of you. It is impudence, I know, but this is what I want. To face you with a *fait accompli*. It will be a real satisfaction for me when your conjectures and opinions, your tattle and accusations, slip from the smooth, hard form which I shall create. Metaphorically, of course. Yet I shall lean over you, and on a hot August noonday I shall throw my shadow at your feet. You will look up and see a fat old man in a tight jacket. He will smile at you slyly, sentimentally and somewhat sheepishly. He will be like our world, like our lives — like us. Lots of pathetically practical risks taken, some nerves, tiredness after walking in the street and a pinch of faith saved, dipped in vulgar fear. You will be moved and proud that I have resisted you so well. Oh, dear friends, this brave operator — it's I.

I beg your pardon. I see that the hall is empty. This means that no one has heard my last words . . . Perhaps it is better so. I have spoken too long, and I should have kept silent about certain things. Not to show too much feeling and not to expect too much — this is the basis of a rational upbringing. What's this? Are the lights going out? Ladies and gentlemen, has everybody gone? Is there no one left but myself? It seems to have got much cooler now, and yet I am very tired.

Excuse me, but who are you? I can't hear you, but I am delighted that you wanted to stay to the end. Have I understood you correctly? You are representing the fire service? I see that you are performing your duties better than I. Sergeant, tell me frankly: what do you think of my address? I must admit that I feel slightly disgusted with it. I have been too original, and this is not in character. To destroy ceremonial one must have a special license from nature, and I haven't got it. I have made myself ridiculous — there is no getting away from it; I shan't sleep again tonight. I have surrendered myself to them, instead of just saying a few words. Sergeant, make a note of this: your duties should consist not only in guarding the hall against an outbreak of fire; you must also watch that smokers should exhale in the normal way — through the mouth or the nose, and not put out the cigarettes against their own breasts. Listen now, this is what my speech should have been:

"Dear friends, dear Minister. At the end of my wandering, it is good to look back. One can see the road one has covered and assess the direction chosen. Without false modesty, I can confess today that you have been good companions on my journey. Your severe criticism, although sometimes it wounded me painfully, made me realize my shortcomings; you were always able to reward injustice with magnanimity; but most important of all has been for me the realization that we are bound together by a common destiny and — in times of good fortune and bad, in sunshine and in rain — we are moving forward together. Today, after forty years of labor, I can proudly say that I am no different from you — that I am one of you."

Do you know, Sergeant, that this would have been the truth? What a strange night this has been . . . But it is all over now. You may take off your helmet.

— *translated by* Celina Wieniewska

(From *Romantycznosc,* short stories. Published by "Czytelnik," Warsaw, 1960.)

Ando

(*Fragment*)

BY Stanislaw Czycz

Stanislaw Czycz is, in his early twenties, one of the youngest newcomers on the Polish literary scene. The short story from which an excerpt follows created a stir in Warsaw literary circles in the spring of 1961 because of its subject matter. Obviously autobiographical, the story is about a trip which two young poets make to an all-Polish writers' congress. Those in Poland officially responsible for such gatherings were disturbed by the grotesque, almost macabre picture the author gives of the occasion – the more so since the tragic end of the story, the sudden death (suicide is implied) of Ando, the author's friend, proved to be a fact. The selected fragment typifies the deep cleavage which exists in the minds of some young Polish (and not only Polish) writers between the "surface world" of art and love and the "submerged city" of daily toil and primitive instinct. Jaroslaw Iwaszkiewicz (see "Sweet Flag" in this book), editor in chief of *Tworczosc* which originally published the work, had the following to say about it: "In Czycz's story, deadly in its sincerity, we find the unadulterated flavor of young life. Self-consciousness, here, becomes absurdity; these young men not only are ashamed of displaying the slightest emotion, but are hiding their intellectual interests behind masks of cynicism and sarcasm. . . . The deserts and spiritual wastelands of Mauriac's characters are harmless compared to the drought that sears these youngsters."

(The two friends, returning from the Congress, are waiting at a railway junction for their train home.)

We walked down from the platform; it was a little warmer in the tunnels and passages under the tracks; there was also, down there, a sort of hall, perhaps a waiting room; I remember some wooden benches, set perhaps against the walls of the passages and people sitting on them, and other people passing slowly by, people for the most part dirty and shabbily dressed; and two women, begging perhaps, but more likely whores, walking up and down one of the passages;

this underground maze at a main station in the center of the mining district suddenly seemed to me to be an entrance to a mine, a mine which we will never leave; one of the passages, I thought, will lead us to the coal face, or perhaps blasting will uncover coal in one of the walls, or show a locomotive sinking into the depths at the moment of detonation, or a whole train shattered into pieces of coal, and these people sitting on the benches will be startled into activity and we, too, with them, will throw ourselves at that coal; but now we still have a moment to while away, a moment of rest on the journey, and if we are waiting for a train it will have been that one;

or perhaps the mine is lower down; on our level there is no coal; coal is deeper down, but not much deeper, and one can in fact reach it by walking down one of the passages, perhaps the one where we are; it seems to be on a slope; we are walking along slowly, but we should be walking slower still, to prolong the moment of rest; moreover, we are not yet quite sober, so we move slowly, slowly; in one of the two or three underground kiosks Ando bought some cheese rolls, we must eat them calmly and walk without hurry, to have some strength for work;

and there is almost joy that we have arrived, that the very long, very tiring journey — and I am not thinking only of the last three days at the Congress (Ha, ha; of course. Wait: I had been very tired, so I can indulge in pathos. Besides, what of it? What of it, you clot?) — the long journey is over; there is at last the harsh — and we were longing for it, we were longing for something like it and this in fact is a good thing — the harsh quietening, calm. And joy that we have reached our destination and that nothing awaits us but work and later a return here, to this underground city; yes, because this is not a waiting room, but a city; and we shall later return here together with those people; together with them we shall rest, sitting on the benches or walking about the underground streets; they are here, I can see them, there are quite a few of them; yes, and none of them, not a single one, is trying to get out of here,

as if not only they could not — and they are sure to know about it just as we do; we now belong to them — as if not only they could not but did not wish to get out;

since that underground city is more real,

more real than the other ones, on the surface — if any of those people makes the effort to remember or, if remembering, he compares;

real; its lights have nothing of the illusory brightness of those surface days; there are no speckled greens, no peacock sunrises, which, in the final event, are only a mockery;

those lamps in the low ceiling shed a stern, utilitarian light. That man who passes us with his head bent slightly forward is not hurrying, and cannot be driven to walk faster by any thought of anything or anybody awaiting him; for even if such a thing existed, he has no imagination which would extend that thing or person beyond its proper, real limits; no, nothing much drives him; he can walk calmly, without hurry; but these two women, for example — and here probably no one has any other, artificial interests — these two, whom I saw, and as in any other city there are probably more of them (Ando had begun to talk to me about women and had said that one does not know whether they really exist; so even if there were no more of them here, and those two I am certain to have seen, this would be a fair number; it's quite possible that there, in those surface cities, there are not many more of them — Ando, I still think is wrong, he has not yet convinced me — not many more because, even in large cities at a given single moment I could only see at the same time, see clearly, that is, no more than ten, "an illusion," Ando repeats, "an illusion, they don't exist and have never existed," no more than ten, I think, and if later, in a subsequent moment, I again saw one or two, perhaps even spoke to one, I could not prove that she was different, that she was not one from among the ten, no, I could never maintain with certainty that there were many more), these two women — colorless, expressionless features, stultified eyes, crumpled-looking faces — looking at their legs, their breasts, hands, necks, I thought that all this was a perfect negation of that of which people on the surface try to convince themselves, and in their belief it is not the exterior that matters, for I had seen beautiful faces there, some with tender and some with wise expressions, bodies harmoniously built, as if pride or nobility or both had shaped their perfect form (ha, ha; all right: he he) — well then, it is not the exterior that matters, but the assumptions about the inner side, about the essence, all those sublime, enchanting fantasies spun at the sight of a façade, and how many, there on the surface, how many tragedies occur because of the gilded frame of a miserable picture, because of a sudden disclosure of something quite paltry under the splendor of gilt, there on the surface which similarly is framed in a false, misleading glitter; the faces, hands or necks of the two women I saw here cannot suggest anything unreal, even if anyone in this underground city had suddenly a wish to look a little lower or a little higher than the spot which contains all their essence — aha, getting satirical, a dash of social satire, what? — no, angel face,

no satire: I don't wish to achieve anything by it, even forgetting that tiredness which I might have exaggerated; yet I repeat it now, perhaps still tired, but differently so, and not really *very* tired — I don't wish to achieve anything. I had looked, I had felt; but I bear no grudge. And this here, even if it were not a repetition of the thoughts I had during tiredness, is not sarcasm; nor is it youthful anger.

No satire; and if I had groveled before a tart (Oh yes, there are things I have written about these matters, texts more than religious. No, they were not insincere), if I had groveled before a tart and if I should continue to do so — and I know I shall — it is not because, ha ha, because I suddenly will forget (I, my consciousness, my sober thoughts — which I won't obey, although they will be there), because I will think that now, this time, the picture will be different (Repaired perhaps, eh? And who was the repairer?). I said: I am not thinking about repairs;

and I need not deal with this here, for I have told myself — with calm — a misleading frame, a façade: a beautiful body, looks and smiles, even certain words — pseudowise and pseudotender, a whole behavior; admittedly it is pleasant, it has its value;

but only an external value of a façade; and why should this façade suddenly suggest sublime thoughts, brightly golden structures, superimpositions onto the one misleading frame of another, more gilded and — despite all subtleties — very heavy; heavy even for the picture and threatening to damage it — should there be anything to damage?

But, as I have said, oh, my friend, as I have said: I could occupy myself with it and not ponder so much over it; but here, in this business with Ando, what matters among other things, mainly perhaps, are such or very similar frames; and similar is the whole cycle from, first, perceiving, then a slight, warm at first, play of imagination, through an obscure, for me, contrary to all common sense and at long last completely absorbing impulse to build or rather to build onto, reality, until the moment when this begins to crush its creator,

although before (often much too late) there can be attempts — hysterical, alas — attempts at escape, at freeing oneself from the structure; it was to have been a game, it was to have given pleasure (exactly, as I have said at the very beginning — not about Ando, about myself — that I am in it, within the frame of art, I am still within); and the similarity of art to the other frame, with tarts, no, not the similarity, the difference sometimes completely stuns me; for those, the others, the frames of art surpass even the most madly gilded frames of sexuality, not having — like the first — any natural source; that's just it: fantasies spun only from fantasy; the frames are empty; their creators become in the last resort only frames; they are nothing but frames;

a glistening devastation which, hollowing out, builds luminous surroundings of hollows, devastation born from desolation, from the glistening of previous hollows; an unbroken, continuing and even regulated madness, having its own, constantly improved conventions, madness or, simply, as our fathers would say, chasing one's own tail.

What? Exactly: this throws you. Ha, ha.

And at first, at the very beginning, the creator thinks that this, that madness, these frames, that these frames are serving him, are subjected to his authority; since he had made them himself, yes, since they had come into being by his own small, perhaps even unconscious effort, they are, he believes, his own light framework,

and later when the framework begins to absorb him and when he tries to escape from it, or from the frames, he at the same time never stops gilding them; he hates to lose them while all the time doubting whether he can ever escape them, and this doubt only increases his ardor for gilding; he reasons that as he cannot get out and, without realizing it, increases his doubt, broadens it, for it is sweet, his whole thinking precedes himself, is only a frame; and now he is not unable to think differently, but he does not wish to do so; so, if he cannot get out, let the thing within which he is stuck (and within which he will die, and die in a ridiculous way: as a frame — my comment, ha, ha, ha), let the thing he's stuck in be something really splendid — a doubting extrication and a simultaneous, sometimes secret gilding.

Ando — these two frames — Ando has already reached the stage of getting out and perhaps even of having shed those secret gildings.

Ah well. Let's go back. One moment. Have I been chasing my own tail? Yes, quite clearly. But I wanted to. Yes, I wanted to chase my own tail. I have quite mastered the art. For how can one speak about chasing one's own tail without actually doing so? Ha, ha. Yes. Let's go back. Let's go back to lyrical reminiscences.

Those hands — I thought — faces or necks of the women I saw here underground cannot suggest anything unreal to anyone — even if someone in this underground city had a sudden wish to look a little lower or higher than the spot in which their essence is contained — nothing unreal, therefore no fever or madness; one need not hurry when going to meet any of them; one can think calmly that even if she is not there, even if she is busy with someone else, one will just have to wait a little, and the thing one is going to get will take place a little later; one need not hurry even when one knows that being late would prevent a meeting.

"But you have a wife," I say to Ando; "You had a wife," I correct myself, for this had been on the surface, and we are not going back there. At the same time I think: these two women; what I have seen is a complete revelation, not only a revelation made by nature itself, for I have seen their looks and their behavior, and this had nothing artificial, nothing to remind one of those women on the surface, nothing of those deceiving trappings of whorishness common to all women; I am thinking this, and I also remember the impression at the moment when I saw these two, a sudden and unique impression: something owl-like, at the same time some filminess, as if the membranous wings of a bat had touched my face; I felt their cool stickiness — and an engulfing wave of sleep — with a prolonged thrill of rapture — sleep induced by the touch of mobile warm pelts; "You had a wife and son";

"Yes," says Ando, "I think I had; it seems to me that I had; and I thought before that I still have";

the passage comes to an end, and we turn back, then we enter another one: people are sitting on benches and walking about, again a

his pay as a syndic, but gives it to the poor as soon as he receives it. I got to know him last year at a conference of burgomasters, presidents of capitals, chairmen of metropolitan town councils, and syndics, which he organized in Florence.

The conference was closed with a Mass for peace, said by Cardinal Della Costa, after which, to the chagrin of all right-thinking people, the cardinal exchanged greetings with the comrade president of the Moscow City Soviet, a similar comrade from Prague, and Comrade Bogomolov, Soviet ambassador to Rome. It was to this incident that the right-wing Catholic illustrated weekly *Oggi* alluded a few days later. On its front page it printed a large photograph of the Pope in Castel Gandolfo, speaking to his flock, and after the explanatory text it added the following reflections: "A scene full of poetry and purity, enabling one to sober up and draw a pure breath after the recently published photographs of a high dignitary of the Church involved in incidents painful to Catholic susceptibilities."

L. says that some people suspect La Pira of common snobbery. But if it is snobbery, it is certainly not common. But L. himself does not think this. Though he is spiteful and gets a kick out of repeating these insinuations, he hasn't the least doubt that he is spreading a faulty diagnosis. La Pira loves wanderers. He loves them "because without love there can be no conversion." Only after liberating it in oneself, so that a constant and definite emotional state is reached, can one effectively weed out the evil and sow new seed. Love should grow stronger as it meets with strongly reinforced evil, when it has to deal with a dominating and leading error. Communism is just this leading and reinforced error. In La Pira's philosophy, which at one time was accepted by the entire group, it is the *ultimate* form of error.

"The error is theirs; the guilt is ours." This classic formula was often repeated in the columns of *Cronache Sociali*, the *professorini's* theoretical journal, which was published from the day of the Liberation until 1951. "The error is that of the Marxists; the responsibility for the error falls on the Christians" is a variant of the same formula. "Through communism God is passing judgment on His Church, or rather on His Christianity." As he relates the formula, Father L. reminds me that this is an exact replica of the opinion of Bossuet, who said of the Reformation that it expressed "God's judgment on His Church." Having this conception of the chief and dominant error of his age, Bossuet also "loved and all his life sought an understanding with Protestantism, at the same time keeping the Catholic faith clear from error." The *professorini* were also fond of quoting Berdyaev's opinion of communism: that it is a "testimony to Christianity's unfulfilled obligation and unexecuted task."

But closest of all to their thinking is Pius XI's painful accusation that "the great tragedy of the Church in the nineteenth century consisted in the Church having lost the working class in that century." The working class "did not remain long in a state of indecision, but soon turned to the antithesis of the Church, namely, to communism." This profound, fundamental sense of guilt filled the hearts of the *professorini* to overflowing with diffidence and shame whenever they had to examine the question of Communists within their own consciences. This premise in its philosophic and historical and sentimental aspects has been preserved to this day in the tone in which La Pira addresses himself to the Communists and whenever he speaks of communism.

The *professorini* read Mounier and Maritain and were inclined to be anti-*petit bourgeois* and anticapitalist. But they were fundamentally different from the French because of their "integralism." Ontologically considered, they erased the differences between the world and the Church. Pius X's doctrine, according to which the world needed the Church just as much as the Church needed the world as the object of its activity, was alien to them. Their ideal was for the Church and the world to be one and the same. Their proposition was that the world should be entirely absorbed by the Church, and the Church should continue its penetration until it had absorbed the world completely.

L. declares that just as Giorgio La Pira was ready to love the Communists because they were the victims of errors committed by the Church, so Professor Giuseppe Dossetti was ready to love the *petite bourgeoisie* and the capitalists because they, too, had in a sense become denaturalized as the result of the Church's lack of control. Capitalism on the one hand, communism on the other, are the right and left wings of one and the same heresy. They will vanish from the face of the earth when the Church permeates the world integrally.

It is absolutely essential to the understanding of this problem to comprehend the profound contrast between the Catholic activists who developed their political and world outlook before the advent of fascism, and those who developed during its existence. For instance, this conveys the difference between de Gasperi and Gronchi on the one hand and La

Pira and Dossetti on the other. The first have the classic nineteenth-century *petit bourgeois* democratic spirit. The second were molded intellectually in an age of directed societies, in an age which recognized no division between society and ideology, in an age of integralist ideologies. None the less, without going into various biographical details, especially where Fanfani is concerned, the *professorini* were, after all, anti-Fascist.

Ignoring the various deviations, their journals are standard Catholic products of antitotalitarian propaganda and essay writing. But one cannot resist the suspicion that the *professorini* group would not have held to their integralism with such characteristic intellectual force if they had sought inspiration for their social philosophy solely and exclusively in St. Thomas Aquinas and St. Augustine, and not also in an incompletely suppressed complaisance with what in Dossetti's language was called "the good side of every error," in this case Italian fascism. At the end of the conversation I remarked, "And so, to make use of the Dossetti metaphor, the *professorini's* integralism and fascism would be the right and left side of the selfsame error." Father L. laughed.

And so as not to be behind with a joke, he told me two amusing trivial anecdotes about La Pira. One is related to the fact that La Pira always has very well-cut clothes. A great Florentine tailor, formerly an unbeliever, whom La Pira converted, dresses him free of charge. The other anecdote concerns the baskets of sweets which La Pira sends every holy day to the city nurseries and orphanages charged to the city municipal authorities. At first a little prayer for the head of the city was attached to every basket. But the socialist councilors, who formed part of the city council's majority, objected.

Fiuggi
June 20, 1956

Another long talk with Father L. about Dossetti. He brought me his photograph from a recent issue of *L'Espresso*. A narrow, ascetic face. Black, mournful eyes, baggy. A thin nose, thin lips, withered, accustomed to spasmodic, pleasant smiles. The lips of an old nun used to faint, colorless smiles. He started the movement or attitude calling itself Dossettism. The movement has faded out; it has passed away like so many other Italian Catholic movements attempting to uproot nonconformism and withering through their too close proximity to the Vatican.

Possibly ever since the days of Galileo, the Vatican has never had any need to break anyone in Italy. It smothers everything at birth. It calls to order in a whisper. And before the movement, the man, or the thought really matures to the point of disobedience it is blown away, it passes from the scene, it loses all actuality. Here everything is too much in the public eye.

The case of Giuseppe Dossetti is particularly bitter. He set out proudly to remold the Christian Democratic party from within. He reached high rank in that organization, the position of deputy secretary general. He was not a camp follower; he marched in the ranks. And he continued to do so until 1952, in which year a whisper reached his ears, recalling him into the shadows. And he slipped back into the shadows. Four years later he returned as a newborn, declaring that he remembered nothing of his past and there was nothing connecting him with it. In Bologna it is known that during the two months before this new birth he had a number of meetings with the archbishop of Bologna, Cardinal Lercaro. He listened to him, and took on a duel with Dozza, the Red mayor of Bologna. He went into the fight as Dossetti, yet not as Dossetti. He gave it his name and himself too, but completely gutted of its former content; the epigone of his movement and, as he was even called, "the worst of his own epigones." And to make matters worse, he lost the fight. They say in Bologna that there is one chance in ten of conquering the Communist Dozza. But if anyone can conquer him, it is only the devout, standard Christian anticapitalist, filled with contrition toward the world of labor. The operation was not successful.

What a thicket there is of psychological and moral problems here! Father L. says that inwardly Dossetti has not changed his views. That he even obtained from Lercara a placet to face his electors in the armament of his former world outlook. He obtained agreement to this for the period of his pre-electoral activity. But only for then. Later on, if he had become mayor, he would have been forced to put into effect the program of the Christian Democrats' right wing. So he chose another possibility. He presented himself in a reactionary guise and as reconciled with great industry, the financial world, and the great landlords. For this L. admires him. "Because," he says, "he didn't wish to lie to the people." Apparently L. considers that in this instance it is more moral to lie to oneself. To break, to flee from oneself for a period imposed from above. Sometimes for all one's lifetime.

Father L. not only brought me the issue of *L'Espresso* with Dossetti's portrait, but some issues of *Cronache Sociali*. This was the journal of the group. It ceased publication in 1951. L. ferreted out these copies in the library, and when I told him I would return them to him tomorrow or the next day, he waved his hand unconcernedly. Nobody needs these things in Villino Santa Chiara. Neither Cardinal Lercaro's article, "The Shameful Agony of the Church," nor Giorgio La Pira's essay, "The Defense of the Poor People," nor any extracts from Huizinga, whether from his *Crisis of Civilization* or his *Martyrdom of the World*.

From an article by E. Dirks, "On Marxism and Christianity," I read aloud one long sentence: "A hundred years ago, when the proletariats grew self-conscious, one cannot say that they renounced Christ, rather must one say that Christ ceased to be a reality, visible and comprehensible to them; they would return to Him, but only through the mediation of Christians who would agree to share the proletariats' fate, their anxieties and their needs." And again: "But no one sacrificed himself. No Christian from higher spheres did so; not one eminent individual succeeded in breaking out of the *petit bourgeois* circle in which he lived. And so Christ remained invisible."

This ended my conversation with Father L. concerning Dossetti.

— *translated by* HARRY STEVENS

(From *Spizowa Brama*. Published by "Czytelnik," Warsaw, 1960.)

The Last Man on the Arena

A Roman Story

BY HANNA MALEWSKA

HANNA MALEWSKA was born in 1911 in Grodzisk, near Warsaw. The daughter of a physician, she took her degree in history in 1933, and in 1937 published her first historical novel, *The Iron Cross*. Her writing career was halted by the war, during which she was active in the Polish Underground and took part in the Warsaw Uprising in 1944. Since then the following have been published: *The Stones Will Shout* (1946);

Harvest on the Sickle (a biography of C. K. Norwid, a Polish romantic poet); *The World Passes* (1955); *Sir Thomas Moore Refuses,* five stories – one of which is in this book (1956); *The Tale of the Seven Wizards* (1959); *The Squires Leszczynski* (1961). This last novel is a panoramic view of eighteenth-century Poland as seen by the modern mind. Since 1945, Hanna Malewska has been a contributor to *Tygodnik Powszechny* and is editor in chief of *Znak,* both Catholic periodicals. She lives in Krakow.

"Illuxit nobis," sang a man who had naked, muscular arms. Almach, the monk, shoved hard against him, felt as though he had struck a tree. The man did not even notice the collision. His face wore a stupefied look, while his fist beat on his chest every now and then.

For the first time in his life, Almach felt not only similar to, but exactly like, all the other people, although they did not speak his native Greek. It seemed to him that what he himself had sought in the desert, and later in the monastery of Soracte, others had learned in the world as well, at least those whom one saw on the streets of Rome, whom great wealth had not separated like lepers from the rest. Because who serves, if not mothers? Who obeys, if not those who toil for their children? And young lovers forget themselves like nesting birds in spring. The world is composed mostly of mothers and fathers. Those who obey include also children, pupils; those who serve — clerks, sailors. Sailors love their ship, as Almach had witnessed during his one sea voyage. Was not the world created so that people could love while obeying? The devil was not its author. The world was good. Why was it bad at the same time?

Countless feet clattered and scraped against the pavement. Heads raised upward, eyes staring beyond the roof ledges. It seemed as if but one face were turned towards the Father.

Et illuxit nobis. Yes, He showed us the light and we are going to Him, unknowing and enslaved, divided and exhausted in our lives of service.

Next to him, a woman sobbing like Mary of Magdala lifted her arms, as though, having squandered human love, she was now holding up an empty cup for the wine from the Cross.

Almach felt that somehow everything had been set right. He prayed for Alypius, the city's prefect, for the bishop, for Quincius, the wealthy Roman, and for the prior, seeing all of them in the athlete with hard limbs who sang like a bear and who beat his chest as if it were a shield. He even saw himself in this athlete, although he barely reached up to his shoulder. And his wretched body seemed to possess an equally restless and frightened spirit.

At that moment he noticed that he had floated with the crowd into a large patch of cooling shade.

Instead of the sky, the walls of an enormous amphitheater now towered like Mount Sinai over his head. But he was not in Judea; he was in Rome. The people around him were no longer singing or praying; they pushed ahead, crowding through a high arcade but so narrow that it suggested a wasp's nest under a cliff. The amphitheater, to Almach, was a sanctified place; martyrs had died here. Once before, long ago, he had dreamed in his hermitage of traveling to Rome and kissing the holy sand of the Colosseum.

Suddenly he noticed a straw-haired Syrian girl — who a moment ago had been reciting the Scriptures after him — reach into a net at her waist and pull out a tambourine. As she lifted it over her head he started back violently. But, as in a dream, he could not move — there was no free space to move into. He had seen three such women before. Each time they would, first lazily, almost unwillingly, begin by stroking their little drums; later it was as though a fire had swept over them.

The monk felt a flash of horror. What if this were a procession of pagans and he himself had been possessed by the devil? Then he understood: the procession was over, and now the participants were hurrying to the circus. Were they the same people?

He was being carried along through the gate, unable to come out of his trance. The arch was decorated with heavily perfumed garlands, and on the other side one could hear the murmur of excited human swarms.

"Will you be in it today, you there, Croton from across the Tiber?" someone shouted over the monk's head. The athlete's bass voice answered slowly and somehow sadly, "God permitting, I will."

Almach could not leave now; never in his life was he able to retreat when such words as "God permitting" were uttered in his presence.

Behind him the crowd pushed harder, blindly, like thirsty cattle running to a water hole. They were late and impatient. The guard at the entrance had been thrown back against the wall, and the monk found himself raised off the ground so high his head barely missed the vault. The huge bright sun of the circus blinded him, yet by the hardness of the arm and the bass voice he recognized who it was that saved him from being trampled.

"Thank you," he whispered, as he wiped his neck that had been touched by the sweaty, hairy arm of the athlete from across the Tiber.

People were crowding into the gateway under the loges. Almach's eyes no longer blinked in the glare. Two women pushed forward waving their arms. He saw them: mother and daughter. They radiated obscene, sinful heat. Their faces were not those of prostitutes, but their nostrils trembled and their movements were like a shameless dance; he found himself drawn into this dance; and there was no escape for him. The athlete, who could be seen above the crowd, cleared the way for himself with his fists. People stepped aside, swearing.

A cool cave. In front of it three palm trees and then nothing — a desert. O God, why had he left it? God was like the horizon; His gaze was like the gaze of the sun; His ear was in the cave; He watched like the stars over the pure palms, the sands and the panthers.

Woe to Almach's vagabond spirit that had seduced him away from there.

"There's room for all of us." A quiet voice amidst the general shouting sobered him up. A little room was made for him on the bench by a man with a face burned by the sun, an old face, but without wrinkles. Almach wiped the sweat, and drew together his torn habit, which had caught on a hook at the entrance. The sun-bronzed man beside him wore the clothes of a wealthy freeman. In him the monk did not notice either contagious fear or the heat of excitement.

Only after sitting down did he realize how weak he felt, but he was no longer dreaming; he was really there.

And more people were there than he had ever seen before at one time in one place. Ascetics, who are prone to visions, must view the Last Judgment in this way. But this was no vision. The amphitheater, on its shaded side, displayed heads and more heads, close together; here in the sun, shoulder was pressed against shoulder, row after row, all the way down to the sand of the arena. The sand was empty, smooth, glaring. Fences in the center marked a square; another fence enclosed a small area in front of the loges. Inside and outside the fences, the surface was raked lightly, like sand on a beach made smooth by the wind; the footprints of the martyrs were effaced beyond recall. Almach sat now on a bench in the sun of Rome, with all Romans having but one face, shiny with sweat, quivering with laughter — just one face, strange, belonging to nobody. It occurred to him that the coarse laughter united deadly enemies whom everything else divided. He raised his hand to make the sign of the Cross over the nightmare, but was unable to complete it. It seemed as if Christ had not been born under Augustus Caesar, and had not suffered under Pontius Pilate.

Then, on the balcony of the loge which, decorated with oak leaves, dominated the others, he saw entering a man in red robes. He was the Prefect Alypius. The crowd rose with a cheer for Caesar's delegate. Alypius waved his thanks and took a seat. Almach, whose eyes had been sharpened by distance and not dulled by books, watched him hungrily; the sight of the man somehow sobered him; after all, Alypius was not a figment of the devil.

Applause rolled along the benches. Speeding on the outside track of the arena were a number of carts pulled by ponies, trailing clouds of dust behind them. Each held a cage with speckled animals, writhing and whirling on their chains. As far as he could see, they were not panthers, only various minor creatures, tormented and furious, howling, barking so fiercely that several women squealed with fright.

A youth seated close by let out a shrill whistle and kicked a girl whose hands were clamped over her ears. He turned around, grinning, and settled back in his seat more comfortably, like a schoolboy proud of his prank.

"Psst" — a murmur ran through the crowd.

In the arena Almach saw a group of men, about the number of a small patrol of soldiers, marching toward the prefect's loge. They were almost naked, like legionaries on a journey, wearing short red tunics that left the right side of their chests uncovered. They were armed lightly. Fair and dark bodies, blond and black heads, all men equal in age and height, handsome, with smooth faces. The crowd stared, hypnotized. "Ah!" came a collective sigh. In front of the main loge they raised their right arms, glistening with oil. They were so well disciplined, and at the same time so proud, that the crowd felt humble at their sight. They reminded Almach of the brave sailors he had admired on his sea voyage; he wondered at their strength and joyous efficiency; he felt as if he had never really known people before.

But could one know people? . . . Both the spectators, massed like black lava, and the armed men, straight as a taut rope, were so separate, so cut off, that there was no way of knowing them. And yet since they had walked together an hour ago, invoking God the Father, he could not tell them, "I don't know you." Horrified, bewildered, unable to separate his cause from theirs, he was falling with them into crime, as into a bad dream. Because, even if the swordsmen killed only leopards, or fought each other only for fun, fighting like panthers and leopards, they became like them. And the beauty of a panther is not human beauty.

"Why have you come here?" the man with the bronze face asked sharply. He must have been a gladiator at one time. "You monks have no women, so maybe this is how you please yourself?"

Almach was sinking. In his hermitage he had heard about Rome — and that they still had a circus, as in Nero's time. It had not meant much to him then; true, old men showered threats of the Apocalypse on Rome — terrible threats, but not effective till the end of the world came.

He still saw in his mind's eye "his" sailors and soldiers who had fought off and captured the pirates at the shores of Syrta. Nobody indolent or cowardly could have saved that ship. Even in the everyday routine, as they handled the sails, there was great beauty about the sailors.

A shiver ran through Almach. His eyes and mouth opened wide. The whole amphitheater rose to its feet and thundered with one voice. A deafening, repeated chorus cry, such as the monk had never heard before. He did not understand the words. There was wonder in them and adoration, fear and passion, rapacity and love. He jumped, as if someone had carried him, onto the ledge of a higher bench and looked down. What brilliance of steel and copper! New men had entered the arena — one by one, not in formation. There must have been about ten of them, all heavily armed, all covered with glimmering scales, only their right arms and knees bare.

One after the other they paraded in front of the prefect, carelessly raising their right arms, saying something that could not be heard over the fanfare. New men, a different greeting. Caesar himself does not get such a reception. They never even looked at the crowds prostrate at their feet in rapture. Almach strained his eyes and saw, or rather guessed, the faces under the shallow helmets — and then he realized that it was true. They were the gladiators. They fought till death. This was what everyone had come here to see.

Pulled down to his seat where he could not see much of the arena because of his smallness, the monk saw something else instead: a street in Antioch where, on his way to school, every day he passed the yellow barracks of the gladiators. And so he had always known that they existed, yet he had been as blind as the crowd here was.

With a noise resembling the roar of waves over a rock, the thousands sat down again, their eyes still feasting on the gladiators. They called their names — the name of Melittus was heard most often, but not one of the athletes acknowledged the tribute.

Oh, no, the crowd here was not blind and did not wish to be blind. They wanted to see everything; perhaps, not necessarily death, but all that of which life is capable.

"It's not true," whispered Almach. He watched the gladiators walk away with vigorous steps and disappear into the shadow of the decorated gate behind the prefect's loge. Wire cages were placed between the fences in the middle of the arena, and on the outside animals on carts were being brought in. First the crowds had to be stimulated by animal blood — only then the men would return. The ex-gladiator seated next to the monk was gazing at the garlanded gate, paying no attention to the animals. "It's not true!" the monk wanted to tell him, but he somehow no longer knew what he meant. Prefect Alypius got up and raised the *mappa.*

"Oh Savior, who art not here . . ." Together with the veteran and the prefect, Almach felt the slow, pulsating chill of waiting. And with each throb reality entered into him, the undeniable reality of all that was going on, and still to come. Gladiators, the most admired of all the beautiful young men in the world, courageous young men, as useful as sailors during a storm and soldiers against the enemy hordes . . . What if people wanted to watch bravery and death? It delighted them more than the pantomimes. Even the frightened ones, ashamed of their cowardice, even those who find their senses so aroused that at Easter time they must confess to impurity — they all come here. Reality. People, and Almach one of them. Why then were his lips repeating, "It is not true"? Did he not feel this morning like everyone else? The only difference, perhaps, was that he had followed Him longer — Him who was not here.

Again Almach jumped to his feet. It was as if, drowning, he had touched bottom and was now starting up. All his life, he had shared in this crime, until he had been dragged here and thrown into the depths.

Oblivious of the cursing spectators around him, he began pushing his way out, not toward the exit, but in the direction of the main loge. He did not hear the howling of the desert beasts released from their cages, running around the arena in their deathly race. Well, it was for this that he had left his three palm trees and boarded a ship. It was for this that he had walked under the Cross with the same circus crowd, all of them equally guilty of murder, with the exception, perhaps, of the Prefect Alypius.

Toward him, toward the prefect, was Almach, the monk, pushing on with all his strength now. From the moment he got up and began to struggle with every forward step, the circus and the gladiators lost their resemblance to a ship and sailors, to any God-created reality. But if they were but a trick of the Enemy, so inhuman a fraud could be exposed. And the man toward whom the monk strove, the man who did not know Palm Sunday, and thus could not have known Good Friday, could be the first man whose eyes would open.

Now Almach saw him quite close — a person in red, representing authority. Pagan, and the son of a pagan, but human.

Meanwhile, things were happening in the arena. The crowd shouted and whistled; the game of death had now caught up with the weakest animals. Bursts of contemptuous laughter came from the benches: hyenas and jackals die so miserably, trying to escape death. There were no lions, as their price was too high; the greedy hyenas before dying devoured their own intestines. Alypius was talking to two handsome women with veiled faces. Someone handed the prefect a drink; he stirred it slowly, in the manner of a man obliged, like the others, to wait, but who chose to use his time differently. An armed guard stood on the highest step leading to the loge, his face a mask of boredom.

The monk stopped for a moment to catch his breath and pull together his torn robes.

The prefect's eyes fell upon him, and froze in surprise. The sight of the monk's rags did not make Alypius laugh. Putting away the goblet, he interrupted his conversation with the ladies. Almach, breathing hard, was praying. They looked at each other. Although Almach had seldom been among people, he could sometimes make out their feelings. The prefect did not think him a half-wit; also, he did not blame him — a monk — for being at the circus. He was just uneasy, because Almach stood there obviously ready for anything.

"Honorable sir," began Almach respectfully. He came closer.

"Will the gladiators be killing each other, sir?"

The guard glared at the man in rags. The women withdrew, as great ladies would at the approach of vulgarity.

Alypius drew the monk toward the back of the loge, and his proud, tired face was as understanding as Almach had known it would be. Yes. Less guilty than the others, the pagan Alypius understood. And it was not the fear of a distasteful scene that furrowed his brows; the deep-set eyes did not need to change their expression to become sad.

"But surely you know," he said brusquely, "that such is the custom."

The steps leading to the loge were like rocks on a shore which Almach had to climb onto. But he had been wrong. The hard land where Alypius stood was called necessity — a sad land, without illusions, compassionate, but . . . Suddenly the monk drew the prefect's hand up to his lips. Alypius pulled it away, and blushed.

"I know, monk, that you are different from the others. But you must turn to your bishop or Caesar, not me. Here in Rome it has always been like this."

"But you are ashamed of it, sir."

"I don't like it, but the masses do. Without some corpses, they would tear into each other."

"Forbid it, sir! Every Roman court should indict us."

"Oh, so now you are attacking me as a jurist, not a monk," smiled Alypius. "Yet politicians and even most philosophers would defend us; you may preach, but not forbid. Can't you imagine what would happen here? This thing has lasted much longer than Christianity."

Seeing despair in Almach's face, the prefect leaned over him like a physician over a sick man.

"Don't think that many gladiators die, or that they are forced to fight. Fewer and fewer are killed, and they get paid better all the time. There are more volunteers than we can accept. But you should not be here. You may leave through there; this exit leads directly to the street."

Trumpets sounded in the arena, and the prefect walked over to the railing, the embroidered *mappa* in his hand.

Like Pilate, he was ignorant of the Word which became Flesh; he did not know that it made no difference whether many or few gladiators died, if they were well paid, or just wanted to fight. Even if the slaughter had been going on for a thousand years, Almach, running through a dark corridor, knew that it could not be permitted to go on for another day.

He saw light. A huge figure crossed the corridor, his wrestler's shoulders gleaming. Almach rushed to the right, where the vault sloped, and he followed the man.

The glare at the bottom of the staircase turned out to be a large whitewashed room, lighted from the top. When his eyes became accustomed to the brightness, he noticed men sitting and standing by the walls, like statues: the gladiators.

They were being served by several young boys — no, by grown men who, next to them, looked childish. Like the ardent faithful in a temple, they cowered in front of their motionless idols in copper and scales and oiled nakedness. Somebody raised a heavy curtain; bright sand glistened behind it.

"The *scutarii* are just about ready to start," the curious one declared. Then he saw Almach and burst into laughter. "What? Do monks place bets now and look over their favorites?"

"Psst," hissed the others, and one of the giants stirred noisily, as if awakening in anger. All heavily armed — they were the ones he had been looking for. The burnished helmets rested on their knees, now he could see their faces, which he had only guessed. But he had guessed well: these faces were shut off from life, artfully peaceful — not heroic, but not slavish either.

Almach's eager eyes examined them for a long time, and his sigh was a sigh of relief. These demigods were, after all, the most subdued of people. Here was the silence of fear and hope; out on the arena the screams, the applause, the prefect's *mappa,* the idolatry of the populace were like many fetters and yokes.

One spoke. He was fair, probably the most beautiful of them all. A youth in gorgeous dress and elaborate curls attended him. Quietly, in a barbaric accent, the fair-haired one addressed Almach: "If you have come to bless us, do so."

Almach's eyes dimmed with tenderness. It was as if a dying man had been suddenly restored to health here. He seemed to recognize the blond warrior. "Was it you I walked with on Via Appia yesterday? No. You must be the one who held me up in the crowd this morning," he said.

"I don't think so," muttered the barbarian.

"Shut up, you circus monk," hoarsely broke in the man who had earlier shown a desire to have peace.

"If it wasn't you, then he looked just like you. Oh, my brother! How can you?"

The curly swells glared at the monk with contempt, but the man with the sword, the favorite of the arena, seemed to consider him; he was silent.

Almach raised his hands. "For Christ's sake, brother, don't go out there!"

"Some day they'll carry me out." The movement of the warrior's eyes and lips must have signified a smile in his tribe. "In church," he added, "I shall listen to you, not here. Go away!"

"Get out! Away with you!" yelled the outraged burghers.

Almach stood in the circle of light, praying silently. The whole world was affronting the gladiators; the whole order of the world; but they could still refuse to please the world. At that moment Almach noticed the athlete he had seen at the procession. He was the one seated next to the curtain looking out from time to time. He wore armor, but had no sword. "Go ahead, monk! Persuade Melittus, I beg you," he shouted in a garrulous voice, like a market vendor. "Take Melittus away from here, then they'll have to use me in his place."

"You in place of Melittus, you woodchopper from across the Tiber?" hissed a youth with rings on his fingers. "There is no use your hanging around here; they'll never send you in place of anyone."

Almach fell to his knees. "Melittus, in the name of Christ!" He caught his hand, but with his iron fingers the gladiator freed himself and moved away. "The devil," pressed the monk, "also has the power to say: 'Today you'll be with me forever.'"

Trumpets screamed on the arena, the strong man from across the

Tiber again stuck his head out, the angry one seized Almach by the arms and lifted him up like a rag doll. "Bless whom you wish, and get the devil out of here!" With his knee he pushed him toward Melittus, who stepped aside in disgust, but caught the falling monk.

"Leave it, Hiero," pleaded an old man, probably the father of the one who had pushed Almach. "The servant will throw out this good-for-nothing, and the prefect will punish him."

"Hey, guards!" The young man who had been betting on Melittus now found it his business to act. Through an opening in the curtain a streak of sun shot in from the arena, as sharp as a sword.

The monk lay where he had fallen, unhurt, feeling like a worm. He prayed that the guards would not come and throw him outside. He was no longer able to pray for the gladiators to stay away from the arena. Surely he had not been the first to break into this place and beg them. Surely there had been a mother from the country? A priest? A philosopher? A girl in love, who had had a disturbing dream? And, each time, the gladiators shook them off. Were they not, in their own way, sailors and soldiers "more ancient than Christian monks"? One thousand years of this. How did they become so used to it? Perhaps some preferred it to everyday hardship, and later found they had no other choice. Others might have been hunted criminals. In any case, they wore, like an armor, the knowledge that of all the people in the world they died with the loudest roar and in the brightest sun.

Did they hate each other? Did they ask themselves: "Which one some day will kill me?" Have they drawn lots to decide who was going to fight whom today? At a signal from the arena they stood up. They looked at one another, aligned in pairs. The die, obviously, had been cast for them. They stood erect, all looking alike, surely not hating each other, just as the crowd outside or Alypius did not hate them. Almach saw amulets on their chests. Melittus was wearing a Cross.

The curtain fell open, revealing the eye-piercing glare of the arena, the glitter of scales, arms and shields pulsating in rhythm with the steps and the music of the flutes and the horns. The footprints on the sand stretched evenly like wagon tracks. Reality! Step after step. The flute is blowing and the buglers know their tune. The prefect waves his scarf. Where are the Christian priests?

Reality. Processions. Monks, churches. *"Timor Dei"* and *"Credidimus caritati . . ."* The civilized prefect of Rome does not like it, but . . . It was twenty-five years ago when he, Almach, had been christened. The original sin had been washed off him, so that he could be a free man.

The little group which, after the gladiators had left, blocked the entrance to the arena thought that the half-wit whom the guards forgot to take away was now running to get back to the front rows. But he rushed on ahead, his back bent, seeming even smaller, since he scurried along a gutter under the loges.

At last the public from their benches saw him too. They could hardly believe their eyes; here was a runt in rags diving under the iron fence, joining the gladiators! The sand in the enclosure had been protected from the animals and the *scutarii;* to put one's footprints here was a crime, as punishable as witchcraft was once. The spectators roared, whistled. A guard rushed in from the gladiators' gate, then a second, a third, horrified. If the prefect does not revenge this insult . . . Standing erect, two of them in combat positions, the gladiators raised their heads toward the prefect.

Alypius stood for a moment, speechless. Then he motioned a lictor to drag the trespasser away, before the guards could beat him to death.

"Don't be too hard on him," he whispered; "he's a monk."

The crowd too had recognized that this was a monk, one of those noisy tramps who revile ancient Roman customs; it was enough to look at him to want to spit. Forgetting the sanctity of the gladiators' sand, people from the first rows started throwing sandals, turnips and stones on it.

Almach sneaked in between the two fighters, who now stood at attention with bared swords: Melittus and the fierce Hiero. He gripped Melittus's right arm.

"Hit him!" roared the crowd. "Hit him!" They had forgotten that the prefect had not yet given his final signal, but the gladiators remembered. Before the wave of the *mappa,* they could not kill — not even this outcast now being stoned by the Romans.

Half of the circus — the sunny side — was up on their feet, yelling curses and throwing stones. Their shouts aroused the others, who still did not realize what had happened. Like an avalanche, people jumped to the lower rows, and the floor of the arena was now littered with a shower of refuse. The lictors could not get through, the guards' whistles were drowned in the uproar. Hiero's eyes seemed to be bulging out of his face; with flushed cheeks he raised his sword. Melittus turned pale.

Then everything broke loose. The barrier of the first row was thrown to the ground. Those who could not reach the sand hit their neighbors and loudly cursed the prefect of the city and the gladiators. Here and there knives flashed. Hiero moved back and called to his comrades: "Attention!" Melittus stood high above the crowd, his sword circling in the sun, slashing at no one knew whom. The eight gladiators at the fence prepared their weapons.

The prefect turned away from the arena to give an order. The sound of trumpets and flutes filled the air. Last time the circus heard such poignant clangor of brass was when the army of Theodosius fought in the streets of Rome and called for help. The echo of the trumpets beat against the walls of the amphitheater, even more ominously. On the steps, men were pushing and trampling over the weak. The furious hubbub had not yet died down, when single people began to steal away from the arena and hide in the crowd. At a sign from their leader, the circus guards stopped in their tracks. The lictors stiffened. On the sand, at Melittus's feet, lay a naked, bloody human flattened into a patch of mud.

The flutes still squealed. As they fell silent at last, the voice of the prefect was heard. He declared the fights were finished for today and postponed: the arena was defiled.

The gladiators still stood with their swords drawn, ready to fight each other or the crowd, whatever the order would be.

Melittus leaned down, lifted the body at his feet, and covered it with a piece of the habit.

– *abridged version, translated by* WANDA JAECKEL

(From *Sir Tomasz Moore Odmawia,* short stories. Published by Pax, Warsaw, 1956.)

The Smile of Jeremiah

BY JAN DOBRACZYNSKI

JAN DOBRACZYNSKI was born in 1910 in Warsaw. He began his literary career in 1934, and is now the author of some thirty books, mostly novels, a number of which have been widely translated. Since his main interest lies in the moral problems of the Christian world, he often chooses Biblical subjects. He took part in the 1939 Polish September campaign and, later, was a member of the Underground Home Army, in the Warsaw Uprising in 1944. Arrested by the Germans, he was sent to the concentration camp at Belsen. He belongs to the Polish Writers' Union, the Pen Club, and the Christian Writers' Club, Krag. The publishing institute of the controversial Pax movement lists him among its representative authors. Pax, a Catholic organization with political interests and wide economic scope, gained a good reputation for its publishing activities, particularly in introducing Western writers to the Polish reading public after the war, but its political aspect remains unpopular. (Note the reference to Pax in Stanislaw Stomma's article, "Positive Thinking," which appears in another section of this anthology.) Dobraczynski's *Letters of Nicodemus* and *Holy Sword* were published in the United States by the Newman Press. He lives in Warsaw.

AT FIRST there was nothing but a wilderness of dried-up weeds crossed by a narrow track of pebbles, mingled with black soil and the knots of long, thin roots. On the slope grew clumps of low fir trees with springy, serpentlike branches, bristling thorn bushes, and shreds of damp moss, beneath which white stones gleamed. Higher up, the bushes disappeared, and barren rocks rose amid the green uplands. The going became hard, and the lonely wanderer was often forced to bend and aid his climb with a long staff, yet he continued to press sternly upward. Crests shaped like ribs, separated by masses of soil and deep gorges, stood out clearly against the vast sky. In one of the gullies he found water; a wonderfully transparent narrow stream flowed down the crevice, forming little pools. Jeremiah knelt down and drank greedily; but when he rose to his feet, he started to walk again — he did not want to lose time. With great difficulty he climbed the slope, struggling against the loose stones. This part of the mountain was strewn with fragments of yellowish-gray or black rock. When he lifted his head a dazzling glare made him blink — he was approaching the snow level, and soon he heard it crunching under his feet. The hard snow, icy and brittle, covered the saddle-shaped ridge of the mountain. A fresh breeze from the summit struck Jeremiah in the face. For a while he paused to inhale it happily, but the bliss soon waned, and once again his heart was overcome by a desperate urge to flee, if possible, from something which he knew he carried in himself. This flight of his was sheer madness — he felt it, and yet he still strove to run away. Across the country of Canaan from the Mountains of Gareb and Gath to Mount Hermon. A merciless hunter followed him, but now on this sparkling ridge Jeremiah realized that he would never escape from the Voice. There was no escape for him since the Voice wished to speak through his mouth; there was no escape when the Voice commanded him to utter cruel, painful, terrifying words. For the first time the speech of the Lord sounded mercilessly in his ears; until now he had been ordered only to warn, to admonish, to threaten. Before the Battle of Megiddo, he had never seen such horrifying visions of the things to come. What he now saw was not just a warning; it was fate itself. In his mad flight, why should he rush to the flowery oasis of Damascus or hide in the dark, cedar-shaded ravines of Ion? The irrevocable verdict would follow him everywhere.

Wearily he sat down on the snow, and suddenly everything became or seemed indifferent to him. He felt his heart pounding violently; he waited — he waited for the words he had refused to listen to by the Kedron. He did not have to wait long. The Voice which he had endeavored to shut out rang in his ears with such strength that he leaped to his feet. A blast of wind smote him, hot as though it had come from some invisible oven. His arms raised in a gesture of worship, he whispered:

"I am here. . . ."

The Voice spoke. And with moans and lamentations Jeremiah repeated the words. It seemed to him that a host of riders skimmed the earth on their horses as lightly as a flock of quails dashing through a cloud of arrows against a shower of spears. Black, terrifying waters surrounded Mount Zion. Then everything became confused, entangled like dry leaves, sand and dust raised in a furious gust of the desert wind. Jeremiah was shaking all over; his trembling lips repeated:

"Summon the weepers, let them come . . . Let them hasten . . . Let them lament, because I have abandoned my home and my inheritance . . . I have given the soul of my beloved to my enemies, and the strange shepherds have trodden down my vineyard . . . With desolation the soil is laid waste . . ."

The prophet's body was burning with fever. In a desperate effort he freed himself from the spell. He moaned:

"No . . . No . . . Lord . . . It cannot be . . . No . . ."

He lifted his hands with their clawlike fingers and tore at his cheeks with his nails.

"No," he shouted wildly, and the mountains echoed his voice. It seemed to him that blood was all around him; he could smell the sickening odor. He wept aloud like a frightened child, but once again he had to repeat:

"Though Moses and Samuel stood before me, yet I have no heart for this people . . . Chase them away . . . Let them get out of my sight . . . And if they ask you whither they should go, tell them: those who are for death, to death; those who are for the sword, to the sword; those who are for the famine, to the famine; those who are for slavery, to slavery . . . And I shall try them with four plagues, even worse than those of Egypt, with the sword for killing, with dogs for tearing, with birds for destroying and jackals and beasts for devouring . . ."

Pressing his fingers into his mouth, biting them till they bled, he stopped himself with a cry:

"No, Lord, it is a temptation . . . Take it away from me . . . It will not happen . . . It cannot . . ."

But the visions would not fade. From the confused mass of men, horses, arrows, swords and spears there arose a dense black cloud of smoke tinged with a ruddy glaze.

Jeremiah howled in anguish and fell to his knees. He covered his eyes and sobbed:

"O, Lord, it must not come to pass . . . No . . . No . . . Mercy, O God . . . Take away from me these thoughts of torment . . ."

He waited for a long while, clawing his breast and cheeks with his nails, plunging his face in the cold snow. Then he rose to his feet, miserable, bloodstained, dreadful to behold. Lost in thought, he dragged himself along the wide ridge of the mountain, unaware of the ice and snow. At a certain point the ridge narrowed into a passage with its sides sloping down abruptly. There seemed to be a void beneath Jeremiah's feet — a gray mist, ascending from the valley. Once again he whispered:

"Take away from me, O Lord, these thoughts of torment . . ."

But like the mist, they were engulfing everything. Rebellion welled up in him. In a savage voice he cried out:

"O, Lord, why have you abandoned me?"

He clenched his fists — "No . . . No . . . No . . ." — and suddenly, bereft of all thought, he leaped into the abyss. Fog enveloped him, and he went down through it as a diver goes down through water, obliviously, in search of a pearl. Suddenly it seemed to him as though a huge hand had taken hold of him and brought him to a halt. He was unaware of whether he was still falling, or whether he was suspended in the milky fog. A gentle slope appeared beneath him. He fell on soft, downlike snow and rolled across it. He was alive. Though bruised and wounded, he could move on. He sat down and began to weep, but now he wept softly.

It was night when he rose and began to descend the valley. The stars paled as the half-moon rose in the sky; the snow glittered, the riblike cliffs were alive with quivering shadows. At first he encountered only bushes which resembled crouching animals; suddenly somewhere inside them gleamed the eyes of a living creature. Jeremiah halted. A black, hairy bear emerged from the thicket and, sniffing at the air, cautiously approached him. It stopped a few paces before him. It shrank back and growled. Jeremiah knelt down, bowing his head in anticipation of the powerful blow, which never came. The bear gave a sharp, nervous growl and plodded away, turning unwillingly to look back at the man. Jeremiah arose and waved his arms impatiently as if to annoy the animal, but it was already gone. Jeremiah flung himself down at the foot of a gaunt and lofty fir tree; he fell asleep.

It was broad daylight when he woke. Below him the slope dropped to a green meadow sprinkled with white and yellow flowers. There were trees, and birds flitted among the branches. Lying on his back, he gazed at the tender sky. His face was burning, his swollen feet ached, his heart hammered unevenly. He placed his hands under his head and wished he might die here. He knew that he would hear the Voice again, but now he awaited it with indifference. As soon as he heard it, he got up. The command was:

"Arise and go . . ."

Smiling piteously, he pointed to his bloodstained feet, to his legs trembling with weakness. The Voice said:

"Eat first, then go . . ."

Jeremiah looked around him uncertainly; he noticed that a nearby bush was covered with red berries. And so he plucked them and ate them, and as he ate he was filled with strength. After a short while he took his staff and climbed down the slope.

He walked on and on. Green meadows gave way to a dry sunburned steppe; a few scattered trees grew close to narrow streams. He did not meet people; instead he saw herds of wild asses, gazelles and antelopes. Hares and quails sprang up from under his feet, and vultures hovered majestically in the sky. It was not until noontide of the second day that, obedient to the Guiding Will, he turned westward to a more habitable land. The country was marshy, covered with reeds and papyrus, but the people there, though not Israelites, greeted him hospitably, offering him fish and oatcakes. He wandered farther and farther, wading through the bogs until he at last reached the foaming, wildly roaring, ice-cold Jordan. Now he walked along its banks and watched how it forced its way through the rocks, falling down the cliffs, its water white, angry and impatient. So he reached the Lake Kinneret, a vast greenish-blue mirror of water, framed with copses and shrubs. In front of him stretched an undulating plain, thick with flowers and grass, young groves of oak and myrtle, oleander, acacia and poplar trees. In the pastures cattle were grazing, and scattered in the fields among the wheat, barley and green corn, there stood small white houses. Here people offered him milk and sweet honey cakes. As he walked along the crest of Mount Tabor he saw down below the green battlefield of Megiddo. The white town clinging to the slope glittered in the sun. He struggled down to the valley of Esdraelon, fragrant with many flowers. There, only a few months before, the battle had been fought; there was no trace of it now. Luscious plants covered the fragments of broken chariots, arms or perhaps here and there a forgotten corpse. Walking through the knee-high grass, he descended to the stream, where he saw a young woman seated on a big piece of driftwood. She was scarcely more than a girl, her features almost those of a child. Her eyes wandered over the glittering river. She did not hear him come, and only when he stood right in front of her did she start. She uttered a cry, leaped to her feet, and began to run. But as nobody pursued her, she looked back and stopped. Something in the attitude of Jeremiah must have made her change her mind, because she retraced her steps.

Jeremiah seated himself wearily on the grass. There was silence; then he asked:

"What do you want with me?"

It was not his habit to speak gently, and if anything, he was even more stern with women. On the threshold of his lonely cave he would sing melodious songs, but when he met people, he could only scold them.

But the girl seemed undismayed and answered quietly:

"I want nothing from you . . ."

Her voice was truth itself. She had large blue eyes. He turned away his head and poked the earth with his staff.

"Go home," he said gruffly.

"I shall go home," she said, "but before I go, let me help you. Your feet are covered with blood."

He repulsed her with a gesture of his hand.

"I need nothing . . ."

"Why do you say that? Anyone can see that you are weary from your journey . . ."

"I do not want your pity."

"Why, Rabbi?"

Girls like this one, young enough to be his daughter, angered him. With his staff he struck off the heads of the flowers around him.

"Do you know me? Do you know who I am?"

"Yes, Rabbi, you are the prophet Jeremiah . . ."

"Why not say the false prophet?" he snarled.

Her lips quivered, and an anxious gleam came into her eyes. She knelt down on the grass, and after a long silence she whispered:

"I do not understand your words, Rabbi . . . but you are the prophet Jeremiah . . ."

"I am he . . ."

He would have liked to add: "Yes, I am he, who was born to suffer, in whom every thought is pain and anguish." But he said no more. The water murmured, and a gull hovered screaming over the stream.

"Let me bring you some bread and fruit; let me wash your feet . . ." she pleaded.

He did not answer, and the girl went away. Water continued to flow, indifferent. His head propped on his arm, Jeremiah fastened a lifeless gaze on the gull flying away with a large fish in its beak. Somewhere on the opposite bank a young masculine voice was raised in a gay tune. With the evening approaching, the sun shone less fiercely and a breeze cooled the air coming from the nearby sea.

He was still in the same position when she stood by him again. She put the basket down from her head and handed him a few pomegranates, cakes, cheese and a jar of wine. Without a word he took the food and began to eat; the wine he did not touch, as the Nazarene vow forbade it. The girl drew water from the stream, filled a bowl with it, and washed the blood off Jeremiah's feet. The man on the opposite bank sang louder and louder. Breaking a dry cake in his fingers, Jeremiah asked:

"Is he your lover?"

She raised her eyes and shook her head. Only then did he realize that her face was sad and tired, with dark rings under her eyes and pale lips.

"What is your name?" he asked.

"My name is Ruth." She lifted her head, and bent it again. "Micah, the merchant, is my father . . ." She took some oil from the basket and poured it over his feet.

"What more can I do for you?" she asked.

He shouted:

"Nothing . . ."

And then, surprisingly, he smiled. Even had he wanted to, he could not have recalled when he had last smiled.

"Sit down and talk to me . . ." he said.

He wanted her to tell him something about herself, but as he looked into her sorrowful eyes, he realized that he could read them like an open book. In them he saw the image of a man, young, lighthearted and boastful. But that was not all. Ordinarily, the invisible things which he was allowed to see were wrapped in a cloud, but he remembered well how once he had seen in a flash the Pharaoh overthrown near a river . . . And now, beside the young man, he could as clearly see a child — the child of this girl. A child . . . He trembled from head to foot. The contrast between this vision and those awful ones which had tortured him on Mount Hermon brought peace. His eyes burning, he approached the girl who stood before him, shy, small, with her arms pressed to her breast, her face pink and gold in the setting sun.

In a voice that broke, he murmured:

"He has not returned to you?"

Surprise, shame, fear, and at last grief distorted her features, and then tears rolled down her cheeks. She wept without a sound.

Jeremiah frowned.

"He must return," he said, and bent to pick up his staff.

She breathed:

"Are you going, Rabbi . . . ?"

"Yes, I am going. I am going to tell him that he must return to you . . ."

With a low, throaty cry she ran toward him, and not daring to kiss his hand, she knelt down and pressed her lips to his foot. Jeremiah shook her off; his vows forbade him the touch of a woman. He made a gesture as though he were stroking her head and shoulders, then he turned and walked away swiftly, without looking back, hurrying toward the road which was turning gray in the dusk.

— *translated by* JOLANTA KASICKA

(From *Wybrancy Gwiazd,* a book about the life of Jeremiah, the prophet. Published by Pax, Warsaw, 1957.)

III

What They Believe

The Priest and the Jester

Reflections on the Theological Heritage in Contemporary Thought

BY LESZEK KOLAKOWSKI

LESZEK KOLAKOWSKI was born in 1927 in Radom. After studying philosophy at Lodz University, he held various teaching positions at Lodz and Warsaw Universities. In 1954 he became a lecturer, and in 1959 professor of history of modern philosophy at the latter. Between 1952 and 1954 he taught at the Institute for Training of Scientific Workers, a school maintained by the Central Committee of the Polish Workers' Communist party. From 1955 to 1957 he edited *Po Prostu*, a weekly for young Communist intellectuals. The magazine was officially censured for its deviation policy – it had been especially critical of the "new class," the party bureaucracy and its police methods – and in 1957 the publication was suspended and never revived. Kolakowski became editor in chief of the bimonthly *Studia Filozofiezne* (which succeeded *Mysl Filozoficzna*) but gave up this post in 1959, though he remained on the editorial board. This essay, "The Priest and the Jester," originally appeared in *Tworezosc* and gave rise to much critical discussion among Communist thinkers. He is also author of *On Karl Marx and the Classical Definition of Truth* (1959), delivered as a lecture at Tübingen University, West Germany; *The Individual and the Infinite; World Outlook and Daily Life; Responsibility and History*, published in French in *Les Temps Modernes*. He is presently living in Warsaw.

WE HAVE DONE all we could to keep alive in our minds the main problems that in the course of centuries have troubled theologians, although today we formulate them in a somewhat different way. Philosophy has never freed itself from the heritage of theology, which means that theological questions were only awkward attempts to solve riddles that are still haunting mankind.

Riddles? It may be that what is involved is not really a riddle but —

frequently — a situation into which we read a riddle because the most self-evident facts appear unacceptable to us.

Nothing is as deeply rooted in man as the belief in a moral law of equalization of temperatures, that is, the belief that the world eventually will reach a state where our merits and rewards, our crimes and punishments are leveled out, where evil is avenged and goodness rewarded — in other words, a world in which human values attain their complete realization. Whatever happens, man ought to rejoice, because the rewards which await him in heaven are generous.

And thus, the first question which contemporary philosophy has inherited from the theological tradition is the problem of the possibility of eschatology itself. We pose it differently: Can the human values we accept attain complete realization? Does history evolve in the direction of final equalization and justice? One ought not to wonder that we do pose such questions to ourselves. Reflection on history has its main *source* in our dissatisfaction with history's results; the most common *hope* of historiosophy is to bring into harmony the essence of man with his existence, that is, to create a situation in which the inalienable aspirations of human nature are fulfilled in reality. Because the attainment of such a state would put an end to dissatisfaction with the results of history, it might be said that historiosophy has adopted as the main object of its hope a situation which leads to its own extinction. At any rate, every optimistic historiosophy must inevitably, by its very nature, be a victim to suicidal tendencies.

It is not difficult to see that secular eschatology — that is, the belief in an eventual elimination of the disparity between human essence and human existence (the belief in the deification of man) — naturally presupposes that "essence" is a value and that the realization of essence is desirable; and it relies on the wisdom of history to bring about this realization. Secular eschatology places its confidence in the final judgment of history. We do not laugh at it, for who does not defer to this belief? For instance, every time someone believes that the unhappiness and torment of people already dead may be avenged by history, or that centuries-old accounts of wrongs eventually may be settled justly, he demonstrates his belief in the Last Judgment. Every time man expects that some day the requirements of his nature will be satisfied, he professes his belief in eschatology, in the end of the world, and thus also in the finiteness of man. Since the eighteenth century, that is, from the very moment when

"History" and "Progress" in Europe made their way to the throne of the violently deposed Jehovah, it transpired that they could substitute for Him successfully in His basic functions. From the day that historical eschatology demonstrated its possibilities, human history became an argument for atheism: a different force took upon its shoulders the labor of God and, as He had done in the past, it could lull its unhappy subjects with the vision of a happy end.

Yet the belief in progress does not necessarily mean that one must indulge in chiliastic visions; the latter require additional presuppositions, namely, the assumption that current history can be characterized by its striving toward a lasting result, one which can be defined and which will end all conflict. It is irrelevant whether we call this result the end of history or its beginning; for every eschatology the end of the history of the earth is the end of human suffering and the beginning of the life of the blessed, about which we know nothing except that it will be a state of permanent contentment.

The problem of the possibility of eschatology is one of the central issues of a discipline which may be called philosophical anthropology, and which today deals with the majority of vital philosophical questions. But theology has always been a projection of anthropology on non-human reality. In regard to the antagonisms between the natural aspirations of human essence and man's entanglement in his external fate, philosophical anthropology today may still search for solutions either in terms of transcendency — as do the Christian existentialists (Jaspers, Marcel) — or in terms of history — as do the Marxists — or, finally, it may recognize the conflict as insoluble; the last eventuality was at one time formulated by Freud, and existentialist atheists have since put it in a different way. Independently of the arguments expressed in more or less "technical" tongues, the question itself has become common currency, and almost everyone, acting under the combined or conflicting pressures of tradition and personal experiences, has a more or less ready answer to it. In this popularized version, answers need not be theses; most often they are attitudes to life which express, if only unconsciously, a solution to the following problem: Is the existence of each of us merely a collection of facts, one following another and exhausting itself within its duration, or is every fact something more than the mere content of the time which comprises it — namely, an anticipation, a hope for other facts to come, the revelation of a fragment of the final perspective of fulfillment? Is each fact an absolute reality, or is it a section of the road at whose end peace awaits us? The answer to the question is of highly practical value, for it determines whether we consider our daily chores a means of saving pennies toward a retirement pension in eternity for ourselves and mankind and therefore, perhaps, disregard current facts and such values as cease to matter when the now passes; or whether, on the contrary, we see in them only their empirical and immediately given content, and therefore tend to ignore those possibilities which may be realized only after certain preparations are made, but which require transcendent interpretation by way of assigning sense to each fact by relating it to something outside it. Risking the loss of current values in exchange for final values, illusionary though they may be, and risking, on the other hand, the loss of greater values by pursuing current values — what, indeed, could be more banal than these two extremes between which our daily life oscillates? But this is exactly what philosophy concerns itself with, having inherited the problem from theological tradition.

The next matter, directly related to the first, is theodicy, also a part of theological heritage. In its modern version, theodicy deals with the rationality of history, that is, it tries to discover whether the unhappiness and suffering of the individual can find sense and justification in the universal reasons on which history rests. Traditional theodicies tell us that in the poverty of the condemned shines infallible divine justice, and that human misery reflects the glory of ultimate goodness. There is a difference between the problem previously formulated and the one posed by theodicy: eschatology assigns sense to all facts by relating them to a perspective of ultimate completion; theodicy justifies partial evil by invoking the order of a wisely construed whole, while the question of whether the ultimate completion is a justification of partial evil remains unanswered.

The problem of theodicy in its modernized version treats of "the wisdom" of history, that is, the problem of conceiving such an intellectual organization of the world in which evil, known to, or experienced by, us, discovers its "sense" and value enmeshed in the wise plans of history. Ideologies based on theodicy do not necessarily have to be conservative, although the majority of historical examples might make us think so. Strictly speaking, theodicy is always conservative where it justifies evil experienced by people independently of their own decisions; it is not necessarily conservative where it justifies evil resulting from someone's free choice. In the first instance, it is simply the ideology of the helpless; in the other, it may be an ideology sanctioning our active participation in human conflict — regardless of whether on the side of good or evil.

Theodicy belongs to the department of popular philosophy, the philosophy of everyday life; and although it is sometimes practiced in the form of historiosophical abstractions, its acceptance or rejection expresses itself also in daily, common attitudes, in that semiconscious practical philosophy which influences human behavior. On this level, its action varies. Someone who has suffered an irreversible misfortune can find solace in the thought that God has used his suffering for some — undefined — good in the world's order; or else that nothing is wasted in human affairs, and the suffering of the individual is recorded in the bank of history, thereby adding to the account from which future generations will draw dividends. Anyone able to nurture such beliefs can certainly derive advantages from them, and there would be no reason to discourage him so long as he does not resort to them in the face of an evil or a misfortune which can still be opposed. But theodicies mostly do serve the following: the belief that — by an act of God or history — nothing in human life happens in vain is so powerful a stimulus to our inborn inertia and such a justification of our conservatism and laziness that, in practical life, it inevitably becomes a shield protecting human inertia against the pangs of conscience and rational criticism.

"Ultimately," one may say to oneself, "our fate is only a part of the universe, a fragment of the enormous whole where the suffering of the individual serves to enrich the universal good, where everything influences all, while the general order of things is maintained. Whatever evil happens, it is a sacrifice on the altar of the whole, and sacrifice is not born in vain." Although sober observation does not support this optimism and points rather to the fact that no wages of history can balance the fate of an individual man; that the suffering of some contributes to the well-being of others, while the suffering of others serves no purpose and is simply what it is — bare suffering; that much of our toil and sacrifice and much of our life is ultimately spent in vain and there is no proof that it amounts to anything else. Although, then, this unifying and balancing vision of the world finds no support in our knowledge of it, the belief is so deeply rooted in our desires for compensation that it appears to be one of the truly irresistible intellectual superstitions known to man. The critique of this superstition would not be — we repeat — of great importance if it acted solely as a tranquilizing interpretation of matters past and irrevocable, and not also as an apology for situations that are, and whose inevitability can hardly be proved.

Theodicy, therefore, is a method of transforming facts into values: a method thanks to which a fact is not only what it appears to be to an empirical imagination, but an element of a special meaning in a teleologically arranged order. This transforming of facts into values is no doubt a vestige of magical thinking, older than the speculative theologies, and presupposes the belief in the sanctifying or damning power of certain events, a belief which has no connection with the empirically given data, while relating to intangible qualities. The assumption that our present suffering must find compensation in some good in the future presupposes faith in the secret good qualities of unpleasant events, qualities connected with the all-wise order of the universe. This belief is of the same nature as any trust in the efficacy of magical practices. Our purpose here is to point to those essential elements in which modern secular thought is also compelled, either in negative or positive terms, to answer questions inherited from theological and pretheological — that is, magical — tradition. Every belief or disbelief in a godless history, or a godless universe organizing its elements in a teleological unity while assigning them values independent of human notions, is a belief or disbelief in theodicy. The question about the existence of an immanent order in the universe is not futile, a fact we accept silently any time we agree to reply to it, even in the negative; this is so because a question fit to be answered presupposes a certain *raison d'être* of that sphere of knowledge from which it derives. Theodicy is thus part of contemporary philosophy; it may be called the metaphysics of values, or speculation on man's position in the cosmos, or even a discussion of historical progress. In all three departments, each of them a part of nonreligious contemporary philosophy, the patronage of theodicy, and through it the patronage of magic, has not become obsolete.

The belief in eschatology, as well as the belief in theodicy, is an attempt to find for human life a support and validity outside that life — an absolute validity, a superreality which any other reality lends meaning to and which, in itself, does not require further interpretation by reference to something else. The absolute usually becomes a moral support because of being a metaphysical support; because, in a metaphysical structure of the world, individua appear as its manifestations, or its accidents, and only as such become understandable. But the role of the absolute manifests itself more directly in other matters, whose importance in the history of theology is well known and, in its modernized form, is still troubling not only philosophers but all those who seek a rationale for their behavior.

First of all, the matter of nature and grace. In Christian history, this was one of the central preoccupations (Pelagianism, the Reformation, Jansenism), along with the question of theodicy (Manichaeans, the Cathari), and the idea of redemption (Monophysites, Arians, Socinians). It is not difficult to see that the problem of the relation between the responsibility of the individual and the determinants acting upon him from the outside is, in all its complexity, as much alive today as it was at the time of the Council of Trent. In its most general version, this is the problem of determinism and responsibility: in what sense and to what degree "can" or "cannot" the human individual resist the influence of forces which, independently of him, are shaping his behavior; and in what sense is he then morally responsible for himself, or to what degree can he place responsibility on other forces over which he has no power? There are many varieties of the problem — biological, sociological, historiosophical, metaphysical — and yet the sources of social interest in it are similar to those in the past; some of the varieties have become questions to be studied and solved empirically, thereby losing their philosophical character. Others have remained within the bounds of historiosophical or metaphysical speculation, with no great chance of being solved otherwise. In considering them, man wishes to discover to what degree certain elements, independent of him — physiological, or historical — can justify him *ex post,* and to what extent they can supply him with an infallible guide to his future decisions. Above all, there has grown up around historical determinism a multitude of complex questions which compel attention as the most vital in contemporary philosophical thinking.

"We have no freedom to do this or that, but only freedom to do what is necessary, or to do nothing at all. And the task which historical necessity has posed is being solved with, or against, the individual." This attitude clearly summarizes the idea of historical predestination, against which all rebellion is doomed in advance to failure; it is, at the same time, the idea of justifying acts undertaken in accordance with the inherent inevitability of history. The words quoted above are from the closing chapter of Spengler's *The Decline of the West,* but they may serve as a terse formula for a more universal tendency. All concepts pertaining to natural cycles of civilizations — such as Arnold Toynbee's — are analogous repetitions of that world vision we know from *De Civitate Dei.* The opponents of historical determinism — Isaiah Berlin, Karl Popper — are continuing, in this sense, Pelagian soteriology. Marxist literature on the matter presents various motifs, usually revolving around solutions resembling those of the Council of Trent, which can be summarized as follows: Acts that are in accordance with the demands of the historical absolute are contained within the framework of determinants derived from it; none the less, there is no irresistible grace, and the individual is responsible for accepting or rejecting the offer to cooperate tendered by the absolute to everyone; redemption is a possibility open to all, although, on the other hand, it is anticipated that not everybody will make use of it; thus, humankind is fatally divided into the chosen and the rejected; in the absolute's plans, this division is irrevocably established, and the results are determined, and yet individuals voluntarily accede either to this or to the other category.

We draw these analogies, not in order to ridicule an actually vital topic in philosophy, but rather to uncover the hidden rationality of theology's subject matter which, in the old version, has lost its vitality. For there is nothing surprising in the fact that certain central difficulties of any and all world concepts have a stubbornly persisting character as to their basic problems, while the actual degree of culture and the richness of vocabulary at our disposal determine the way in which we express them. Our explanations are thus directed, if at all, against that attitude of contempt which freethinkers and rationalists adopt in regard to problems that were flesh for past ages, as if we ourselves were not engaged in solving the very same questions by means of a different technique; this haughtiness is as unreasonable as derisive laughter at medieval man would be, because he transported himself from one place to another by means of the horse and not the jet plane. Airplanes now serve more effectively the purpose that horses once served, just as historiosophical reflections deal more effectively with the very problems once dealt with by the medieval disputes on the Trinity and irresistible grace. Why should anyone wonder at the fact that humanity wants to realize the role which independent forces play in man's behavior? Neither is there anything strange in the desire to know not only the forces which act upon us in the form of energy transferrers, but also the elementary and autonomous forces, that is, the absolute. If the absolute is a historical process, secular historiosophy simply takes over the tasks of theology which, in its old version, had become all too obviously anachronistic. Probing into the problem of nature and grace can serve a manifold purpose: it may aim at finding in the world a principle in whose authority one is able to have total confidence, and which relieves man of his responsibility and solves all conflicts for him; what is aimed at may be the highest tribunal on whose justice one relies without fear, and which will allow no harm to be done to us if we adhere to its guidance; it may also be that we want to acquire the certainty that in our lives we have chosen the better side, and thus all we do is just. Some solutions to the enigma of nature and grace serve as ways of shedding responsibility, which the absolute takes upon itself — this is the Calvinist solution. Another doctrine accepts responsibility, but only under the condition that acts are performed in accordance with clearly defined rules whose acceptance inevitably must lead to effective results — this is the Catholic solution. Still others accept the principle of unconditional responsibility to the absolute, but coupled with uncertainty as to the legislator's intentions — this is the Jansenist solution. In all cases, it is assumed that the absolute possesses both the legislative and the judicial power; the object of another argument is to determine whether the absolute's decrees can be well known to man, exactly how they are known, whether — if they are known — they can be carried out, and whether the transgressor can claim ignorance of these decrees if they are not fully known. Roughly speaking, these were the questions that served as focal points for all theological discussions in the sixteenth and seventeenth centuries — debates on nature and grace, predestination and justification of one's faith and acts. The very existence of a principle which is the source of all obligation and — simultaneously — a tribunal deciding in each case whether the law was observed was not a subject of controversy at that time; those who today reject the existence of such a principle altogether reply in a simple negative to a question theology has solved in a positive way so unequivocally that it sometimes was deemed unnecessary to spell it out.

If we put aside social conflicts which have a bearing on the controversy over nature and grace, we can see, from the point of view of individual motivation, two contradictory tendencies: on the one hand, there is the desire to find outside oneself support for one's own existence, the desire which denotes fear of an individual, isolated life, a life relying exclusively on man's own decisions, and thus, in final terms, the desire to rid oneself of oneself, to jump out of one's skin; on the other hand, we observe fear of the unreality of one's behavior and decisions, fear of harboring within oneself an alien force that not only carries out human intentions, but is also a will undertaking them instead of man. The conflict between striving for individual self-affirmation and striving for self-annihilation — in other words, the conflict between fear of getting rid of oneself and fear of oneself may be considered the most universal subject matter of philosophical thinking; more precisely — the history of philosophy confirms that such conflict really exists.

Let us remark in passing that the problem of original sin, very closely connected with the idea of nature and grace, also has its contemporary, although modified, form since it treats of the satanic element in man, and thus also of rebellion against absolute power; in its modern version, it is the problem of utopia, that is, an attempt to break the historical absolute — power — against which any rebellion is seemingly condemned in advance to failure. The problem of redemption and incarnation also lends itself to a *sui generis* secular interpretation: it is the matter of the individual's role in history, that is, of that mechanism which allows the historical absolute to become incarnate in exceptional individuals, or, in more general terms, the question as to whether those individuals really draw their energy from transcendent sources or rather are in themselves a spontaneous "principle of creativity" in history.

All the above-mentioned matters bear on the relationship between man and the absolute: something historiosophy has inherited from theology. However, many important questions in the theory of knowledge also originate in the very same sources, although they are not connected with historiosophy.

The most vital among them is the problem of revelation. Capricious divinity never reveals its secrets fully, yet a dimmed reflection of its wisdom does sometimes fall on mortals, depending on how much their owlish eyes can stand before being struck blind. Revelation is simply the absolute in the order of perception; it is a collection of unquestionable data; it is a way of communicating with the absolute. We need revelation not so much for learning what the world is really like, as for being able to appraise other opinions about the world. Thus, revelation is — in terms of usage — the textbook of the inquisitor. It is a granite throne from which we can mete out verdicts without the risk of error, and without which our rickety skeletons could not sustain us. Propped up by revelation, we can do more than move the earth: we can stop its motion.

Revelation is the eternal hope of philosophy. And so we see that the so-called philosophical "systems" which are supposed to give us certainty in the final stage of their investigation give it to us always at the very beginning; by force of an almost automatically accepted succession, they begin by establishing sure knowledge, the absolute beginning of all reasoning. It would seem that once the absolute of the beginning was given, so would be its end; that once we managed to stand on solid ground, moving forward would cease to be interesting. Since we have at our disposal what is most certain and unshakable, all further thinking would be as smooth and easy as the motion of a glass ball on ice. Revelation is "the first push" given to thought, after which thought moves onward automatically; yet it is only an apparent motion, for automatism is precisely the antithesis of thinking; thinking in its narrow sense, which interests us here — that is, creative thinking — is a function which cannot be performed by an automaton. Philosophy is an effort to question incessantly all that appears evident, that is, to disavow existing revelations; nevertheless, the untiring temptation to possess one's own revelation keeps on laying traps for critics; every philosophy aspiring to become "a system" questions the revelations of other systems only to establish immediately its own; there are few methods of thinking which do not tacitly subscribe to the Thomist principle whereby the aim of all motion is rest. "*Impossibile est igitur quod natura intendat motum propter seipsum. Intendit igitur quietem per motum . . .*" The premise of this assumption is that the essence of motion is its opposite, namely, absence of motion; motion realizes itself by annihilating itself, or in other words, motion is an infirmity or insufficiency of that which moves; motion reveals need, whereas need is the negative component of nature; therefore, the nature of all things realizes itself in fulfillment. In philosophical thinking, this principle appears as the conviction that thought moves only because it is imperfect, and only to attain perfection, immobility; thought, as every motion, attains satisfaction and fulfills itself only when it ceases to be motion, that is, when it ceases to be. But the urgent need for finality, the need for revelation, is one of the needs most easily satisfied; that is why its seekers find it almost as soon as they become aware of the need; once the revelation has been found and thought has reached its much desired fulfillment, philosophy begins to construct what it thinks is a "system"; in fact, however, the alleged beginning is already the end, and the structure has been given a roof at the moment when it seemed to us that we had just laid the cornerstone. Any philosophic finality is nothing but a substitute for revelation, which, being allegedly the starting point for theologians, is in truth all that is needed; for indeed theology begins with the conviction that truth has already been given to us and its intellectual effort lies, not in pitting it against reality, but in assimilating the essence of something that has been totally completed.

The original key formula of secular revelation is the Cartesian *cogito:* an attempt to question all that is obvious, and all the traditional finalities, in such a way as not to allow the act of criticism and destruction to be completed before a new finality — the self-knowledge of man's own thinking process — has been attained. Descartes undertook his act of criticism fully aware that there must be a limit to criticism, that sand is usually removed to enable people to stand on solid ground; to him, critique would have been without meaning if it were not to stop at a static point, and so his critical task was to reach a point above all criticism; the goal of criticism was self-annihilation, the goal of motion the absence of motion, a point of immobility; the exposure of the shortcomings of successive revelations was to lead to the discovery of a revelation free of shortcomings. The progress of post-Cartesian philosophy was, to a considerable degree, a succession of imitations of the same procedure; philosophers accepted *in toto* Descartes's question, thereby half accepting his answer, while the persistent work of modifying the *cogito* formula has lasted until the present century. In particular, the entire evolution of European idealism has brought to light the basic quality of the Cartesian revelation which it shares with other revelations: its starting point is also the point of attainment; since the awareness of the thought process is the ultimate datum of cognition, the whole of reality cannot go beyond the thought process or, to use Gilson's words, "as we begin with the immanent world, so we end with it." This seems natural: reality will always have in man's vision such nature as is inherent in the ultimate data from which he tries to reconstruct it. For to declare that certain data have the privilege of being final is to deny the reality of everything that cannot be in some way reduced to them. If, then, the immanent world is the absolute of knowledge, it is, at the same time, all that knowledge can achieve; just as Spinoza's *causa sui*, being the starting point of the thought process, is inevitably its point of attainment, the only world whose reality can be defended. So also people for whom the physical objects of daily reality constitute the only collection of absolute data must recognize that those data necessarily exhaust all possible data, while people who assign this character to sensory phenomena will construct the world exclusively on the basis of sensory phenomena. In the motion of philosophical thought, the absolute starting point predetermines everything else, and he who attains the absolute ceases to move; any further motion on his part is illusory, as is the motion of a squirrel running up a rotating drum.

And yet the nostalgia for revelation lives in the heart of philosophy, while the need for ultimate satisfaction has still not been extinguished in its faithful. Taine's positivism had to find satisfaction in the "ultimate law" or the "eternal axiom" of reality, which discovers the unity of the universe, and to which all our knowledge must finally be reduced in some way. The great ambition of phenomenology was to present reality in the absolute and final sense, and since reality thus conceived could not be anything but immanent reality, the idealism of Husserl's late work seems to be the result of the previously mentioned inborn logic of a doctrine whose main task originally was to overcome subjectivism. The inner antinomy of this search for revelation was — in the case of Husserl — an illustration of all such analogous searches; the statement that ultimate data can have only an immanent character, whereas transcendent reality is provided — as Husserl said — with an epistemological zero indicator, presupposes that the ultimate data cannot be established without a clear concept of transcendency, while opinions about it were left in abeyance. However, the very concept of transcendency could only have resulted from that natural, precritical cognitive attitude, no results of which were to be considered. Yet it appeared now and again that the verbal definition of the original principle, which attributed an ultimate character to pure phenomena, had required an earlier use of a concept derived from outside these phenomena, thereby also requiring borrowing from certain data of natural knowledge; without them nothing could be achieved. The epistemological absolute appeared then to be as burdened with the dead weight of nonabsolute knowledge as the Cartesian *cogito,* which is nothing else but a presumption of a fictitious thinker, a distilled intellectual substance, totally independent of all such content as experience and acquired knowledge have left to it. This is so because the absolute is impossible to describe without simultaneously describing its opposite, and by this very fact it betrays its fictitiousness. Every critique presupposes an object to be criticized; a thought process in which we "put in brackets" transcendent reality presupposes that the latter was given to our thought, regardless of how many "distinguos" are added to the word "given."

Modern positivism has not saved itself, at least in its first phase, from the pursuit of the epistemological absolute; Moritz Schlick presented us with another version of the same maneuver which, in so many other doctrines, was to provide us with secular substitutes for revelation.

The problem of revelation is the problem of the existence of ultimate data; it is accompanied by another question: to what extent is conceptual thinking able to encompass and express ultimate data? This is the problem of mystery which, in contemporary philosophy, belongs as much as the former ones to the heritage of theology. In its modernized version mystery is identical with the limits of rationalism; it covers all the questions that primarily concern the rationality of certain elementary components of perception, and certain indivisible fragments of reality itself. The deliberations of the personalistic doctrines about the noncommunicable character of personality are a projection into the human world inquiry of the questions which theology addressed to divinity; personalism in its metaphysical version — that is, the monadology of the human world — did not attack theology but borrowed its troubles. In this case no more than in the previous instances, we do not want to imply that the troubles were illusory; the question about the rationality of the indivisible whole which human personality is, is a real question; if at one time it was a question about the mystery of the divine personality, it was formulated in sufficiently general terms for the theoretical priority to remain in the hands of theologians; in the evolution of the very word "persona" — the mask — there took shape a difficulty which has tripped philosophers ever since. This difficulty usually is solved by means of a rather simple slogan, "personality is inexpressible," but the slogan itself, even if true, is just as sterile as the statement that God is a mystery to mortals.

The problem of the relation between faith and reason has also reappeared in a modernized form. We concern ourselves with it every time we try to find out to what degree experience and rational thought can unequivocally resolve conflicts and what the role is of unprovable factors in our image of the world; the controversy over the unprovable assumptions of empirical knowledge on the one hand and, on the other, the existence of preferential criteria in regard to conflicting sets of experience has inherited much from the old tradition. If certain facts cannot be integrated with a previously accepted coherent set of principles which explain our past experiences, how much within our rights are we to ignore these facts or to advance interpretations whose purpose is to align them, sometimes falsely, with the system? These are the daily troubles of scientific thinking, similar to those that occurred in the past when revelation was the skeleton which organized all our knowledge into one compact "system." At the bottom of these controversies, there lies the antagonism of the same two tendencies which were present in nearly all the above-mentioned problems: on the one hand, the integrationist and monistic inclinations, a hope — in ultimate terms — of containing the world in one formula, or at least of discovering a principle that would explain the whole of reality; on the other hand, the pluralistic urge to disregard coherence in knowledge, a lack of ambition to construe a forest out of a single tree, a readiness to accept single facts as absolute even if, when confronted, they should contradict each other. It was William James who, in a radical formula, expressed the antimonistic attitude toward knowledge: if the facts contradict each other, we still can accept each of them separately, since there is no reason to suppose that one inflexible elementary law rules the universe and arranges its history; we have the right to assume that the way in which things happen varies, and that the effort to reduce variety to uniformity is most frequently futile and artificial; let every fact be its own explanation and the general knowledge elastic enough to react separately to any situation; if, in a series of experiences, the world crumbles before our eyes like a heterogeneous mass thrown together accidentally, we have the right to assume that the world's structure is precisely what it seems — chaotic, free of uniformity and order, full of accidents, more akin to a garbage heap than a library where every item has its clearly defined place and where everything has been inventoried.

And yet this obsession with monism, the stubborn passion to arrange the world in accordance with a single unifying principle, this search for a magic formula to make reality decipherable, proves to be more lasting than all the other adventures of man's intellectual development. Philosophy itself favors it; each epoch which prides itself on having created a great scientific synthesis seems to reveal more and more of an orderly world—while presenting us with more and more general principles, compared with which all those known before appear incidental. Thus philosophy, especially since it has developed the aspirations of a scientific discipline, eagerly calls upon science to bear witness to its ventures. But when it tries to renounce its monistic hopes, it does just the opposite—it denounces science and explains that a scientific vision of the world is not a reconstruction of an organization actually inherent in the world, but the result of just such natural propensity of the human mind.

All the above-mentioned examples are nothing but attempts to justify theology, not by rebuilding its whole structure systematically, but by illustrating some of its subjects; these examples were drawn from the speculative theology of scholasticism. But the wealth of mystic theology was not lost either, and it retains its splendor in contemporary thought.

The problems of mystic theology are particularly alive in the following four departments of modern philosophy: the practical interpretation of knowledge; dialectics; the explanation of the world in terms of the whole; and finally, in matters relating to the substantial character of the first reality.

With regard to the first, one ought to note that the mystics were pioneers in the field of the pragmatic approach to knowledge. Because the qualities of the absolute elude the investigation of the instruments at the disposal of human speech, which is used only for describing finite things, the only concept our knowledge has of the absolute is of a practical nature; in the strict sense of the word, this knowledge does not say what the qualities of God are, but instructs us as to the best way of paying homage to Him and how, by self-renunciation, one can approach His glory. Moreover, this knowledge is not so much a series of prescriptions one can learn by heart before applying them in practice, as the actual application of them; reason does not precede will — rather the acts of will become simultaneously acts of understanding; our knowledge of God is as great as the love we give Him.

Advanced by the first pragmatists and still retaining its force, the practical interpretation of knowledge is a generalized version of the mystics' program; let us ignore the question of what the world looks like "in itself" and accept instead scientific theories as practical guidance for our behavior under certain circumstances. Pragmatism rejects as irrelevant all queries about the nature of reality, and substitutes for them practical questions.

The second guardian of the properties taken over from mystical theology is dialectics. We know that the attempts to apply everyday concepts to the absolute existence have led to antinomies, hence the mystics became masters of a thinking which proceeds by thesis and antithesis; to say that no categories of human speech apply to God is to say that every time we speak of Him all categories apply to Him; thus God is and is not, He is all and nothing, maximum and minimum, affirmation and negation. In the mystical texts we also find the modern idea of alienation, as well as the idea of the world's development through its own negation. Alienated from its source, the world, an emanation of God, being finite, is the negation of its source. But in its reverted motion it tends to annihilate itself and again become identical with its genesis; this vision of Erigena contains in itself almost all the rudiments of dialectical logic. As in Hegel's logic, alienation in mystical theology did not have to be a negative phenomenon: the absolute secretes its theophanies by force of the fatality of its own nature, and by secreting them becomes, so to speak, enriched because it can regain them anew. Likewise, original sin and the fall of man can be considered a necessary phase previous to man's future happiness to which he can look forward because of his Savior's act of redemption: "*O felix culpa quae talem ac tantum meruit habere redemptorem*" — thus speaks the well-known medieval song; blessed be the sin which deserves such a savior.

Historiosophical reflections on progress which fulfills itself through its "negative aspects," and on alienation by which man is enriched as he overcomes it, are variations on the same theme.

As the third accomplishment of mystic theology from which contemporary thought has borrowed, we mentioned questions dealing with the unifying interpretation of existence. Thus the theory of "Gestalt" appears in mystical texts in an almost perfect, although somewhat generalized, form, the modern equivalent of which can be found in Bergson's speculations rather than in the methodology of the "gestaltists"; a really independent existence is the prerogative of the absolute only; all the finite fragments we distinguish in the universe, and the differences between separate things, are either a kind of pathological alienation which awaits its end in the universal return of the world to the absolute's womb, or else a deformed product of our imagination, which tries to impose upon an indivisible whole a principle of multiplicity and differentiation completely alien to it.

Also the mystical problem of applying the concept of substance to the absolute has begun to flourish anew in our century. The question as to whether the original reality has the character of substance, or whether its substantialness is a secondary phenomenon, an attribute of our perception, or even its creation, whereas the original reality is something not substantial — event, relation, act — this question is obviously of theological origin. The questioning of the idea of substance in favor of the metaphysical priority of other principles which were traditionally considered secondary predicates has, in our century, appeared in theories which are otherwise completely different; Giovanni Gentile's actualism, Alfred Whitehead's and Bertrand Russell's theory of events, and Natorp's theory of relation — to mention only three cases, each of a different origin — all meet at a certain, quite distant, point in their genealogy, a point which, to each of these philosophers, would seem totally alien to his thought. But every one of us has spiritual ancestors whose portraits he prefers not to display in the family dining room, though much malicious gossip goes on about them among the neighbors. Besides, we ourselves do not deny that our deliberations at this moment are somewhat reminiscent of the famous *Liber Chamorum;* in this case, however, the author has no intention of removing himself from the disreputable register.

Our list, so far, has been merely a collection of loose cases with one common feature: this was to show that many basic problems which are today considered by various philosophical doctrines — sometimes diametrically opposed to each other — as well as by "everyman's" philosophy, which always revolves around the same questions as "technical" philosophy, are a continuation of theological controversies, or rather a new version of the same propositions which, in the original and less elegantly phrased version, we have known from the history of theology. And yet, led by the very same instinct which, as was said, lies at the bottom of the monistic tendencies of the human mind and gives birth to monistic interpretations of reality, we also want to formulate a coordinating principle which will permit us to span the conflicting views of the world in a systematic way.

The majority of the cited examples revealed that there exists in philosophy an antagonism centering on the same scheme: for or against eschatology, that is, for or against the ordering of the facts of current life by reference to the absolute which eventually is to be realized; for or against theodicy, that is, for or against seeking justification in the absolute for every individual evil in this world; for an interpretation of man in the categories of grace, or rather, in the categories of nature, that is, for or against assigning to the absolute all responsibility for our actions; for or against revelation, that is, for or against seeking a principle of knowledge which is permanent and inaccessible to criticism, and which gives us the guarantee of infallible thinking; for or against the monistic concept of knowledge, and thus, for or against striving for intellectual power over reality by way of possessing a code of supreme and elementary laws explaining everything; for or against the unifying interpretation of the world, and thus, for or against such vision as lends everything a meaning by referring it to the absolute, a manifestation, a part, or an accident of which it constitutes. In short: for or against the hope of finality in existence and knowledge, for or against seeking support in absolutes.

We have tried to present the nature of this conflict as a constant struggle between two summarily defined but essential tendencies to which philosophy tries to lend a discursive character — a situation in which the human individual can rely only on himself, a situation in which he cannot "define" himself and identify himself absolutely with anything else. Such a situation breeds fear, which finds expression in man's seeking support in the absolute reality, and thus in self-annihilation; in man's seeking for himself and his acts a definition which refers him to something he is not. On the other hand, there is the affirmation of the individual existence as an irreducible fact, and thereby the rejection of all reasons justifying individual existence, the refusal to accept any absolute reality, the refusal to recognize immobility as the genuine nature of something that is mobile, the refusal to consider the prospect of finality.

And to what peculiarities of human nature — to use this much abused term — ought one to ascribe that indestructible tropism toward absolutes, that hope for the revelation of one ultimate principle which would explain the whole world and shoulder the burden of man's existence, behavior and thought?

There are various doctrines explaining the hunger for self-definition by reference to the absolute, a feeling which may well be hunger for nonexistence. Theologians have long tried to convince us that it is the creator-given-and-oriented gravitation that rules man's thought; they call it natural religious feeling. This, however, is equivalent to justifying one's own doctrine by facts whose acceptance must be preceded by the acceptance of the same doctrine you try to justify. And anyway, by what right are we to call religious feeling something that may just as well manifest itself outside all that which both in our daily life and in science we commonly term religion? I think we ought to define religion before we speak of *homo religiosus;* otherwise we may fall into a trap — a common one, to be sure — and define religion through religious feeling, characterizing the latter in a way which presupposes the knowledge of what religion is. It would be simpler, would it not, to view religion as we know it in its historical formulae, as an instance of a more universal phenomenon which may also occur outside religion.

But even if we disregard this one, we still have at our disposal a whole series of other explanations which are merely different ways of expressing the same thought, and which, unfortunately, give rise to all too many doubts to be satisfactory. Let me mention four such attempts:

One of them, formulated by Freud, and later ignored on the whole by his disciples, is the theory of the death instinct, that is, the theory in accordance with which there exists in animated matter a constant nostalgia for reverting to the inorganic state, a constant tendency to reduce tensions and, ultimately, to liquidate them entirely — in other words, to discontinue organic processes altogether. The death instinct thus would be hostile to the libido and — at the same time — explain the striving of the mind to discover in the world such principles as would reduce personal forms of existence to impersonal ones.

Another doctrine has long been known in its methodological

(Ockham), as well as theological (Malebranche) and physicalist (Maupertuis), version; Avenarius and the empiriocritical group have investigated it in deatil; it is the principle of economy. In its summary metaphysical shape, this principle implies that in nature — and thus also in the behavior of organisms and in thinking — there is a latent tendency to maximal reduction of effort and the use of the simplest means. Freud's theory may be considered as the economy principle specifically applied to the organic world. The principle of economy, as the principle of the natural tendency of all systems to equalize tensions and differences, might also help to interpret man's thinking as an attempt to reduce individua to an undifferentiated absolute, an attempt to explain monistic realities.

The third possibility, one formulated in the Gestalt theory, is the principle of simplification, according to which all Gestalt systems or entities have an inborn tendency to acquire forms as simple, regular and symmetrical as possible. This principle is again another version of the principle of economy, and can be used in this case for similar purposes.

As the fourth possibility on the list, we quote Sartre's formula maintaining that existence "for itself," that is, human existence — defined as pure negativity in relation to the rest of the world, freedom but a freedom-*privatio* — is imbued with a constant and contradictory desire to be transformed into an existence "*in* itself"; it would like to shed the nothingness which torments it, but nothingness, that is, freedom, is at the same time precisely what defines human existence; to want to shed nothingness, to return to the world "in itself," is therefore tantamount to annihilating one's self as individual existence, and thus simply annihilating the existence itself.

All the explanations above represent — as one can see — translations of the same thought into four different tongues. They all give rise to doubts and difficulties. Both the theory of the death instinct and the principle of economy, as well as its kindred versions, are attempts to raise (or, if one prefers, to lower) the principle of increasing entropy to the dignified level of a universal metaphysical theory, applicable not only to all forms of energy that are known and presumed, but also to human behavior, feeling and thinking. If this principle of universal tendency to equalize tensions and liquidate irregularities and differences were to be accepted, it would be possible to interpret the history of philosophy within the principle's framework, and all the previously mentioned forms of nostalgia for the absolute which have given substance to philosophical life for centuries would simply be individual cases of its line of action. The very essence of philosophical research could be derived from the same propensity human thought shares with all the other systems of energy; the content of the different metaphysical doctrines would have its basis in the processes of energy transformation on which the human brain depends; and the strong links between conservative thought in the philosophic sense, and social conservatism and that inertia of public life which we call reaction, would be still another individual illustration of the said principle.

However, had such a principle governed human thought exclusively, it never would have caused the previously mentioned chronic conflict in philosophy, which, to our mind, effectively directs its course: a conflict between the search for the absolute and the urge to escape from it; between the fear of oneself and the fear of destroying oneself. As things now stand, thought which is subject to the process of increasing entropy — that is, conservative thought — has been opposed in the course of intellectual history by a mode of thinking which exemplifies reverse processes — processes of increasing tension. In all fields of culture, in philosophy as much as in art and custom, there always has been present an antagonism whereby everything that is new derives from an unceasing need to question the existing absolutes, although every new form of thinking that tries to disassociate itself from the accepted absolutes establishes — sooner or later — its own final absolutes; although every rebellion against accepted truth eventually passes into a conservative state, it prepares the ground for a new phase in which its own absolutes become in turn the object of criticism. Can any mode of thinking, even the most radical, escape this fate? All historical examples make us doubt it; besides, the hope of formulating such a mode of thinking would mean a hope of achieving an ultimate method contrary to its very premises. In this regard, the history of ancient skepticism provides a highly revealing example: a doctrine which assumed the function of questioning all accepted truths and dogmas itself became an atrophied and barren dogma of questioning; the critique of the immobility of all accepted principles became the immobility of universal criticism; for no principle of universal criticism is safe from the antinomy of the liar.

And so we do not know of any absolutely elastic ultimate method which history could not threaten with ankylosis. We know only of methods which retain vitality because they have managed to develop instruments of self-criticism. It is our opinion that there is more than one such method. There is more than one method which creates instruments to criticize itself over a relatively long period of time; in our century, we believe that this has been attained by Marxism and by phenomenology and psychoanalysis. To state this is not tantamount to accepting the various and contradictory propositions these methods contain; the statement is only meant as a recognition of the ability of these methods to go beyond the absolutes they advance, and to detect the hidden premises of their own radicalism; in this lies their chance to live not only as congregations of perennially acquiescing believers, but also as thinking organisms capable of further evolution. Although within each of them there exist a current of orthodoxy and a group of people who know only how to repeat invariably the original formulae, each one of them has also produced offspring capable of life. The other "great doctrines" of the twentieth century — such as the philosophy of Bergson, for instance — never went beyond their initial phase and have remained in history as closed systems that may claim admirers but no offspring.

The antagonism between a philosophy consolidating the absolute and a philosophy questioning the accepted absolutes appears to be incurable, as incurable as the existence of conservatism and radicalism in all areas of human life. It is the antagonism of a priest and a jester; and in almost every historical epoch, the philosophy of the priest and the philosophy of the jester have been the two most general forms of intellectual culture. The priest is the guardian of the absolute who upholds the cult of the final and the obvious contained in the tradition. The jester is he who, although a habitué of good society, does not belong to it and makes it the object of his inquisitive impertinence — he who questions what appears to be self-evident. The jester could not do this if he himself were part of the good society, for then he would be, at the most, a drawing-room wit; a jester must remain an outsider; he must observe "good society" from the sidelines, for only then can he detect the nonobvious behind the obvious and the nonfinal behind what appears to be final; at the same time, he must frequent good society so as to know what it deems holy, and to be able to indulge in his impertinence. The jesting role of philosophy was mentioned by

Georges Sorel in connection with the Encyclopedists — but in pejorative terms; a jester was merely a toy of the aristocrats. Yet, although it is true that philosophers entertained monarchs, their antics had their effect in earthquakes. There can be no agreement between a priest and a jester, unless, as it sometimes happens, one becomes transmuted into the other (it happens more often to a priest; so Socrates became Plato). The philosophy of the jester is a philosophy which in every epoch denounces as doubtful what appears as unshakable; it points out the contradictions in what seems evident and incontestable; it ridicules common sense and reads sense into the absurd — in other words, it undertakes the daily toil of the jester's profession along with the inevitable risk of appearing ludicrous; depending on time or place, the jester's thought can oscillate between the various extremes of thinking, for what is holy today was paradoxical yesterday, and absolutes revered at the Equator may be a sacrilege at the Pole. The jester's attitude is an endless attempt to reflect on the various arguments of contradictory ideas, an attitude dialectical by its very nature — simply to overcome what is because it *is;* a jester does not jeer out of sheer contrariness; he jeers because he mistrusts the stabilized world. In a world where allegedly everything has already happened, the jester's contribution is an always active imagination which thrives on the resistance it must overcome; it was Fichte's admirable observation that thought cannot function without overcoming obstacles, just as a car cannot start on ice, or an airplane in a vacuum. For the same very good reason, a philosophy must be regarded as illusionary if it is reduced to pure autoreflection or else contained in the closed world of a monad. The assumption that the subject can be identical with the object in the act of perceiving is contradictory; to presuppose such an identity is tantamount to presuming immobility, a situation where no perception is possible. If, then, philosophy undermines the absolute, if it rejects the uniformity of the principles to which reality can be reduced, if it affirms the plurality of the world and the mutual nonreducibility of things, thereby affirming human individuality, it does not do so in the name of monadology, or in the name of the concept of the individual as a self-sufficient atom, because the affirmation of individuality is possible only in contradistinction to the rest of the world, in its relation to the world — relations based on factual dependence, responsibility, resistance.

A philosophy which tries to do without the absolute and without the prospect of completion cannot, by its very nature, be a consolidating structure, for it has no foundations and desires no roof; its function is to undermine the existing foundations and pull down the roofs. In the intellectual life it has all the vices and virtues of an indiscreet person whose sense of respectability has not developed. That is why in certain epochs the conflict between the philosophy of the jester and that of the priest resembles a contest between the irritating features of adolescence and the irritating features of senility; the difference is this: only the former are curable.

Someone might say that our reasoning tends to submit to the temptation of the very same monistic thinking it criticizes, that it betrays a tendency to submit a multitude of facts to one ordering principle. But it is not the ordering of facts that is contrary to the antiabsolute philosophy. Order can be a handy slogan for the police as well as for a revolutionary. There is only one kind of order hostile to an antiabsolutist philosophy: an order which has formulated fully the plurality of existing worlds, an order which has tasted the satisfaction of a fully accomplished task. A policeman's ideal is the order of a comprehensive dossier; while the ideal of the philosopher is the order of an active imagination. Both the priest and the jester violate the mind: the former by strangling it with catechism, the latter by harassing it with mockery. At a royal palace there are more priests than jesters — just as in a king's realm there are more policemen than artists. It does not seem possible to change this. The preponderance of the believers in mythology over the critics seems inevitable and natural: it is the preponderance of a single world over many possible worlds; it is the preponderance of the simplicity of falling over the complexity of climbing to the top. We have observed the validity of this preponderance when, with astonishing speed, new mythologies replace old ones. In the intellectual life of societies, wherever the machinery of traditional beliefs has gone rusty, new myths flock into being, created en masse from technological progress and scientific achievements. Thousands find consolation in imagining friendly inhabitants of other planets one day coming to the earth to solve the problems humankind cannot cope with; for others, "cybernetics" raises the hope of solving all social conflicts. A rain of gods is falling from the sky on the funeral rites of the one God who has outlived himself. The atheists have their saints, and the blasphemers are erecting chapels. Perhaps the desire for the absolute, the striving to equalize tensions, must embrace a disproportionately larger number of units in the system than the increase of tensions, if the whole is not to blow up. If this is so, then the existence of priests is justified, although this is no reason for joining their ranks.

Priesthood is not merely the cult of the past as seen through contemporary eyes, but the survival of the past in unchanged shape. It is thus not only a certain intellectual attitude toward the world but, indeed, a form of the world's existence, namely, a factual continuation of a reality which no longer exists. In the attitude of the jester, on the other hand, there materializes that which is only a possibility and which, in him, becomes real before it becomes factual. For our thought of reality is also part of it, no worse than the other parts.

We declare ourselves in favor of the philosophy of the jester, that is, for an attitude of negative vigilance in the face of any absolute. This we do not because we want to argue; in these matters, a choice is an appraisal. We declare ourselves in favor of the nonintellectual values inherent in an attitude the perils and absurdities of which we know. It is the option for a vision of the world that provides prospects for a slow and difficult realignment of the elements in our human action that are most difficult to align: goodness without universal toleration, courage without fanaticism, intelligence without apathy, and hope without blindness. All other fruits of philosophy are of little importance.

— *translated by* Pawel Mayewski

(From *Tworczosc*, a monthly, No. 10. Warsaw, 1959.)

Why I Am a Catholic

by Antoni Golubiew

Antoni Golubiew was born in Wilno in 1907. Having majored in history at Wilno University, he became a writer of historical fiction, as well as an essayist and journalist. *King Boleslaw the Valiant,* a six-volume novel published in 1955, has had great popularity. It is based on an eleventh-century saga of the life and deeds of the second Polish king, the actual founder of the state, who was a promoter and defender of Christian faith among Northern Slavs. Mr. Golubiew is also a contributor to *Tygodnik Powszechny* and *Znak,* Catholic periodicals. Other of his works include *Letters to a Friend* (1955), essays on religion and philosophy, one of which follows; *The Search* (1960), essays on modern intellectual attitudes. He lives in Krakow.

. . . IN THE COURSE of modern history man has reached out to interstellar space; today he can calculate the speed, temperature and chemical composition of distant nebulae; he has also penetrated into the atom and has perceived new whirling worlds there. He has mastered many of energy's secrets, harnessing it to his own service; he has come to know the structure and development of vegetation and animals; he has armed himself for the struggle against disease, learned how to cut a thousandth part of a millimeter and measure incredibly small dimensions. Is it surprising that, intoxicated with these achievements, he believes himself capable of determining not only phenomena, but the very essence of man and the world? Provided with precision tools, he inclines to assume that anything he cannot grasp with his instruments simply does not exist. This has been suggested by the fact that formerly any inexplicable manifestation, such as an eclipse of the sun or plague, was explained by a direct intervention of higher powers, gods or God. One intellectual error led to another, namely, to the theory that only that exists which can be perceived directly by the senses or indirectly by means of suitable instruments.

A young man who comes into contact with the splendid world of scientific discoveries is dazzled by it. His horizon extends, and his brain utilizes the primary method — commonly still imprecise and imperfect — of natural science thinking. With its aid he tries to solve questions to which hitherto faith has provided the answers.

In the story of my life, spiritual difficulties and conflicts have been many. The discrepancy between certain scientific statements — for example, concerning the origin of man and the universe — and the picture of Creation such as I absorbed in my early youth caused me much trouble. And the natural science explanation of facts which formerly had been ascribed to supernatural causes seemed to shake the foundations of my religious world. I confess that there were times when I fled from these conflicts to fideism, the simple faith based rather on instinct and tradition than philosophic thought. But I did not draw conclusions too hastily. I did not reject the beliefs of my childhood without a sufficiently strong proof that God did not exist. That proof I did not obtain. And yet it is just as necessary to demonstrate that something does not exist as that it does. This is true both in regard to the existence or nonexistence of vegetation on Mars and the existence or nonexistence of God.

As I grew better acquainted with the methods of natural science and the scientific statements themselves, my difficulties diminished. I began to realize that natural sciences speak of phenomena, never of the essence of the world they investigate. My first — and unjustified — doubts as to the greatness of their achievements occurred when I learned that they cannot answer such questions as "What is gravity?" "What is force?" "What is life?" and so on. When they describe phenomena and things, classify them, and order them according to certain rules, "they draw," to use the popular saying, "the map of the world," but they do not explain it. At that time I had not yet come to see that my charges against natural science were untenable, since the problems which interested me belonged in the majority of instances to the sphere of philosophy, and not of natural science.

In search of a solution, I wandered — without realizing it — on the border between natural science and philosophy. Nor at that time did I know that many a natural scientist, not acquainted with the methods of strict philosophic thinking, also falls into this error. At that time I put my trust in the scientists, because I had not checked on their reasoning and researches; I simply had faith in their learning. Against their authority, the wisdom not only of my mother, but also my father, a well-educated man, and of the schoolmistress whom I had liked so much and who had presented me with the "naïve" vision of the world, not to mention the prestige of the Father-confessor and certain worthy but absurd teachers, seemed dubious. I was not in a position to struggle on my own through the maze of problems confronting me, so I had to trust wiser people than myself. But I did not trust them unreservedly; the former authorities continued to hold sway because of their inflexible moral attitude. And thus I survived the difficult time without surrender.

Meanwhile, the new masters were not content with imparting to me the particular discoveries of natural science and stressing the disparity between the ancient picture and the new one of the world, but, more or less consciously, they formulated the thesis that only that exists which can be explored by the methods of natural science. In other words, everything that we believe but cannot confirm by these methods is fiction, poetry, even deliberate bluff. Methodologically, it was an arbitrary assumption, but still is amazingly widespread. Are you surprised that I succumbed to it? I had had no mental training, and apologetics acquired at school was obsolete. Above all, it provided no precise method of philosophic and theological reasoning.

The conclusion from the "new masters'" teaching was that the only thing in existence is matter. Now this sounded very unsatisfactory. The time when a young man has to decide on his future requires an answer to the questions, "What is life?" "What is its goal, its sense, its value?" Not only natural science but philosophic materialism, too, cannot give an adequate answer to these problems. Arbitrarily rejecting an extra-material world, they simplify the image of existence and create the illusion of having solved all difficulties.

Let us return to the borderland between natural science and philosophic materialism. The belief that matter is all that exists must lead to the further conclusion that it is infinite and everlasting. This idea was quite popular among natural scientists for a long time, and the law of the conservation of energy seemed to confirm it. It was considered that if we set out on a journey into the universe in any direction whatsoever, we are headed for infinity, and this infinity must extend not only in the direction of the macrocosmos, but the microcosmos as well. In my school years I was also taught that the atom was indivisible, in the sense of its homogeneity. In other words, the atom could not be split, although it could (theoretically at least) be cut in half, those halves again into halves, and so on ad infinitum. The concept that matter, finite and limited by its very nature, is infinite always caused me mental anguish. I found the infinity of the universe just as difficult to understand, since the naïve question arose: "And what beyond?" And yet the idea of the infinity of matter in space (at that time the ether theory was still prevalent, and consequently space itself was material in a sense, though scientists were not quite certain on the point), that idea seemed to clash with experience, which is constantly bringing us in contact with spatially restricted matter. This in turn led to a discrimination between boundless space and quantitatively bounded matter; but there were serious gaps in this theory also.

I shall not go into the complications in my attempts to understand the "division" of the atom. Much greater difficulties arose when I contemplated infinity in time, backward as well as forward. The idea of movement and change implied a beginning and end, and more particularly a beginning. But, as thought of by the natural scientists, a beginning forced the notion of a first cause, and so it transcended matter, which, if it had a beginning, necessarily led to something which is not matter.

Although these misgivings did not redirect me straight back to the faith of my childhood, they did point to one thing: natural sciences and the materialistic monism, as postulated by many scientists, not only do not provide solutions to the difficulties tormenting me, but constantly add more problems; they cannot — at least in the present state of knowledge — provide an answer. Of course, one can *believe* that they will do so at some future time. So we are back at faith again. But on what is this faith to be based? Faith of this kind does not possess a real basis in the facts. Was I, after rejecting religious fideism, to fall into scientific fideism?

The last half century, so far as science is concerned, has been like the explosion of a bomb. Old theories have been discarded; new ones have been proposed. Technical achievements made clear to everyone that natural science research is not barren speculation. And now I began to discover that according to contemporary views the universe is probably finite, and that attempts are being made to measure it, to weigh the whole of the matter contained within it. The atom has been split, and new worlds have been revealed in it; but these worlds, too, are finite. It seems that we have penetrated to the smallest particle of matter, the neutron, which has no electrical discharge, is of insignificantly small mass, and in rest is most likely equal to zero in weight. The human mind began to reach out to the bounds of the universe, and overthrew — it would seem — the hypothesis that matter is infinite. That was not all. The idea that the universe is everlasting also may fade into the past. The universe had its beginning, and scientists are trying by various methods to calculate its age. And the end of the universe also — at least as far as movement and change are involved — appears to be inevitable; here too we find serious attempts to calculate its future length of existence. There are even hypotheses claiming that space itself must be finite in time, since its "extension" leads, in some manner incomprehensible to science at present, to inevitable catastrophe — of course in some unimaginably distant future. Science is more and more definitely dissociating itself from speculation on such subjects as what was "before," what will be "after," what the universe is in its essence, what is beyond its "bounds"; science is confining itself to the investigation and ordering of phenomena, to the construction of such a pattern of the universe as will clarify phenomena. And yet this same science is drawing closer and closer to acceptance of an undefined and unknown first cause for all the phenomena observed today.

Obviously, it would be naïve to think that we have reached the end of scientific knowledge. But forecasting the future of this knowledge would take us into the realm of fantasy. Here we can only stand on the ground of what we know, or what today we consider a result of empirical research. That renunciation by contemporary science of "everlasting and infinite matter" meant a great deal to me. The former "contradictions" between the faith of my childhood and contemporary scientific knowledge were left far behind. Now I had to struggle not so much with religious skepticism as with scientific skepticism, with the difficulties I had to face because of that assumed basis of natural science, that "everlasting and infinite matter" which involved an absurdity. Today I know that such an assumption is quite unnecessary; science can accept the idea of matter having an end in space and time; there is no contradiction between the belief that time has a beginning and an end, and in some form of incessant act of creating matter, and the results of scientific research. Indeed science today directs (only directs!) the human mind to truths which exceed the material order. I am still filled with admiration and enthusiasm for scientific research, my confidence in it has increased since I came to know its scope and methods better, and the doubts which it temporarily aroused in my mind it has itself been able to dissolve. My confidence grew as natural scientists established with ever growing precision the range of their investigations, and have come up with ever more spectacular results.

Of course, the instances I have mentioned were only part of my troubles. I could draw similar examples from the sciences concerned with life, biology, genetics, physiology, etc. My first contacts with research in human physiology or heredity, and even the study of Pavlov's work, which explained the physiological phenomena arising in the process of thinking, occasioned more than one conflict. Here the fault was my lack of understanding, when I was young, of the fact that man does not consist of a soul (separate) and a body (separate), but is a psychophysical being. The slighting of the body, as expressed in religious teaching, was bound to take its revenge. Later on, Thomism cleared these difficulties for me, but in my early days the important fact was the discovery that Pavlov was profoundly religious — not a weighty argument, scientifically speaking. However, I am not writing a scientific treatise, only the story of my life, in answer to your question, my friend, why I am a Catholic. In my life, Pavlov's religious outlook was important for a simple reason: where his scientific experiments were concerned, I had to believe him, since I myself had not conducted any. Why had I to believe him in one thing, and not trust him in another? Pavlov's religious faith demonstrated that the great intellect on whose authority I relied, and which had accepted and employed in scientific research the methodology of materialism, itself saw no contradiction between its researches and religion. I, too, do not see any contradiction there, now I have come to realize that man is a psychophysical being. In time, cybernetics, especially the analysis of the operation of so-called "thinking machines," also helped me to understand a great deal.

But my final breach with materialism came about as an aftereffect of two other issues. They had nothing to do with the methods of scientific thinking, or with the scope of scientific investigations; none the less they emerged within the sphere of my probing into scientific problems. I have already mentioned that in my early youth I was spared the unhappiness of disbelief because of my ingrained respect for moral principles, in other words, a hierarchy of values. Well, in the conception of "infinite and everlasting matter" I saw no place for any hierarchy of values. Value necessarily requires a point of reference; every deed, thought, or desire can have value only in relation to some constant and absolute standard. Meanwhile, if we accept the conception of materialistic monism, the idea of everlasting and infinite matter, then we lack a point of reference. Everything — both the great thing and the small, an object and a deed, or a thought — is a manifestation of the incessant fluctuation of matter and energy. It is not possible to discover an ultimate purpose in infinite matter; nothing is tending anywhere; everything appears and disappears, or is subject to change. In face of all this one cannot speak of forms higher and lower, but at the most of forms more or less complex, more or less advanced in development. But what is the measure of that complexity or development? Man, humanity, is equally only a temporary vibration of matter, possibly its "sickness," its "madness," in other words, a declension from its own laws. A freakish concept of this kind provides no basis for evaluation.

So perhaps the concept of value is a fiction, having no correspondence with anything real? Perhaps there is no hierarchy of values, there are no poles of good and evil, and all things are absolutely equal: man and the meteor, a musical symphony and a flea, gravity and the death of Leonidas, a wrong done to a little child and the revolutions of a galaxy around its axis? Such would be the logical end of evaluation if I accepted materialistic monism and the concept of "everlasting and infinite matter." I clearly saw the nonsense of such equations, though I was not able to demonstrate why they seemed so absurd. There is, I suppose, scarcely anybody who could agree with them in all their implications and consequences. We feel the disharmony inherent in them; we know that one cannot reason along these lines. For a hierarchy of values to have any meaning, there must be, as a point of reference, an absolute, a supreme value. Since, in the monistic concept, "everlasting and infinite matter" cannot be a point of reference because this would lead to a vicious circle, the supreme value must be *outside matter*. This point of reference, being a measure of this universal and supreme value, my mother taught me to call God. The concept is certainly a long way from the God which Catholicism teaches, but even further from monistic materialism. And if that is so, the bound has been exceeded, and man is condemned to seek God — the highest value and the measure of all things.

There is another obstacle to my accepting materialistic monism: our means of cognition of the world, if only the material world. The very formulation "matter cognizing itself" seems to me to contain a contradiction. For cognition implies possession of at least partial freedom (or, to put it more exactly, independence) *in relation to matter*, a freedom to accept correct judgments — that is, those in harmony with reality — and to reject false judgments — those not in accordance with reality. Meanwhile, acceptance of monistic materialism postulates one of these two possibilities: matter is subject to the incessant play either of fortuitous and uncontrolled forces, or of forces ordered according to certain laws (yet another problem and another difficulty); true, modern physics admits to a certain extent an intermediate standpoint, but in principle it embraces the second alternative. Now, neither of these alternatives allows room for that independence of intellect which is indispensable to the act of cognition. The absolute consequence of these assumptions would be the listing of the act of cognition among just such plays of forces as the aurora borealis, the chase of electrons "under tension" or the assimilation of phosphorus by plants. But then there can be no talk of truth or falsity.

Perhaps this is exactly the case? Perhaps there are no such things as right or wrong judgments, they do not differ in any respect, or we cannot choose between them? Such reasoning would lead to total cognitive skepticism, or rather to agnosticism. Yet after all, even agnosticism is a judgment: "I know that I know nothing" is a definite statement, and the agnostic considers it to be true. But if he expresses, even in a single instance, a judgment which he regards as true, he is making a breach in his own reasoning—he is canceling it. Thus agnosticism devours itself. There are, however, many other judgments which we consider to be absolutely true—for instance, our judgment as to the fact of existence. The fact is that a system as complicated as materialistic monism leads to an inner contradiction, which the human mind cannot accept. I presume that if anyone does accept it, it is only because he does not realize the contradiction.

But the difficulty consists not only in the problem of intellectual independence. The world of thought is not subject to the laws universally binding in the world of matter. I admit that a blow on the head causing damage to the brain, and even the effect of disease on an organism, or the defective functioning of any organ of the body, renders the efficient functioning of the cognitive faculty impossible; but this demonstrates only one thing: that which is endowed with the cognitive faculty, the mind, cannot operate in earthly conditions in disaccord with the normal functioning of the body. The functioning of thought on the other hand, although bound up with the physical body and dependent on certain processes occurring in that body, has no material features; it is not subject to the "law of space." With the greatest of ease and "in the twinkling of an eye" thought reaches so far that light must consume millions of light-years in order to get there. It passes beyond the bounds observable by the senses (if only with the aid of instruments — we are still talking of the material world, those regions of the universe not yet reached by the most powerful telescope). It knows no barriers, penetrates into the interior of the earth and the sun, does not succumb to the highest temperature, and does not cease to function in regions with a temperature close to absolute zero. It peers into the interior of electrons, weighs the mass of stars, calculates the path of the nebulae. Nor does it succumb to "the law of time"; without hindrance it reaches millions of years backward, and even hurries forward. And more: thought governs the world, changes it (truly only on very small sectors), directs energy according to its will, reverses the "normal" course of causes, introduces new causes according to its fancy. Still more astonishing is the capacity of thought to create abstract concepts with which we embrace at will a number of units. When we think "man" or "star" we are in a sense embracing every man or star — present, past, or future — and not simply as a collection of all people or stars, but jointly, and at the same time separately. The linking of two grains of sand with two other grains is a material process, but the capacity to achieve the operation $2 + 2 = 4$ is something which exceeds the possibilities of matter (calculating machines do not carry out the operation by themselves; they were constructed by man). All this distinguishes the faculty of thought from the order of matter, and forces us to admit that something exists which possesses cognitive capacity and also an undoubted, though restricted, freedom in relation to matter, but also something which is completely different from the world of matter. That "something" my mother called the spiritual world; and, when speaking of man, she called it simply "soul."

But again, that spiritual world, or that human soul, is perhaps a product, a creation of matter, the result of laws functioning in matter or even the fortuitous play of energy? If we resort uniquely to natural science methods, we are unable to formulate any opinion on the subject. Natural sciences cannot explain either the manner in which a process occurs or what conditions cause it. Science can only say what material conditions must exist for man to think; in other words, science does not step beyond matter. We would be compelled to take on trust the axiom that the world of matter created the world of spirit, and take it without the least shadow of proof or even justification. The very idea that matter transcends its own nature and creates something completely foreign and even superior to itself (since thought can cognize matter, and even, in a measure, control it) seemed so artificial that I have seen no reason to accept this breakneck hypothesis, which explained nothing and piled up innumerable problems. To believe, I must understand why I am to believe, why I am to submit to someone else's authority. Otherwise I should fall into the common error of fideism.

I have shown you, friend, a section of the road which I traveled through coming into contact with the great discoveries of science. I shall not emphasize how precious those discoveries are to me and how very proud I am of them. I have exposed my difficulties, and the paths which unexpectedly directed me back to the truths of childhood. I suppose that there are gaps and inexactitudes in my reasoning, which I have put before you in a fragmentary way, by reference to a few characteristic examples. I also think that in its general conclusion my reasoning is sound.

But this road is infinite, and I am traveling on.

— *translated by* HARRY STEVENS

(From *Poszukiwania.* Published by Znak, Krakow, 1960.)

Catholicism Today

BY JERZY TUROWICZ

JERZY TUROWICZ, born in 1912 in Krakow, received his higher education at its university, where he majored in philosophy and history. A journalist, he began his career shortly before the war on the staff of the Catholic paper, *Glos Narodu,* and soon became its editor in chief. Since 1945 he has been editor in chief of *Tygodnik Powszechny,* of which he was cofounder. Very active in the organizational part of the international Catholic movement, he lives permanently in Krakow.

IN ORDER to evaluate Polish Catholicism properly, it is necessary to view it against the background of the twentieth-century problems of the Church, the trends and tendencies working within it today.

These trends fall between the two opposing poles described as "integralism" and "progressivism," and, in their extreme form, point to two kinds of heresy in contemporary Catholicism. Perhaps it would therefore be safer to use the terms "closed attitude" and "open attitude." At any rate, the two tendencies determine the framework for future development.

The problems which the Church faces in the contemporary world are, generally speaking, those of quantity and of quality. The problem of quantity is connected with the evangelization of the world, the preaching of the Gospel; it exists not only where peoples who never knew the Gospel are concerned, but also where nations which for centuries belonged to Christian civilization have again become, in part, a field for missionary work, because of civilization moving away from Christianity. The problem of quality refers to the level of "Catholic consciousness" among Church members, the profundity of their faith and the extent to which it shapes their behavior and outlook. In other words: quality here means the degree to which the natural order is permeated by the supernatural order, the degree to which God is present in people's lives.

The period through which the Church is now going can be described as satisfactory and unsatisfactory at the same time. It is satisfactory because of the great attempt at holiness manifest among her ecclesiastical leaders as well as the gray mass of the faithful; because of her high moral authority in the contemporary world, the awareness of her fundamental tasks and functions and her evangelical dynamism.

Yet it is an unsatisfactory period since Catholics have to contend with a sharp conflict between the Church and the "world." Someone may say that the Church has always been in conflict with the "world" as it was conceived by St. Augustine. True, but today the conflict seems sharper than in earlier epochs. It could also be said that the conflict is beneficial because through it the Church purifies herself and improves her "quality." This may also be true, but nevertheless there are losses in "quantity," an important fact. It is not numbers that matter; every human individual, every soul, counts. In today's conflict, the Church is losing ground in many sectors, perhaps temporarily, but she is still losing. We are now reaping the fruits of a process initiated about five centuries ago, when Europe began to drift away from Christianity. Nineteenth-century rationalism and scientism have broken down, but out of the dizzying successes of science and technology a new materialistic rationalism is being born.

What are the problems the Church has to face today? It seems to me that these are the most important:

1. The spread of atheistic materialism of the Marxist type, particularly in the countries of the socialist bloc.

2. "Practical materialism" of the Western brand, which prevails mainly in the United States and the countries of Western Europe, but also elsewhere (for example Japan, where it grows together with the economic standard). A consumer's attitude toward life, enhanced by the increasing possibilities of satisfying any appetite, the tendency toward an easy life, the fading of the notions of want and sacrifice — all these entail secularization and religious indifference, if not atheism. Although Marxist atheistic materialism seems a more immediate danger to religion because of its connection with a political system, "practical materialism" may develop — especially in the long run — into a much greater threat to the Church.

3. The situation of the Church in the missionary territories. In spite of great efforts, the results, particularly in Asia and Africa, are rather meager in comparison with the tremendous needs. In addition, progress has now halted in many areas. The growth of national consciousness among the colored people striving to achieve political independence goes together with a reaction against the whites, and often against Christianity. One must also reckon with the recent Moslem ideological revival. As a result of the so-called "population explosion," the absolute number of Catholics is increasing, but in spite of this their relative percentage decreases quite substantially. This is true not only of Asia and Africa, but on a world scale. In the areas which have been Christian for centuries, such as Latin America, the picture does not look any brighter. Great poverty of the masses, social injustice, and often the lack of a sufficient social and political awareness among the Catholic ruling groups may cause alienation from the Church. The "quality" of Catholicism in these areas suffering from an insufficient number of clergy also leaves much to be desired.

4. The level of the Catholic culture among the masses is a worldwide problem for the Church. It is so not only in the new areas but in those with old Christian tradition too. Faith does not shape human life

as it should. Here is a specific example, small but significant: recent polls have shown that in the United States, 85 per cent of Catholics practice birth control, and sometimes abortion as well.

5. A difficulty of world-wide dimensions is the shortage of clergy. Only in a few areas is there a satisfactory number of priests. Large territories — in both Christian and missionary areas — suffer from the shortage.

6. And finally, the problem of the reunification of the Church. Almost half of the Christians in the world are outside the Roman Church. The matter is not easy, and one should not expect rapid changes. However, if these changes are to materialize at all, a great effort is necessary as of now.

Let us now briefly and not systematically examine what answers the Church is trying to find to these problems.

In the field of efforts to make the administration of the Church more efficient, we note at the same time a centralization stemming from the understanding of the world role of the Church, as well as decentralization, a trend toward the autonomy of territorial units and the strengthening of the position of bishops. Much energy is being devoted to the modernization of the work methods of the clergy, religious instruction, and education of priests. A liturgical reform, the introduction of the evening Masses, and more liberal fasting rules brought almost revolutionary changes. Also the Catholic Action, the development of international Catholic organizations, the growth of Catholic charitable activities should be stressed.

The progress of the theory and practice of missionary work among the laity, the creation of a lay theology, the idea of introducing a secular diaconate — these are symptoms of the tendency among Catholic laymen to assume new functions in assisting the work of the clergy. Before our eyes, secular Catholic institutions have come into being and have flourished. A spiritual and intellectual renaissance of the old orders, such as Benedictines, Dominicans, Franciscans, Carmelites, can be observed in the West. The Jesuit order is prospering, and it is worthwhile to note the decline of the old "conflict" between Jesuits and Dominicans. The ranks of the contemplative orders with most severe rules, such as Trappists or Carthusians, are swelling significantly. This can be seen for example in America, but not only there. New orders are springing to life, such as Minor Brothers and Minor Sisters Charles de Foucauld. The latter fact, the twentieth-century realization of Franciscanism proclaiming the presence of Christ among the poorest, undoubtedly constitutes one of the most impressive phenomena in the life of the Church in our time. One can say that a new spirit has entered the Church, and it manifests itself in a variety of forms. It pervades the charitable works of Abbé Pierre in France, the activities of the Belgian Dominican Nobel laureate Father Pire, the social and political activism of the Italian Giorgio La Pira, the numerous manifestations of the Catholic "nonviolence" action, the disinterested attitude of French Catholics toward the Algerian problem, the action of the Catholic Worker group in the United States, the struggle of the Catholics and the Church against racism in the United States and in South Africa. The experiment of "worker-priests," though seemingly unsuccessful, is being continued in many ways. New theories and research material have appeared in the realm of sociology of religion. The Économie et Humanisme group, under the direction of Father Lebret, is working on new forms of Christian civilization in the area of social and economic problems.

In its missionary activities, the Church tends, above all, to create the cadres of native clergy, to establish local Church hierarchies, autonomy of the churches, and to integrate the Gospels into the national cultures.

The development of theology finds its expression, among other things, in the development of Catholic dogma and the doctrine of the Mystical Body of Christ, that is, the Universal Church. New fields are opening up: lay theology, theology of work and of "earthly realities." Scientific knowledge of the Bible and patristics are achieving great progress, and there is a revival of the liturgical movement among the faithful. Personal and social ethics and the Christian social doctrine are steadily advancing, basing their development on the directives of the great papal encyclicals on social problems. The Catholic educational theories and Catholic philosophy follow chiefly the Augustinian-existentialist line, sometimes perhaps to the detriment of Thomism. An impressive blossoming of Catholic artistic culture, literature, theater and plastic arts, especially modern church architecture, with many new names of great artists, must also be recorded.

At last an event of cardinal importance: the Ecumenical Council announced by Pope John XXIII. This council certainly will play a serious role in the return to Christian unity, but above all it will provide an opportunity for the whole Church to work on its response to the contemporary world.

Now, what about Poland? The situation of Catholicism in our country differs from that in the rest of the world. The prewar achievements — whether organizational forms or personal cadres — were largely destroyed. In 1945 it was necessary to begin from scratch, almost. Conditions were more difficult than before the war, and this was due not only to the losses wrought by military operations. In spite of this, after fifteen years of work, results are now once more considerable. The Catholic University is active in Lublin, the only Catholic institution of higher learning in the area between the River Elbe and Shanghai. The school of the history of medieval philosophy, created at this university after the war, is one of the foremost centers of this kind in the world. The Catholic press, the weekly *Tygodnik Powszechny,* and the monthlies *Znak* and *Wiez* play an important part in the intellectual life of the country and the shaping of a new intelligentsia. There are several publishing houses. Their resources are limited, but nevertheless after the war several hundred — original and translated — Catholic works appeared under the imprint of (to mention only the most important ones) *Pallotinum, Albertinum, Znak Publishing House, Catholic University Press,* and *Pax.* Many eminent contemporary writers in Poland are Catholics. From 1957, Znak, a group of Catholic representatives under the leadership of Stanislaw Stomma, has been active in the Polish Parliament. This group does not constitute the political representation of Polish Catholics, but testifies to the Catholic attitude in political problems while trying to lay the foundations for realistic political thinking. There are many active centers of religious life: the orders of Jesuits, Dominicans and Carmelites; the shrine of the Black Virgin in Czestochowa always attracts masses of pilgrims; the Benedictine monastery near Krakow and the institute of Franciscan sisters in Laski, near Warsaw, are valuable sources of spiritual and intellectual life. That intellectual life of Polish Catholics develops not only thanks to the specific character of the "Polish experiment" in socialism, but also in close contact with Western thought, both with more traditional Thomism as represented by Maritain and Gilson, and the French "new theology" of de Lubac,

Congar and Danielou. A great influence is Mounier, as well as the existentialist attitudes of Teilhard de Chardin, Simone Weil and Gabriel Marcel.

It would not be right, however, to draw too optimistic conclusions from all this. Not only because our assets are quantitatively modest and not up to our needs. Regardless of the peculiarities of the Polish situation, Catholicism in Poland is going through a process of transformation similar to that occurring in other countries. Secularization and religious indifference increase, and the internal vitality of Polish Catholicism is weakening. Violent social and demographic changes have greatly affected national customs and standards of conduct, which are particularly manifest in the disintegration of the family and loose sexual behavior. The problem of the youth becomes of crucial importance. The percentage of so-called "Catholic youth" (especially in the middle classes) is decreasing. And finally, the working methods and the speech of the Church in Poland when addressing the masses do not seem sufficiently adjusted to contemporary needs and modern mentality.

It must also be said that the religious life of the Polish intelligentsia is still characterized by the heresies of a rather shallow Catholicism: traditionalism, sentimentalism and utter individualism. The religion of the masses, although often simpler and purer, also suffers from a lack of understanding of what is the essence of the Catholic faith. In comparison with the prewar atmosphere, there are a few changes for the better, such as the lessening of non-Christian, nationalistic tendencies based on a false understanding of the commandment to love one's neighbor. The question of the rational content of Polish Catholicism, however, remains open; we still don't know to what extent religion influences people's outlook, and their strength to resist both rationalistic materialism and the pressure of changing mores.

The present shortcomings of Catholicism in Poland can be explained by many historical circumstances. A possible remedy could be to integrate it more closely in the processes developing inside the Church everywhere in the world. By this I mean adaptation to contemporary needs: a revision of the methods of work, change of language used, a deepening of culture.

— *translated by* Maria de Gorgey

(From *Tygodnik Powszechny,* a weekly. Krakow, December 11, 1960.)

On Moral Responsibility

BY ADAM SCHAFF

ADAM SCHAFF was born in 1913 in Lwow and graduated from the university there in 1935. He continued his studies in Paris and Moscow and received his Ph.D. in Moscow. In 1945 he was given the chair of philosophy at the University in Lodz, and in 1948 he became professor of philosophy at the University of Warsaw, which post he still occupies. He is a member of the Polish Academy of Sciences. Engaged in Communist activities since his student days, he is now a member of the Central Committee of the Polish Workers' Communist party. One of Professor Schaff's interests is in semantics and he visited the United States in 1960 to do research on American Indian dialects. His essays, *The Philosophy of Man* (one of which is presented here), were discussed in the American press in 1961. He lives in Warsaw.

LOOKING BACK on the past few years, one can state with some degree of certainty that the central problem underlying the philosophical concerns of a large number of Polish intellectuals, particularly young intellectuals, is the problem of moral responsibility. The existence of this problem is the main cause of "the explosion" of existentialist moods in Polish philosophical circles which, traditionally, have tended to seek solutions within the rational, even the positivist, framework. For the question of moral responsibility is linked by a thousand threads with the problems of the individual — his status and fate. The subject of moral responsibility invaded philosophy from life, from politics. And this is precisely what gave it significance and force. It was not an abstract matter; on the contrary, it vibrated with conflict and posed difficulties which begged for philosophical interpretation, the more so because it concerned a society living amidst conflicts and cruelly tested by them. It is not incidental that the circles — including youth — which were clearly allied with neopositivism felt no need for "existentialism" and are still approaching it with reserve, if not hostility. However, Marxist intellectuals, and particularly Marxist youth, eagerly embraced existentialism, although unfortunately they often accepted it along with its own subjectivist method of interpretation. But one must be careful when denying the validity of the existentialist attitude, for in this case it developed out of the personal experiences of individuals who interpreted the political difficulties of the past also as a problem of moral responsibility for their own acts and approbation of the acts of others.

Responsibility is a value connected with an act, and it exists as a social and individual psychic phenomenon only when human action has occurred or been omitted. Consequently, we can discern various types of responsibility, although we shall analyze only the one type of interest to us here.

If someone who is obliged to act, acts wrongly, or refrains from action, he is responsible for the damages resulting therefrom. Depending on the nature of the damage incurred, he bears financial or penal responsibility. An architect who builds a house faultily bears civil responsibility, if the damages do not involve penal liability. A driver who violates traffic laws is administratively responsible if his action does not fall into the category of a criminal offense.

This is not what we have in mind when we speak of moral responsibility. Moral responsibility exists in cases which, for one reason or another, are not subject to legal sanctions even though they meet with public disapproval. Take the following example: a man refuses to speak with a person who is obviously in despair. On the same day, the person deprived of human sympathy commits suicide. Public opinion holds morally responsible the man who denied the victim an outlet for his feelings. The man himself feels remorse and understands his responsibility for what happened, although his action is not punishable legally. This is a typical case of moral responsibility, but we shall not discuss it here either.

What we are primarily interested in is the special situation which provided the basis for a moral upheaval within Polish society between 1955 and 1957, and still troubles it; in other words, we are faced with the problem of moral responsibility for a *political* action taken in a conflict situation. What concerned each of us then, and still does, is not whether one should condemn a conscious moral transgression. We were concerned then, and are concerned now, with how a person ought to act when conflict arises between, say, organizational discipline and the feeling that the action enforced by it may be incompatible with one's personal moral standards. This is a great problem, and we must pose it openly, calling things by their right names.

We thus shall analyze a special type of moral conflict, one neither seen nor understood by our "moralizers" of 1956-1957 who, while embracing existentialism, ignored what was truly creative in existentialist thought.

As for myself, I believe that existentialism made a great theoretical contribution when it brought to the surface the vital significance of moral conflict as part of the human condition. Existentialists used this discovery to support the thesis that the individual is alone, isolated, "condemned to choice," etc.

The whole subjective baggage of existentialism is strapped to these very conflict situations. But the way existentialists make use of their discovery in no way reduces its significance. On the contrary, we must consider it even more carefully; cleared of the useless accretions, the problem may then emerge in all its striking vitality.

A situation laden with moral conflict occurs when an action leading to results that the accepted system of values regards as positive leads at the same time to results which that same system regards as negative. Thus the person who acts receives simultaneously moral stimuli prompting him to act and other stimuli hindering his involvement in action.

This is so because the situation is complex, and embodies many different tendencies and interests which, being at odds with each other, cannot be resolved. Such cases are the most absorbing from the theoretical viewpoint and, unfortunately, quite frequent. I say "unfortunately" because they often become the cause of a broken life and — in extreme instances — result in the violent ending of it.

Examples are numerous — both in the personal and the public field. In this category belong all the occasions when a man wants to do good and, having done it from one point of view, inevitably does evil from another. The symbolic victims of such incongruities which fatally give birth to tragic heroes are Orestes and Antigone.

But, as I said before, we want to focus our attention on the conflict situations which relate to Poland's political life over the past few years. In bringing them into the open, we are, of course, dealing a blow to "moralizing" — both officially religious and cryptoreligious, since the latter, in lay form, communicates essentially the same content: absolute commandments and interdictions. For one must realize that wherever absolute moral principles are preached, there — regardless of form — religious values are being propagated, the only difference being that an openly religious attitude is at least consistent: it communicates heteronomous norms established by a superior being and therefore eternal, unchangeable and absolute. He who maintains that the norms he prescribes are absolute because they derive from the categorical imperative, from human nature, etc., makes indeed the same claims religion does — namely, that these are heteronomous norms, only seemingly connected with the human world. Human nature, natural imperatives, etc., are of an unknown, or in any case nonhuman, origin; they appeal to the mystical "spirit," "human nature," etc. They have nothing in common with the only real human world — that of human society — and are not *ex definitione* its creation. The absence of the Creator appears here as an obvious and embarrassing inconsistency.

Well, this kind of moralizing goes bankrupt when confronted with moral conflict. The panacea of moral rules becomes ineffectual when they clash in objective practice. For where moralists consider their task finished, having delivered their sacred commandments and interdictions, the real problem begins: often in obeying a commandment one simultaneously violates it. The difficulty lies, not in one's unawareness of moral laws, but in one's having to choose one of them in a situation where any choice is incorrect. One therefore must choose what will be better and result in lesser evil. But on the basis of what norms? Both the religious and the lay moral codes fail to provide an answer. Both of them teach: do not kill; but neither takes into account a situation in which, obeying the commandment in regard to one person, a man violates it — if only indirectly — in regard to another person or even many people. For instance: I obey the absolute commandment and will not kill a traitor, but by doing so I cause the death of my comrades-in-arms. Herein lies the problem. It is easy to preach and defend absolute norms; but it is difficult to solve real-life conflicts. Of little value is a moral code which fails one the moment reality makes its entry. Moral law designed only for "converting" thieves, criminals, etc., and inapplicable to the interests of honest men who wish to know how to live with dignity when circumstances force them — against their will and intentions — to do evil, is of no great avail to humanity. That is why the holy enthusiasm which infected some of our "ideologues" at a certain period of recent Polish history led to paths of confusion and blurred the vital issues involved. If all we can do in a complex situation is to repeat that morality comes before politics, we make a show of intellectual poverty; in fact, we say nothing that could be of help. For the problem begins at the moment when we want to decide what is moral and what our choice should be in two alternative conflict situations.

Take a concrete example; it seems that only by this approach we can obtain effective results in initiating a dialogue which will bring people closer to Marxism. Well, what is the moral conflict in a situation where, on the one hand, organizational discipline obliges me to act and, on the other, I feel doubtful about the action, or simply am convinced that the action I am to perform is wrong?

Discipline in an organization derives from the common aims of the group I have joined of my own free will because I believed in their program. Organizational discipline within the group is both a condition and a guarantee of its success in battle, since a political organization is a fighting group. And so its discipline is my discipline, for I accepted it on joining, and the group is my group, my organization. This condition is *sine qua non;* otherwise the problem would be based on a misunderstanding and no conflict would be involved (we are not considering cases of moral fraud, where a person deceives others by joining the group in name only). But if my membership is honest, the problem of discipline is extremely serious to me; it determines the success of the struggle in which I am participating. To oppose organizational discipline is to reduce my organization's fighting capacity. The question is: do I have sufficient reason to oppose it? Perhaps my doubts — which are not shared by the others, who are decent, sensible men — spring from a subjective error, from inadequate knowledge and experience? Then should I not — despite my doubts — march in the ranks, valuing unity above all else? For to maintain unity is my moral responsibility.

Now I am torn by fear lest the action demanded of me, or of which I must approve, should be wrong — precisely in terms of those aims which are dear to me and in whose name I have joined the group. Perhaps this action will compromise my group's objectives in the eyes of the masses, divide its forces or demoralize its ranks. Obviously, I feel responsible for the outcome of the action, and if I have doubts, it is only because I am not fully certain of my stand.

How then ought I to act when I find myself in sharp moral conflict? If organizational discipline wins out over conscience, I remaining morally responsible for the unity of the fighting ranks, am shedding personal responsibility for the consequences of the action. If I decide otherwise, I must perhaps sacrifice — at the cost of consistent behavior — a much greater aim, in which I am also morally involved. This is an objective conflict, and to choose between the two alternatives is extremely difficult.

All this has nothing to do with the positions taken up by our "moralists." People who maintained that "morality comes before politics" were not aware of any moral conflict; they assumed that politics was completely devoid of morality, and organizational discipline involved no moral issues. Such thoughts and statements could have come only from outsiders, who did not really belong to the group; its discipline was not their discipline. This state of things may have been temporary, or the result of ideological shock, but it did in fact exist.

The situation, however, becomes really dramatic when someone connected with the group, being in fact part of it, and not in name only, experiences a moral conflict; then he must make a choice which, by retaining one value, may cost him the loss of another. How should the man behave? What must be the criteria of his choice? Can he be helped, and if so, how?

Under such conditions we are usually guided by what we consider the balance of gains and losses; we decide on the more advantageous alternative. It is of course important to have a proper system of values and a scale of comparison. In the given case, both are there. Yet no one can provide universal rules of behavior: first, because situations do change, and they must be considered concretely; second, because the concreteness of a situation depends on how one feels about it. Therefore, it is impossible to speak of these matters in a categorical and absolute way, without examining all the related conditions.

In the last resort, the decision — as in all cases where choice is involved — must be made by the individual concerned. No one can make his choice for him. What someone can do, however, is help a friend come to his decision by providing arguments "for" and "against," and suggesting why another person in the same circumstances would act in this and no other way.

This absolves no one from the necessity of making a choice, of moral responsibility for it. Nevertheless, the help thus given is real, and throws additional light on the existentialist interpretation of man's aloneness. In a sense, man is undoubtedly alone: he must choose for himself, and no one can choose or assume responsibility for him. This leads to mental anguish, sometimes to breakdowns and, in cases where the individual cannot cope with his inner conflict, even to catastrophe. But the existentialist version of aloneness and "being condemned to choice" has little in common with reality. This is so because the individual moves within a system of values and personality patterns of a social character; because, while examining his conscience at the moment of choice, he is also subject to social arguments. In this sense, the individual is not isolated, left to himself, alone.

Returning to the problem of choice and the responsibility for making it under conditions where the individual goes through a conflict between the duty to act (originating in a desire to fulfill the demands of discipline) and the unwillingness to act (arising from the subjective feeling that the action is wrong) — one can say, in effect, only this: there are *no* universally applicable solutions to the problem. "Moralistic" slogans such as "Morality comes before politics" are based on a profound misunderstanding as to the nature of the conflict, in which *both* sides — this should be stressed — evince the feeling of moral responsibility. Such slogans can be offered only by men who are not at one with the fighting group. Those who experience the conflict as members of the group, its factual and not merely formal members, should appraise each instance on its own merits, taking into consideration the particular role played by group solidarity in implementing aims. This recommendation is based on the assumption, which also has moral implications, that, in case of doubt, group interest must be the prevailing factor, while personal reasons are waived in the name of a *sui generis* reason of state. But this is only an assumption, not a final judgment. The final decision belongs to the individual and to him alone. If, after a thorough analysis of the situation when all arguments for discipline and collective good have been weighed, a person is fully convinced that the action in question is so wrong and harmful that it endangers the basic aims of the group — then moral responsibility instructs him to renounce solidarity in this instance and to act according to his conscience. Then, indeed, the individual is "condemned" to choice, and past experience shows that neither public opinion nor group opinion absolves him from moral responsibility (even if it were known that the individual's motive was not personal gain, but group solidarity).

I would like to illustrate the matter by the example of the creative artist or scientist. Here, the conflict which may arise, and has often arisen, is between discipline and the search for truth. The matter, a delicate one, is more often than not submerged in silence, and very wrongly so. I say "wrongly" because Marxism best demonstrates that it would be "supernatural" for such situations not to arise. Only a cult of infallible personality could exclude them, but this cult is incompatible with Marxism, which, in the words of its founder, proclaimed as its principal rule a *sui generis* methodological skepticism: *de omnibus dubitandum est.* One of the new developments is the condemnation of all such cults, their harmful effects and their nature inconsistent with Marxism having been proved. However, violations of the ever so correct principle of the scientific and artistic truth taking precedence over other considerations were so great in the past that the idea has taken even deeper roots in the consciousness of intellectuals, particularly in Poland. Therefore, the matter cannot and should not be bypassed in silence. Especially since there can be no divergence between politics and the search for truth when the latter is conducted from a Marxist position. A conflict is possible, and it sometimes does occur in cases when faulty politics, and organizational discipline, are clashing with truth. But then faulty politics is not politics at all. Proper Marxist politics is *ex definitione* bound up with the search for truth, because it is bound up with the fight for human progress, and so this is the only way a creative person should view the conflict between politics and truth once he believes that he has discovered truth. Moral responsibility dictates this attitude to him, even if the truth he has found is not yet universally accepted. What would happen to progress and experimentation if only accepted truths were allowed? The history of science and culture shows that we would sink then into a bog of dogmatism and intellectual stagnation.

The beautiful and profoundly philosophical Brecht drama *The Life of Galileo* ends with a moving monologue — the protagonist's self-accusation. The old scientist, overcome by the realization of his cowardice, refuses to shake hands with his student, who is about to reverse his unfavorable opinion of the master because — despite persecution and peril — he managed to complete his revolutionary *Discorsi* and hide them from the Inquisition. Galileo is stricter in his opinion of himself, and his last words express the essence of what we have discussed here. Let us then conclude with Galileo's words, if only because it would be difficult to find a more truthful and beautiful expression of the philosophical questions surveyed:

"Even a wool merchant must be concerned with the fact that he not only buys cheaply and sells profitably, but that he also trades freely. It seems to me that in this regard scientific work demands exceptional courage; science trades in knowledge, which it gains through doubt. Supplying knowledge about everything to everyone, it tends to create conditions where man must be heir to doubt. . . . As a scientist, I have had exceptional opportunities. In my time, astronomy has reached the masses. In these circumstances, one man's consistency in action might have been of great import. . . . I have betrayed my calling. Someone who does what I have done cannot be tolerated in the ranks of science."

— *translated by* PAWEL MAYEWSKI

(From *Przeglad Kulturalny,* March 30, 1961, Warsaw.)

Positive Thinking

BY STANISLAW STOMMA

STANISLAW STOMMA was born in Wilno in 1910. After the war he received his doctor's degree in law from Krakow University and later joined the faculty there. Since 1957 he has been a member of Parliament (Sejm) and leader of the Catholic Deputies' Club. Coeditor of the Catholic monthly *Znak,* he also contributes articles to *Tygodnik Powszechny,* the Catholic weekly published in Krakow. The following selection is from *Thoughts on Politics and Culture,* published in 1960.

I WANT to deal now with important and difficult matters of Poland's existence as a state and a nation. There are many people in our country — frustrated, bitter — who dismiss these matters with a wave of the hand. There are others who speak of public affairs in pessimistic tones with a kind of *Schadenfreude.* Those are tragic attitudes, which have to be opposed. We must face up to the problem: where we stand and whither we are going.

I am not a Marxist, nor a Communist, and I am addressing myself to people who, like me, do not subscribe to the Communist ideology. Their position in today's Poland is, of course, the most difficult. I realize that non-Communists in Poland were deprived of historic future through no fault of theirs, and because of this, I bear various ruling forces many grudges. But it is exactly with those nonparty persons, alien, like myself, to Communist thought, that I want to enter on an argument.

The actual state of minds in Poland must give rise to alarm because no nation can afford a passive stand in matters of its destiny. One may count on some economic help from these or other foreign quarters, but Poles themselves must hammer out their own fate. For passive attitudes Europeans will pay dearly in the future. Poles are already paying for them; such national difficulties as result from natural causes — drought, the rigors of winter, etc. — in Poland are taking on proportions too large to be natural. Our efficiency, our capacity for common effort, are low.

My fellow citizens nowadays are often trying to justify their passive attitude by their dissatisfaction with the economic system, but this means that perhaps they have not given the problem enough thought.

We live in an era of global solutions. Times have changed, and since economic independence and political isolation of individual states are no longer possible, sovereignty as it existed before 1914, or even between the two world wars, is not possible either. Europe has entered upon a period of economic and political integration, processes uniting states into large political-economic blocs are likely to continue and intensify, and it is necessary for individual countries to learn how to coexist within those larger bodies; objective social laws are working in that direction, and they cannot be resisted.

Let us then open our eyes wide and observe the world. What happens in the West? We can see there a latent conflict between a group of six and another of seven states; it is actually a contest of methods and means of economic integration. There already exists a far-reaching coordination within each group, and the object of the conflict is how to settle the relations between both groups and create a common superstructure. Undoubtedly, after a period of lesser or greater friction, we shall witness the establishment of new forms of an even closer coordination between all the Western states. Independently of this, we know that they joined in a political and military union: NATO.

If such is the case in the West, it would be naïve to think that the same tendency toward uniformity would not prevail in the Eastern socialist bloc, which — as all know — is a much more closely knit structure. It is, therefore, perfectly obvious to every sensible person that the logical and irrefutable consequence of Poland's belonging to the Eastern bloc must be her adoption of a socialist system, as a historical and political necessity.

Some time ago the above statement caused irritation to a spokesman of the Pax group:* he declared that the socialist system should not only be accepted as a fact, but also fervently espoused. A polemic on the subject would lead to a far-fetched doctrinal discussion, and this we do not deem necessary; very few people are capable of doctrinal attitudes and of accepting total solutions; most humans reason practically and react to the concrete. Persons urging doctrinal discussion are those who wish to divide, but we believe that our people should rather unite in pursuit of wisely defined goals determined by national interest. That is why we shall confine our discussion to the level of national affairs.

And so we live in the socialist part of the world and under a socialist system, which means that we must build our prosperity upon the foundations of socialized economy. The question is: What will happen within the framework; what will this economic life of ours be like? One thing is certain: economic life must develop, prosperity must grow, and the national wealth must increase. On this depends not only the well-being of each of us separately, but the power and the importance of the country as well.

After World War II, Poland took a big step forward in the field of industrialization. This was achieved at the cost of maintaining the national living standard at a low level. Soon it became evident that the supply of goods was not keeping up with the rising demands of the market, and that these goods were not properly adjusted to the needs and purchasing power of the people. This led to serious economic difficulties. We realize full well that such problems cannot be solved from one day to the next; we remember the words of First Secretary Gomulka in

---

* A controversial Catholic organization.

his first public speech as prime minister: "Even Solomon cannot pour from an empty jug."

Under the circumstances Poland had to seek foreign aid. We obtained special (outside the regular trade agreement) commercial credits from the Soviet Union and, before that, small credits from the United States; such help, of course, is not without importance. However, no country can live on foreign aid for any long period of time, not to mention that heavy foreign debts automatically lower a nation's political prestige. It is not a matter of economic separation; we simply must possess as much of our own resources as will, in step with a reasonably organized exchange, assure prosperity to the country's citizens. Only a satisfactory economic standard permits a country to retain political sovereignty as it is now understood. In the meantime, let's call a spade a spade: Poland is still below the normal standard of economic life.

Of course, emergence from the impasse is not a simple matter. Two sets of conditions for economic rehabilitation may be mentioned here. Set one includes the plan and organization of Polish economy, its administration, etc.; in other words, it is a set of data dependent on the government. Set two is of a social character. The impasse will never be negotiated if people remain passive, if they lack initiative and ingenuity, as well as the will to wage a collective struggle for improvement.

Under socialist conditions the motivating forces propelling economic development are completely different from those under capitalism. As is well known, the problem of economic incentives made its appearance in Poland after the 1956 crisis. Since then much has been written and said on the subject. The cabinet minister responsible assured the nation that the government attached considerable importance to the study of economic incentives to be introduced into socialist economy. At the same time, he warned against our overestimating the problem; the road to improvement, he said, leads through the greater "activism" of the workers and a sensible administration of every enterprise. We understand that the minister was right. Individual economic incentives cannot play a decisive role in socialized economy.

In a capitalist society the driving force is provided by the "activism" of a group striving to achieve the highest profit. The sum total of the various "activisms" creates the economic stir, which is, at the most, regulated by the state. Prosperity is supposed to come as the result of these efforts, which are of course based on competition between diverse groups.

There obtains an uneven accumulation of wealth, as well as a considerable difference in the degree of influence exerted by the competing groups on national life. Socialism, on the other hand, wants to eliminate the internal economic struggle between groups, and the resulting irregularities. Socialism lives by the following principle: *an individual can get rich only in step with the increase of the public wealth, and as a result of an increase in the public wealth.* This is the basic dogma of socialism; one may agree or disagree with it, but reckon with it one must.

Under capitalism, the starting point on the road to prosperity is the material success of the individual. Under socialism the first step must be the achievement of public wealth, which only later on can be distributed among individuals.

Of course, such a basic change means upheaval. *In Poland, the change has been wrought in the economic system, but not in the nation's mentality.* The psychological readjustment is hampered by numerous errors in economic administration, bureaucracy, neglect of the common worker, and finally — a problem not enough noted, though of considerable importance — unnecessary doctrinaire wrangling which weakens the ties between the individual and the state. Work on the removal of these obstacles was begun soon after the October Revolution, but it has not run a smooth course.

We in Poland must come to understand our own situation and learn to draw sensible conclusions. *Only an increase in the national wealth will secure for our citizens a steady improvement in their standard of living.* Such is the iron-clad law of the system.

If there is a discrepancy in the above reasoning, it should be pointed out. If there is none, then we must accept as correct the conclusion that the paramount condition of Polish national existence is a change of the nation's attitude toward economic life and public property, as well as respect for effort undertaken in the common interest. Only a psychological reversal can hasten the tempo of Polish progress.

It is not difficult to foresee the objections my opponents will raise. It is improper — they will say — to demand effort from citizens regardless of what kind of state they are living in and by what principles that state is governed. My opponents may submit that citizens are obliged to help increase the national wealth only if they are given assurance of fair treatment by the authorities in power. Also doubt may emerge as to the adequate distribution of incentives and investments; or the question of ideological conflict assailing our country may come to mind.

And yet, the gist of the argument remains unchanged. The ideological conflict is an ideological conflict; Catholic postulates in Poland are clearly defined, and we must have sufficient courage to uphold them. Who declares himself a Christian must participate actively in the fostering of Christian culture, but no conflict can justify passive attitudes, and even less can it be an excuse for sabotaging the country's vital interests.

While fully aware of the importance of the ideological struggle, we feel, nevertheless, obliged to declare ourselves emphatically in favor of an active, constructive economic attitude, and a positive change in the public's treatment of national wealth. Just because of the ideals we believe in, Catholic opinion in Poland should be characterized by a sense of responsibility equal to the particularly difficult tasks that fell to the lot of the Polish nation. This sense of responsibility implies concern for economic development. Under the conditions imposed in Poland by the ruling system, there is no alternative to the acceptance of the tenet about individual prosperity being possible only through the increase in the common goods of the nation.

Once more, I want to formulate what is the essence of our program: the best medicine for all social ills is democratization. Respect for the will and opinion of the citizens means that citizens should take an active part in the running of the country. Because the potential of a nation's spiritual force can be developed only under democratic conditions, democratization is our goal. To achieve it, we must think and act realistically — we must attempt to create objective conditions for the progress of democracy. But democratization is not only a postulate to be presented to the government, it also has its social connotations. There is no need to stress the fact that the measuring rod of any society's maturity is its ability to face up to economic demands. And this we must do, although our difficulties are great.

— *translated by* EWA MARKOWSKA

(From *Mysli o Polityce i Kulturze*. Published by Znak, Krakow, 1960.)

Polish Economics

BY OSKAR LANGE

OSKAR LANGE was born in 1904 in Tomaszow Mazowiecki. He graduated from the University of Krakow and in the early thirties began his professorial career there. He left the country in 1934, and in 1938 became professor of economics at the University of Chicago; he remained in the United States until 1945. He is now professor of economics at Warsaw University, also a member of the Polish Academy of Science, president of the Economic Council and vice president of the State Council. Dr. Lange is a leading authority on economic problems of underdeveloped countries, and the author of the well-known *On the Economic Theory of Socialism*. Two of his more recent works are *Econometry* and *The Political Economy*, Volume 1. He is a member of many learned societies in Poland and elsewhere. Dr. Lange lives in Warsaw.

THERE IS no question that political economy and other branches of economics, such as sectional economics and statistics, are faced with serious new problems. These are already under consideration today, or they will have to be considered in the immediate future, by the branches of economics concerned. Here I must explain that I am thinking in terms of Marxist political economy, since to my mind it is the only one that can be regarded as covering the entire socioeconomic field.

Actually, two types of problems are involved. The one type relates to new phenomena in the development of capitalism, while the other relates to the political economy of socialism. One could mention a third group, those which result from the coexistence of capitalist and socialist countries in the world.

At the moment I want to discuss only the points arising out of the economy of socialism. By the very nature of things, this group is the one most intimately affecting us, the one of most practical importance in the directing and administering of the Polish national economy.

The political economy of socialism is a new branch, if only because the socialistic system itself is comparatively new. The political economy of socialism is now in the stage of being created. A number of questions have already come to the fore, and today they are the subject of scientific debate in the socialist countries. There is the matter of the proportionate development of national economy, the basic problem of planning. Then there is the matter of the part played by the laws governing value and prices in socialistic economy. Finally, we have the matter of economic incentives. These various questions are closely linked with one another. For instance, the law of value affects the proportions of the separate sections of national economy, as well as the policy of economic incentives. In these departments the economy of socialism already counts certain indubitable achievements to its credit. The fact has a further bearing on the development of sectional economics, such as agriculture, industry, and trade, and the auxiliary economics, too, such as national planning, econometry, and even the "border sciences," such as cybernetics. All these side branches are of considerable importance in the development of economic science, and especially in its practical adaptation to the socialistic economy.

When discussing the administration of socialistic economy, the methodology of its planning, we must remember that socialistic economy — as distinct from capitalistic and precapitalistic economy — is based on scientific principles. Socialism is obviously the great historical undertaking to build social life on scientific foundations. This explains the special significance of political economy and other economic sciences, as well as the auxiliary sciences, in the directing and running of socialistic economy. Socialism affords the possibility of a rational organization of economic life — rational from the point of view of the community as a whole. But we have to translate this chance into reality. And at this point the state of economic science becomes of great importance. It depends on the state of the science whether the possibilities provided by socialistic conditions of production can be exploited in a better or worse way. In other words, the state of the economic sciences governs, *inter alia,* the standard of efficiency achieved in the functioning of socialistic economy.

In this regard a notable part can be played by new methodological elements which are now more and more appreciated. We all know that there is a powerful tendency to reduce economic investigation to mathematics. The trend is very strong in Poland; it is also to be observed in the Soviet Union and several other socialistic countries. This is the result of the tasks which socialistic economy sets the economic sciences.

For we are continually having to deal wth quantitative facts, such as quantitative production, costs, profits, and prices. And it is obvious that all these call for a strictly mathematical approach. There are other areas, too, in which the application of mathematical methods is particularly useful. For instance, in the prognosis of so-called automatic social processes, of which we must have some knowledge in order to plan. Or else, the prognosis of the development of population and its age composition in successive years. It is mathematical demography which renders this kind of prognosis possible. In principle I would also include econometric investigation in the future shaping of demand in the field of prognosis. In this regard the question is primarily one of the dependence of demand on the national income.

Among the other new elements in the methodology of economic investigation the so-called theory of programming should be listed, which directly affects planning. The plan must fulfill two conditions. Above all, its parts should be coordinated; it should be free from internal contradictions, such as arise, for instance, in planning the development of certain productions which in turn necessitate the consumption of more coal than was allowed for in the planned increase of output. A plan which contains such contradictions would not be intrinsically coordinated. So the planners' first task is to establish the methodic criteria which assure harmony in the plan. This is achieved by balancing the items one with another.

Further, the plan must be optimal — to yield the greatest results with the given outlay of resources. Or, which amounts to the same thing, to achieve the given result with the least possible outlay of resources.

In the realm of efficient planning the weightiest problem is to ensure effective investment, by which we connote the influence of investment on the growth of national income. In this direction too there is the necessity for analysis (partially using mathematical means) of the various investment projects, together with the variants of these projects, from the viewpoint of the effect they achieve, as well as of outlays.

This last element also raises the question of value and prices, for it is impossible to get a sound appreciation of the outlays without taking the value into account.

All this sphere is covered by what is usually called the theory of programming, the application of new methods to the planning and administration of socialistic economy.

I have mentioned cybernetics. In its origins this science was far removed from economic problems—it came into being during the study of automatic machinery, and also during study of the automatic processes occurring in organisms, in biology. There is an analogy between the process of automatic regulation of temperature in the human body and certain automatic mechanisms applied in industry, for example. And against this background an entire science has evolved which has unexpectedly proved of great importance in a number of serious problems that confront the administration of socialistic economy.

The best way of elucidating the role of cybernetics in our country is by an example. At one time there was a lively discussion in Poland over what was called the model of economy, over the question of centralization and decentralization. We know that in principle socialistic economy is and must be centrally directed. Without that, it would develop spontaneously; the deliberate shaping of economic development would not be possible. So in the planning of this economy centralization is unavoidable. But on the other hand, we also know that a certain degree of decentralization in current administration is necessary simply for the sake of elasticity. So we tried empirically, using the experience we had already gained, to establish the correct relations between centralization and decentralization. Now it transpires that for this kind of problem in particular, the conceptual apparatus developed by cybernetics provides us with welcome scientific criteria.

In the case which interests us at the moment cybernetics gives a very simple answer: decentralization is necessary wherever the time required to transmit information from the field to the center, for the converting of this information into decisions, and the return transmission of the decisions from the center to the field, is so long that irrevocable changes have occurred in the field, and the decision arrives too late.

This raises two problems: that of the period of time needed for the transmission of information and replies, and the rate at which the center digests the appropriate material and processes the information into decisions.

How serious this matter is, is indicated by Poland's difficulties before 1956. When, toward the end of the six-year period of planning, considerable difficulties arose in economic administration, an endeavor was made to get over these difficulties by resorting to greater centralization. The result was not that we mastered the situation, but a direct increase in the number of spontaneous processes as the effect of decisions arriving too late.

I give this instance in order to show how vital the questions raised by cybernetics are to the administration of socialistic economy. I would say that we are still far from a systematic science of administration, and therefore of the economy's optimal organization, centralization and decentralization — far from a solution to the question of incentives functioning within the economy, or the method of selecting optimal variants. But economists in the socialist countries have already begun studying these problems, and one may expect that considerable achievements will be registered in the immediate future.

As I now turn to the question of prognostication of the direction in which economic sciences will develop in the years ahead, I have to make one essential reservation. Namely, I consider that no prognosis can be generalized so as to assure its application in all countries. I know, for instance, that in the Soviet Union just now the question of the price system has priority in scientific debates; they are discussing a rational, scientifically worked out system of prices as the basis of economic accountancy and as a means of creating economic incentives.

So far as Poland is concerned, it seems to me that in the immediate future, problems which are more practical than scientific will tend to predominate. I am thinking of the economic stimuli. As mentioned before, there was extensive discussion at one time in Poland concerning the "model," and many changes were made in the economic administration. Enterprises were allowed a considerable increase in their independent activity. Associations were set up as associations of enterprises, and not as offices forming departments in ministries. A completely new structure of industrial administration was created taking the form: the ministry, the association, the enterprise. A new model of investment was instituted, on the lines of: central investments, association investments, enterprise investments. The enterprises and associations were given some autonomy in effecting certain investments. Further, the economy of the national councils was placed on an independent basis; they were given their own financial footing; and a large share in the administration of economy — such as trade, local industry, local planning — was handed over to them. The national councils obtained even an advisory voice in drawing up the plans for key industries situated in their areas. Then we had workers' self-government, and cooperation. On the organizational side the scope of cooperation was widened; for instance, dairy cooperatives came back, and housing cooperatives are developing. So on the organizational side important changes took place. It is now necessary to summarize these changes and generalize them, to scrutinize them and see how they look and work in practice.

And here the problem of stimuli makes its appearance. Indeed, the organizational changes have necessitated the introduction of a certain system of incentives. Self-government in enterprises, for one, led to the establishment of such stimuli as would ensure that the enterprises profited wisely by their self-dependence; otherwise independence would only be detrimental.

In short, organizational changes must be synchronized with a system of incentives. In this respect — even without scientific analysis and judging only from everyday experience — one can say that many difficulties still confront us. And so the question of the interplay of organization and stimuli will be one of the most important subjects for scientific and empirical treatment.

The view is gradually gaining ground that in scientific matters in the field of political economy Poland is beginning to occupy the position of one of the leading countries. This opinion spreads despite the fact that, owing to the restricted range of the Polish language, not everything we do gets known abroad.

However, contact between scientific work and practice and the nation's economic life has been far too small. This gives rise to a tendency toward a distinctive dualism in activities — on the one hand practice does not take advantage of the help which science can give, or does so inadequately; on the other hand, scientists frequently tend to lose contact with practice.

And yet it is in the close contact between scientific research work and the practice of economic administration that I would seek the main solution to the tasks which face Polish economic science at the present time.

— *translated by* HARRY STEVENS

(From *Przeglad Kulturalny,* a weekly. April 13, 1961, issue. Warsaw.)

Travel by Air

BY ANDRZEJ KIJOWSKI

ANDRZEJ KIJOWSKI was born in Krakow in 1928 and graduated from the university there, having majored in humanities. He began to be known as a book critic in 1950, and since 1955 he has been on the editorial staff of the literary monthly *Tworczosc*. He has also been a book reviewer and columnist for *Przeglad Kulturalny* since 1958. He has published the following: *The Devil, the Angel and a Peasant,* short stories (1955); *Five Stories* (1957); *The Pink and Black Literature,* literary essays (1957); *The Accused,* a novel (1959); and *Critical Miniatures* (1959), a selection from which follows. Mr. Kijowski, whose opinions are so popular with the younger generation that they give rise to cabaret songs, lives in Warsaw.

IN TODAY'S POLAND the attempts to write a realistic novel seem so far to have aimed more or less directly at its nineteenth-century "positivist" model. Particularly where the psychological master key is concerned, which at that time was the relation of the individual to society, a relation changing in step with the decline of the romantic individualism and the emergence of a new, social, attitude. This process had been presented as a matter of free option; it resulted from intellectual choice.

However, that change had been in ethics, not psychology. The psychology remained the same as before, only man was entrusted with other burdens to carry; it was a difference in trend. Psychology remained the same because the social principle remained the same: a society based on free interplay of forces. A definite activity or a definite social consciousness is, or at any rate can be, a matter of good will, sense of duty, conscience, capacity for objective thinking, or the outgrowing of one's class.

Not so in socialist society. Socialism is a reality objectively given *in toto* with all the duties and decisions ready, and not to be evaded. In it, one can have a divergent, nonsocialist conception of life, but he cannot follow a divergent social routine. For the faithful of the traditional individualistic psychology, it is a paradox not easily digested. This was evident in Polish literature of the years 1949-1955, when writers tried, within the categories of the individualistic psychology transferred crudely from the positivist novel, to show how people grow into socialism. In those years was created the problem of acceptance. For example, we meet an old scientist, attached to idealistic philosophy or to his belief in the nonpolitical nature of knowledge, who under the pressure of facts becomes convinced that, etc. We meet a workman unwilling to admit the superiority of collective to individual labor, whose prejudices are overcome by the enthusiasm of the Polish youth, etc. In real life it does not happen like this at all. The socialist way of life, and even socialist convictions, take root in an imperceptible, involuntary manner. An old humanist may well retain his reservations as to the Marxist theory of knowledge, or Marxist methodology, but this has not the slightest bearing on his social practice, which must conform to the actual society, must conform to reality. This reality has to be accepted in its given form; it is inescapable, just as, for instance, modern techniques are inescapable even with people who do not recognize or understand their rules. To this very day I do not properly understand why an airplane flies, but despite all the diffidence, I trust myself and the members of my family to this machine.

The airplane and technology are good examples; I will therefore consider them further. Please follow my reactions after I had decided to take the risk. To begin with, I am afraid. I examine every tiny screw most carefully. Maybe, during a flight, I noticed a little stream of oil running over a wing. I draw the mechanic's attention to it, and he ignores me. I feel offended, and am still very anxious. Then the plane begins to rock. I curse the day when I decided to fly, and I dream of the plush seats in a first-class railway carriage. I try to shirk all responsibility; in my mind I search for those who have persuaded or forced me to fly. But the plane stops rocking. I see familiar scenery. Now I begin to think I have borne myself not at all badly, and I was right in deciding on this flight despite other people's warnings. At last we land. Now I look at the motionless machine with tenderness, and I feel that I have come to know its workings perfectly; I have fathomed the secret of its efficiency. But the next time the story will of course repeat itself.

Modern man constantly has to cope with a reality which takes shape independently of his will and choice, while its mechanism remains too complicated for anyone but a specialist to understand. This is so not only where technology is concerned. Above all, this applies to the social reality, the institutions and principles of which are founded on a definite technique of social life. In our country socialism is simply the technique of modern existence. The "positivists" of the old days compared society to the human body. Today it should rather be compared to a mechanism. All the facts of social life reveal a tendency toward institutionalism, and many symptoms of personal life pass into the category of social phenomena.

Man's behavior in modern society is like the behavior of a nervous passenger in an airplane: fear, uncertainty, an attempt to divest himself of responsibility, finally affirmation *post factum,* and then the entire cycle over again. It is a continual passing not — as in individualistic psychology — from decision to action, but in the reverse: from action to its intellectual confirmation. Not from ideology to practice, but from practice to ideology. First the process of adaptation, the process of submitting to necessities, a process in which all the vestiges of the old psychology play their part: a feeling that human personality is being violated. Then the process of affirmation, which consists in finding one's own chances of freedom in the new situation. These chances lie — according to Marx's classic definition — in an understanding of necessity.

A naïve contemporary novel in Poland tries to present the act of affirmation as an individual's magnanimous gesture in resigning his rights in favor of society, a belated gesture of the past century. The man living in a socialist society is confronted with a completely different moral task in relation to himself and the community: he must separate himself from the crowd, must exclude himself from the mass process, which affects everybody in the same way notwithstanding their degree of consciousness; on the other hand, he must become conscious of the weight of personal responsibility which rests on him.

In brief, it is not a question of understanding and accepting the new historical situation, but of understanding oneself in a new historical situation.

— *translated by* HARRY STEVENS

(From *Miniatury Krytyczne,* essays. Published by Panstowy Instytut Wydawniczy, Warsaw, 1961.)

What Is Socialist Literature?

BY STEFAN KISIELEWSKI

STEFAN KISIELEWSKI, born in Warsaw in 1911, was the son of a novelist, and the nephew of a well-known playwright. A journalist, writer, composer, music critic and politician, he is also a champion of "modern" art. Kisielewski studied at the universities and music schools of Warsaw and Paris. He is now coeditor of the Catholic weekly *Tygodnik Powszechny,* and is considered an *enfant terrible* because of his controversial column, "Nails in the Brain," which he signs as Kisiel. Since 1957, he has been a member of Sejm, the Polish Parliament, and is a member of the Catholic parliamentary group Znak. So far, he has published nine books, among them four novels, two books of essays on music, and two volumes of essays on a variety of subjects. Several of his musical compositions have also been published and are being performed by symphony orchestras in Poland and abroad. Currently, he lives in Warsaw.

SHOULD PEOPLE who are not socialists concern themselves with definitions of socialist literature? A literary margin has been set aside in Poland for the use of authors who do not share the Marxist world outlook, and it is occupied by quite a few. Then why meddle in somebody else's affairs?

The problem, however, is not as simple as it would seem. In the past, I myself believed that if somebody considers socialism as just a sociohistorical fact, and not the triumph of a certain philosophy, he will, if he is a writer, find for himself — political system notwithstanding — other themes, all-human and eternal. A certain great artist once said that it's entirely sufficient to write about love and death, that these subjects will "guarantee a living" for many generations of writers to come, regardless of sociopolitical conditions. In other words, love, death, fear, sorrow, joy, jealousy, hope — those are matters, and thereby literary subjects, connected with human nature, unchanging in their essence, independent of whether industrial and agricultural production is socialized, nationalized, or in private hands.

This I believed for many years, but then, to a certain degree I changed my mind. Someone might ask if I now believe that a change in the economic and political life induces changes in morals, as is maintained by Marxist dialecticians. It is impossible to answer the question by a simple yes or no. Choosing a compromise between a sweeping statement and the splitting of hairs, I would say that while the essence of moral problems, most fully and subtly codified by the Christian moralists, does not change as a rule, their factual and psychological implications do change as the result of revolutionary transformations of production-ownership relationship and the methods of administration. It may be said that humanity, in some strange way, is always the same, while always being new. This is especially important to writers of the realistic school for whom a factual-social, or psychological-social change in the human setup is tantamount to a change in the literary "meat" — and literature depends primarily on that "meat," the quality of which is a more convincing proof of a writer's knowledge of life than the problems and theses he advances.

I believe that contemporary social reality in the countries subjected to the unusual, almost unprecedented in its reformative purpose, experiment of total socialism is a veritable gold mine of subjects and problems, regardless of anyone's attitude toward the new policies. I see here a tremendous and not-to-be-bypassed chance for writers approaching moral problems from the Christian or, more specifically, the Catholic point of view. How do the "eternal" human problems shape up against the background of the new forms of ownership and power; how do these matters reflect on the psyche of various people, young and old, individualists and socialists; what are the new forms of the traditional conflict between individual and society, or public and private interest; where is there room in all this for a new Rastignac's* pursuit of a career, the "full life"; how does the human personality change after having been drawn into the rhythm of collective work under the slogan of building a completely new future; how and to what degree do the psychological characteristics of man change in collective existence under the influence of an extraordinary social situation? These are just a few subjects at hand. Extremely important and yet, unfortunately, seldom touched upon by the pens of our writers.

Attempts to alienate moral problems from sociopolitical reality can-

---

* A Balzac character.

not give good results in a "normal," realistic novel (unlike the modern symbolic, allegoric poetry). Contemporary novels with a social moral give the impression of artificiality or complete abstraction, because moral problems there are not refracted in the prism of the actual social experiment, but seem to be distilled from life, rinsed clear of reality. There is in these books a subconscious evasion, a flight from the obvious. Of course, when consciously attempted, such an alienation is something different: it becomes the expression of individual loneliness, protest, disagreement with life; I mean biological life, not necessarily socialist. Such a voluntary alienation distinguishes the interesting literary debut of Stanislaw Stanuch: *Portrait from Memory,** a novel expressing a protest, which has a long tradition in world literature, for example in the works of Knut Hamsun and in our time Kafka and Sartre. Of course, what in Stanuch's book is a conscious design and a successful method, in the works of false realists becomes an error, or a failure.

Should Polish literature be socialist then? To my mind, this depends on what we understand by socialist literature — whether it is a literature describing socialism as it is now lived in our country or a literature helping socialism on nonliterary, tactical and educational grounds by means of a deliberate use of light and shadow. Stefan Zolkiewski says that socialist literature is not enough, that what is needed is social-realist literature. Hah! But it is just this adjective-supported realism burdened with immediate educational tasks that does not seem like much of a realism to us. The burden of tactics and education thrust upon writers, in other words, the concept of a subservient literature, of practical use to the rulers, was a few years ago responsible for the phenomenon called "schematism." It is indeed extremely difficult to avoid schematism in trying to embed the novel in the reconstruction process of a whole social system and awareness.

Zolkiewski pronounced himself in favor of that second type of socialist literature — a literature engaged in helping socialism on nonliterary grounds. I am naturally for the first alternative, namely for describing socialism, without anger or prejudice. I would even venture to defend my attitude from the point of view of socialism itself. For the question should be asked, does socialism really need assistance from lit-

---

* In another section of this book.

erature, and if so, can literature provide it? It is not impossible that the writer's role, even in a socialist system, should be different from what Zolkiewski wishes it to be.

To attempt an outline of the role of a writer in a socialist society, I shall borrow notions and metaphors from the essay, "The Priest and the Jester," * by Leszek Kolakowski. The author contrasts there two intellectual attitudes: the conformism of the "priest," unshakably faithful to the generalized knowledge of the world, solid and absolute, and the skepticism of the "jester," a nonconformist suspicious of all authority, rejecting the pressures of "theology," be it clerical or secular.

This antinomy (Kolakowski decidedly favors the attitude of the "jester") is not overly interesting in the field of philosophy: it is reduced in its essence to Kant's already traditional *Critique of Pure Reason* and ends up, like the other, with the unattractive "practical reason." This seems a bit inadequate in an era when generalizations ("working ones") are utilized not only in philosophy and theology, but even physics — achieving great and practical results. On the other hand, the "priest" and "jester" conception may prove extremely useful in the field of literature.

Since the time of Voltaire and the Encyclopedists, the largest as well as the most valuable part of literature has been a "jester" literature. It was perhaps most interesting in the era of capitalism's infancy; for example, the nineteenth-century French novel in a period when the *bourgeoisie* was laying the foundations of French industrial and financial power. That literature was far removed from national optimism, although even Marxism considers the bourgeois Industrial Revolution in its early stages as a manifestation of progress. Writers at that time jeered at both *bourgeoisie* and capitalism, sparing nothing. Balzac flayed (often subconsciously, because he was really impressed with capitalism), Flaubert jeered and probed mercilessly, Zola lashed (*Germinal*), and Maupassant ridiculed and tore to shreds. And what happened? All these writings turned out by "jesters" not only failed to harm the *bourgeoisie,* but were finally accepted as its representative literature.

In America things took an even sharper turn. In the last half century, while the United States was building its extraordinary industrial potential, there appeared a long list of writers reviling the

---

* See page 301.

process, boiling over with "anti-Americanism." Before the war: Upton Sinclair's *King Coal,* Nobel Prize-winner Sinclair Lewis's *Babbitt,* Theodore Dreiser's *An American Tragedy,* John Dos Passos's *Manhattan Transfer* and Henry Miller's *Tropic of Cancer* and *Tropic of Capricorn* (the last book, its anti-Americanism outdistancing anything written on the subject throughout the world, was the only work which encountered temporary repression: the author was accused of "pornography" and unable for some time to publish his works in America — today it is almost a classic).* After the war the names speak for themselves: Steinbeck, Faulkner, Caldwell and — perhaps the least "jester" of them — Hemingway. Another characteristic fact: these authors of virulent and passionate disclosures of the dark back alleys of America not only are not considered its enemies, but rather are proclaimed as the pride of American literature.

Stefan Zolkiewski will say that all the above writers represent "critical realism" within capitalism itself. However, I remember that some ten years ago Erskine Caldwell visited Warsaw. The Polish writer who interviewed the author of the book then famous in our country, *Tobacco Road,* tried to suggest that Caldwell's books contain essential criticism of social conditions in America. Caldwell emphatically protested, saying that he dislikes and avoids generalizations, and in his work he purposely chooses rare and striking cases of bestiality because they interest him and suit his talent well. Whatever the motives of the statement, Caldwell showed the good instinct of a "jester" who refuses to be a "priest" even in jest, and who goes so far as to refuse to make any criticism absolute.

Now, the question arises: Is not Marxism in need of its own "jester," its own doubting literature? It is not, if one believes that Marxism is the final stage of human knowledge and its ultimate, though still incomplete, practical fulfillment. But dialectics tell us that evolution never ends, change and conflict never cease. If so, socialism certainly needs its "jester," a new one: new conflicts require new "jesting." "Jester," of course, must not be identified with "enemy." Perhaps the

---

* The author of the article, whose handling of chronology seems a little arbitrary, is obviously unaware of the fact that most of Henry Miller's books, with the exception of his harmless wartime travelogues, are still taboo in the States. *Tropic of Cancer* appeared in New York only in June 1961, twenty-seven years after its publication in Paris.

masses are inclined to read "jester" books in a political, unreasonable way, but there are solutions such as the publication of limited editions for the intellectual elite. We must not renounce the services of a "jester"; his function, though perhaps not the most important, is nevertheless as essential as the functioning of bile or the pancreas in a living organism.

International politics, as well as anti-Marxist or anti-Communist vulgarities spread by some Western and *émigré* factions, are doing great harm by meddling in Polish literary affairs. It all began even before the October crisis in 1956 which, in my opinion, was to a large extent warped by nonessential, purely personal literary fuss. A small group of writers, who in the past period had been in Poland the exponents of schematism, but wished to rehabilitate themselves during the "thaw," made a lot of noise, which was immediately taken up by the Western press and radio. The din they created drowned all common sense, and tiny personal-literary problems were irrelevantly placed next to the most important socioeconomic problems of national existence. This demagogy brought little profit and much harm, literature included. While before, there had been the threat of Marxist schematism, there now loomed an anti-Marxist one, even more dangerous (God preserve me from my friends . . .). Finally, the poor genuine literary "jester" finds himself now between the frying pan and the fire; both sides — for extraliterary reasons — demand of him a simple declaration. And he doesn't like that at all.

The Marek Hlasko* affair is a perfect case in point. When he wrote "The Eighth Day of the Week," he assumed the classic attitude of the "jester," the prerequisite of which is that the author be a part of the things he describes and his criticism the criticism from an inside position. However, when he wrote "Cemeteries," while still in Poland, he shifted to the attitude of the "priest," as he described things he did not know (the internal life of high party ranks) using obsolete Orwellian schematism. Thus, we lost a writer, and what's more, the "jester"-type writer we need so much. Writing "for the West," he chose schematism — and schematism, regardless of its brand, destroys a writer.

To return to literary attitudes in countries building socialism on the Marxist-Leninist principles, I believe that the attitudes of "jester" and

* A Polish writer who "chose freedom" a few years ago, and lives now in the West. The above-mentioned story was turned into a film and shown in America.

"priest" are not the only possible ones. There is still the attitude of complex acceptance which takes into consideration the contradictions in the world and, regardless of the side the writer had on the whole committed himself to, endeavors to give full literary expression to complexity. I see such complex acceptance in Sholokhov's books and also to a degree in Alexei Tolstoy's *Road through Misery*. What a mistake not to read Sholokhov! I learned from an *émigré* publication that he is a "schematist." Apparently the author of that opinion hadn't glanced at *Quiet Flows the Don* for quite some time. It is — in my opinion — the least schematic book ever written on the Eastern side of the world — much less schematic than Pasternak's overpublicized *Doctor Zhivago*, which was based on the conventions of the Western intelligentsia. In Sholokhov's method, there is something of the nonintellectual, unsophisticated, truly "plebeian" method of the great American realists — something of Steinbeck and Faulkner *avant la lettre*. Had Sholokhov, and not Pasternak, received the Nobel Prize, the literary discussion between East and West would have become serious and literary. As it is, the matter degenerated into a political prestige showdown.

I am one of those writers by now utterly bored with being stuck on the "non-Marxist margin." I should like to take up "socialist literature" as I understand it, that is, write about socialism from the standpoint of a mistrustful but objective local "jester." I don't believe it would either hurt or hamper the Polish progress; I don't think that the color black, used among other hues, would discourage people from working.

Avoiding the attitude of a "priest," at the same time many of our authors avoid in their books the topical subjects of the day. This is a great shame — to stand over a rich mine and not exploit it! Should these hugely interesting times remain without a complex, truly literary testimony for the future to appraise? But contemporaries also find in a many-sided report a better political guidance than in a story deliberately simplified. *Quiet Flows the Don* and *Road through Misery*, while making no attempt to conceal the shocking picture of either the Revolution or counterrevolution, undoubtedly divulge to many the authentic mechanism of history.

— *translated by* EWA MARKOWSKA

(From *Tygodnik Powszechny*. February 7, 1960. Krakow.)

Is "Socialist Literature" Enough?

BY STEFAN ZOLKIEWSKI

STEFAN ZOLKIEWSKI was born in 1911. He received his doctorate in humanities from the University of Warsaw. During the Occupation he remained in the city editing papers related to the Communist party, with which he has been associated since his student days. From 1945 to 1949 he edited *Kuznica,* the party literary weekly. He was first elected deputy to the Sejm in 1947. From 1955 to 1959 he held the post of Minister of Higher Education, and since 1945 he has been professor of Polish literature at Warsaw University. He is editor in chief of *Culture and Society,* a sociological quarterly, and till 1962 he was director of the literary weekly *Nowa Kultura.* In addition to his other activities, he is a member of the praesidium of the Polish Academy of Science. Among his many books are *The Old and the New Literary Science; Dispute about Mickiewicz; Culture and Politics.* The essay which appears below was first published in *Nowa Kultura* in 1960. Mr. Zolkiewski lives in Warsaw.

MY VIEW that the progress of social realism in Poland will play a decisive part in the development of literature, in accordance with the essential problems of Polish social life, has met with objections. My opponents consider that we need to postulate a "socialist literature" *pure and simple,* and that it will be distinguished in the multitude and variety of its forms of expression by a social function: its ideological influence in favor of socialism. The concept of "socialist literature," they say, is bound to be broader than the category of social realism, and therefore to engender a more elastic cultural policy.

I think my opponents are wrong. The social function of a literature can be studied by a sociologist empirically investigating its influence on its readers. The ensuing knowledge is of great importance not only theoretically but practically; it provides indications for the future. But in the actual practice of literary life this cannot be a substitute for a well-founded prognosis of the direction taken, and the social influence exerted, by a definite type of work. What are the features which the works of art falling within the category of "socialist literature" should possess to enable one to foresee more or less accurately the nature of their social influence? My opponents do not consider the question, and yet this is the nub of the matter. In consequence, as they reject the necessity for a definition of the artistic character of the works in question, the critics must include books within the category of socialist literature uniquely on the strength of not even their ideological or philosophic, but rather trivially political, contents. Yet the ideological sense of a literary work may not be condensed in the author's own journalistic commentary encased in the story; that sense is usually communicated through the writer's whole approach to reality, his vision, and therefore through means subordinated to his own specific judgment and perception of the world.

This is so even in lyric production, irrespective of whether the poet considers it necessary to add a commentary no longer in the guise of allegories and metaphors, but in the discursive language of the publicist. How often such a commentary is shallow and far below the level of the artist's vision! And so the specific features of a literary genre can affect a book's ideological impact. These features are relatively constant; they restrict the author's freedom in expressing his approach to reality. This is the reason why certain literary genres die out, or disappear for a time, independently of the changes in public taste. For instance, because of its formal traits, the classical descriptive poem so determined the writer's relation to life that Polish romantics were unable to make use of it when they sought to express revolt against social order, their basic attitude. Well, the genre became extinct. In other cases the form underwent appropriate modifications, while preserving some of its characteristic features. We may instance the evolution of the prose novel. The same applies to the philosophical content of a work, the author's *Weltanschauung*. For after all, it is the fate of the protagonist, the organization of his life story, the kind of conflict he encounters and its solution that convey the philosophic meaning of a book. We find that, in important respects, the philosophic judgment of the world as formulated by the romantic writers, who individually were so different and original, is similar; this is due to the romantic stylistic conventions which they all share, or rather, their common principle of choice and integration of the artistic means of expression. Poetics is never a formal game; it is an achievement of the mind in judging the world, interpreting its conflicts, its sense or nonsense, and seeking artistic expression for its own essence; it is therefore a necessary and specifically correct structure, justified by the work's stylistic unity. If there is a conscious design to seek only chance and arbitrariness, as in pure Dadaism, I consider that we pass beyond the boundaries of art; we find ourselves in an artificially invented marginal area of attempts without a future. Surrealism, on the other hand, deserves the name of poetics, because it sought expression of a definite essence, although it claimed some genetic associations with Dadaism. Dadaism quickly waned, whereas surrealism gained a wide and lasting influence on the further development of twentieth-century poetry.

Now, if our opponents are afraid to postulate a definite creative method and corresponding poetics, they are really left with only that journalistic commentary, or some minimum of political content implying direct approval of socialism and its efforts. What they have in mind is only the subject matter and the author's positive attitude to politically active themes.

But that is an extremely narrow and spiritless view. If we are to conjecture about the social influence of a work on such a basis, we have to restrict "socialist literature" to a few themes. All the rest, and consequently all literature not concerned with directly political themes, would be discarded.

I am convinced that my proposal is of the wider scope. Moreover, it answers the particular demands of our literary reality. Meanwhile, the concept of "socialist literature" disregards precisely all that is specific to literature and the laws of its development.

For what are we arguing about? Using deliberately simplified terms, we ask: Are there to be various poetics and one ideology? Or one world outlook, and therefore one poetics defined widely enough to embrace the historic wealth of literature and the creative method of social realism?

One reservation right at the start: The social and political life of the Polish People's Republic presupposes free development of their creative powers for writers who are not Communists and Marxists; who, for instance, reconcile a religious outlook with the will to participate actively in the construction of socialism. Our struggle for a literature of ideas does not cancel out these freedoms. Yet we want to see the development of a literature consistently bound up with the socialist reconstruction of life. We reckon that the future belongs to that literature.

We do not decree what a writer should think and how he should view the world, but we wish to convince people of the truthfulness of our ideas. So now we can return to our question.

I consider that the reason for the existence of many differing poetics is that they allow the expression of various kinds of human attitudes to reality. Various in an intellectual sense. Sometimes, however, it happens otherwise; the aristocratic interpretation of the poetics of sentimentalism, an interpretation contrary to Rousseau's and Diderot's intellectual propensities, attempted in many respects to serve the same essence as the then traditional poetics of pseudoclassicism in the second half of the eighteenth century.

In the history of twentieth-century literature you will find the same approach to reality, the same basic ideas answering the revolutionary needs of the workers' movement and socialist construction, in works marked not only by the writers' different talents, but also by the distinctive features of literary schools. Because socialist realism was not the implementation of an aesthetic doctrine, as futurism was, or even certain early products of the surrealists; social realism was born of social struggle. It laboriously sought its own means of expression. It took on a different guise in Germany in Brecht's works, different in Gorki's literary activity in Russia, different again in Sholokhov's books in the Soviet Union, different in Kruczkowski's plays in Poland. But the creative effort of all these writers only marks certain stages and modifications in the maturing of an artistic method under definite and differing conditions. In the later development certain features of their research proved more durable, others less. Some were taken over by related literary schools; others were rejected.

The poetics of social realism cannot be treated statically by the historian, either yesterday or today; on the contrary, it is necessary to observe the dynamic process of its formation, its changes, its endeavors to set rules, and then struggle against the rules.

The process covers a comparatively few years. And disparity is still very much alive in the socialist literary field today.

In the recent history of Polish literature we find attempts to set rules and introduce uniformity into Polish poetics. A similar period was observable in the literary life of the Soviet Union after 1935. I do not propose here to consider the errors of cultural policy which later weighed heavily on this standardization. But I would never treat the very wish to formulate rules as an error in cultural policy; on the contrary, I would rather adhere to the hypothesis that codifying tendencies are a normal feature of contemporary literary life. I think they will be a component of future literary life also.

It must be said that in the conditions of capitalist encirclement, partially continued in the years of the "cold war," Soviet culture had to be to a certain extent self-contained. The capitalist world isolated itself from Soviet art, which was and still is insufficiently popularized. As Ehrenburg remarked, there are more translations of contemporary American or French writers into Russian than of Soviet writers into English and French.

Because of its isolation, Soviet culture did not feel the need to assimilate the numerous important values necessary for the finding of a common language with people who, thanks to their class position, were susceptible to socialism, but whose upbringing in a different culture required the supply of new ideas to be in a language close enough to their own.

The effort to codify the creative method and the poetics of social realism in the Soviet Union during the 1940s, undertaken in the era of isolation, did not take into account the many experiences of social realism outside the Soviet Union, nor the various artistic values which, theoretically, it could have assimilated with advantage. The impact of the Soviet formulas on the social realists in then capitalist countries varied; it depended on individual and extraindividual factors. For instance, the formulas did not have any great effect on Kruczkowski's work in Poland. But it had a considerable influence on Aragon in France (compare the poem cycle *Hourra Ural* — 1934 — with the novel cycle *The Communists* — 1949-1951). In *Holy Week*, however, the same writer explored new possibilities of development in social realism by appropriating in a creative way the artistic discoveries of other literary trends of the twentieth century.

Let us not forget that the present-day state of the world is different. Today the cultural expansion of conquering socialism is achieved by way of wider contacts with the cultures of the rest of the world. This means not only the winning over to the idea of socialism of whole mass movements of national liberation, but the critical assimilation by socialist culture of new values created by other cultures and artistic traditions.

The policy of the peaceful competition of systems and active coexistence is already strengthening these processes, and may strengthen them even more.

The superiority of the socialist system, its greater dynamism, gradually excelling that of capitalism, makes for an ever growing scope of cultural contact. This compels socialist culture to emphasize its distinctive features all the more strongly, but it also encourages profiting by the new vistas. The exchange takes on one aspect where socialist culture develops in association with the traditional culture of China, and another where socialism, fighting for the ideological orientation of the intellectuals in Italy, borrows some means of expression born in the minds and imaginations of the creative elements in twentieth-century Western Europe. And so the present time is favorable to the shaping-up of a social realism based on half a century of its own varied artistic experiences, the lasting acquisitions of individual geniuses and interesting schools, plus the essential achievements of others, for the enrichment of the means of expression as assimilated by our own creative method.

"International cooperation in the field of culture presupposes mutual exchange of that which is the best; realization of the achievements of others; mutual enrichment." (Ehrenburg, in *Literaturnaya Gazeta* magazine, Autumn 1959.)

"How can that be? someone will ask. "Assimilation of the achievements of other poetics means exactly the principle of many poetics, as postulated by your opponents." Oh, no! Only certain elements of artistic technique are involved, without the self-contained structure of a whole literary craft being appropriated. The deliberately selected elements must become an integral part of a new whole, must join a new stylistic unity. The ideological essence of the socialist world outlook cannot be expressed in the poetics of a Joyce or a Beckett. On the other hand, one can, I presume, assimilate certain technical discoveries peculiar to a given literary technique. For instance, in Aragon's *Holy Week,* the

Proustian disintegration of a fictional character is not a nonrealistic intrusion of alien poetics; the process has been completely absorbed into a new stylistic wholeness and unity. The practice can be accepted since, as Aragon's experience proves, it releases possibilities inherent in social realism and it enriches and strengthens its expression, without distorting the ideological content. This is an innovation achieved by Aragon, the social realist, but no longer in terms of Proustian poetics.

The Soviet attempt to codify social realism in the forties cannot be considered as a rigid norm. Life, which constantly sets our method new questions and problems, will not allow that. And so today social realism is entering on a new phase of development. This is obvious both in literary practice and in the theoretical discussions of Marxists all over the world. According to the laws of literary development, there will be one definite creative method, one poetics, though, I think, incomparably richer than that evolved at any time during the past fifty years.

There are those who consider that the literature of the twentieth century is distinguished by a specific syncretism of poetics. It is said to be the sum total of the contributions of many artistic orientations during the first twenty-five years of our century. I consider this opinion to be merely a more cautiously worded version of the trivial idea of the single sack of "modernity," as opposed to social realism which is allegedly a last-century tradition. A fine outdated tradition indeed, when you consider the work of Brecht or Mayakovsky! But there is more to this notion of syncretism than that. So far I have nowhere seen a proof that it is not at variance with historic reality. On the contrary, the literature of the twentieth century has developed in the form of many definite literary trends, such as futurism, expressionism, surrealism. Certain of them have passed away quickly, like futurism; others lived long, but lived the life of epigones, such as expressionism; others have had a lasting influence on the further progress of art, for example, surrealism. Various kinds of realism, as for instance, the Italian and American kind, have always lived a separate life. No one will deny the distinctive character of the development of social realism.

The evolution of other literary trends since 1950 by no means testifies to syncretism. On the contrary, it demonstrates, for instance, the vitality of surrealism in the poetry of certain literary schools in a number of countries. If there are certain futuristic or expressionistic elements in their poetry, it is easy to identify them as grafted on and destroying the stylistic unity.

The same is true of prose. Here too it is difficult to discern syncretism of method, be it naturalistic, expressionistic, or constructivist. Instead, we are easily recognizing the epigones of expressionism. And both Italian neorealism and social realism have their own definite styles.

For syncretism is something completely different from the assimilating by a given poetics of isolated means of expression discovered by another trend. Cases of assimilation are therefore frequent and easy to point to.

The actual development of twentieth-century literature is being achieved within the confines of many literary trends, differentiated ideologically and correspondingly different as techniques. And the historical experience of twentieth-century literature all over the world shows that the consistent expression of a socialistic attitude to reality is provided in literature by the works of social realism.

The postulate of "socialist literature" is a trick of self-deception. If we analyze the true meaning of this postulate, we must say clearly and doctrinally that we are fighting for a literature of social *realism*. This concept alone enables us to use the one language of the twentieth-century literary theory which not only allows us to reach an understanding with the theoreticians, creative artists, and active workers in culture, as well as Soviet or Chinese readers, but which is also the language of Aragon and the bourgeois eclectic historian of French literature, de Boisdeffre. This concept is used by Lukacs as well as his critics; with its aid both Gorki and Brecht formulated their classic and still vital theories. The café habitués of Warsaw don't like it? Then let them talk about something else, or by signs.

We can and we ought to contemplate great chances of evolution for social realism as far as forms of expression are concerned, but the limit of these chances must remain the unity of the social realistic style. It is impossible to accept Kafka's poetics wholesale, and squeeze socialistic substance into it. Such a hope is absurd. The struggle for a definite ideology in art, creative method, and taste is also a struggle against other ideologies, creative methods, and tastes. There is no escaping from that. Such is social life, and such is the progress of culture. It demands choice.

Between those who judge that the distinctive task of present-day literature is to weigh the metaphysical, supratemporal doubt whether life has any meaning at all and those who think that it is literature which, in measuring up to the problems of our time, will historically clarify what meaning life has, and what is the mechanism of its transmutations, there is a fundamental difference in ideology, in approach to reality, in vision of the world. And consequently there is a difference in means of expression, a constant choice and integration of the artistic conventions. To the first group, knowledge of the historical and psychological reality and the mores of our times will not be of much use. The second group, on the other hand, cannot afford to ignore any important element of history, customs, mentality, or any deformation of the writer's attitude toward the world he describes. But that surely means that the poetics of realism come into play. If, moreover, the writer's attitude toward the world is Marxist, his method will not be just realism; it will be social realism. This method was not meant for extolling schematic production processes without people, as happens with graphomaniacs. It was meant for resolving the deepest problems of human existence. The answer to the same question about the characteristics, necessity, value, and meaning of freedom can be in one poetics existentialist, and in another Marxist. Only this second answer appeals not to mythology, but to history. To human realities.

Certain people would like to abandon their choice to accident and chance. But choice is the very essence of the human condition. And the wider the sphere of well-motivated and consistent choice, the wider also is the part of human culture in reshaping the world.

— *translated by* HARRY STEVENS

(From *Nowa Kultura*, a weekly. January 17, 1960. Warsaw.)

The Solitude of Poetry

BY MIECZYSLAW JASTRUN

MIECZYSLAW JASTRUN was born in Korolowka in 1903 and holds a Ph.D. from Krakow University. From 1928 to 1939 he was a teacher, but made his debut as a poet in 1929 with a book entitled *Meetings in Time.* This was followed by four more volumes of poetry published prior to World War II. Under the Germans, he continued as a teacher in schools organized by the Underground Polish Administration, and also contributed to the Underground press. *A Human Matter* and *A Guarded Hour* – both volumes of poetry – are of that period. After the war, he published, among other volumes, *A Poem About the Polish Language; Poetry and Truth; Hot Ashes;* and *Bigger Than Life,* a selection of poems. His romantic biography of Mickiewicz, Poland's greatest poet, published in 1949, has been translated into many languages. He is also the author of a collection of essays on poetry, *Between the Word and the Silence,* a selection from which follows, and has written an autobiographical novel, *The Beautiful Sickness,* published in 1961. Mr. Jastrun, in addition to the above, is known as an accomplished translator of French, German and Russian poets. He is presently living in Warsaw.

Specialization is probably the most striking feature of contemporary culture. Aristotle could still master the totality of scientific and artistic phenomena of his times, and even many centuries later, Kant and Hegel did not consider themselves ignorant in matters of science reaching beyond their particular fields of interest. Who among contemporary philosophers would dare to say with such assurance, and self-sufficiency: "Starry sky above me, and moral law within me"? This starry sky has become much more complex, and moral law much less certain.

It has been said that in our epoch philosophy is no longer possible. Particular scientific disciplines have become so difficult that they are accessible only to the narrow circle of the initiated. To master even one of these disciplines, a philosopher would have to devote nearly all of his life to it — no time would be left for a synthesis. In this sense, one may speak of the dehumanization of culture. The age of sages is past; the age of the specialists has come. Since philosophy, in the traditional sense, is no longer possible, its function is all the more eagerly taken over by poetry, which, after all, always was philosophy's neighbor and close kin. Sometimes the boundaries between them become hazy. Who is to judge today whether Heraclitus was a philosopher or a poet as great as Sophocles? Was Nietzsche a poet only in his infrequent, very dynamic verses? Are there not numerous pages of Bergson worthy of appearing in the works of Proust or Thomas Mann? Are not Sartre and

Camus also poets in their philosophical writings and essays? Are certain of Pascal's thoughts not the purest poetry?

Twentieth-century poetry broke on the whole with the sentimentalism which, in the last century, seemed to be an integral part of all lyric production. It is rather in Poland and in some other Slavic countries that one expects emotional exuberance. For in Poland romantic poetry, with its roots reaching deeper into the national consciousness than elsewhere, played an unusual role.

Tradition remains alive only when we struggle with it. It is a grave error for historians of literature to interpret the national spirit of the age in an oversimplified manner, ignoring the complexity of various cultural and life processes. Instead of using their imagination, they try to read the future by observing the hands of a clock which is still busy measuring the past.

And now for the antinomies of contemporary poetry. The American poet Karl Shapiro, speaking of modern poetry, adds the reservation that its "metaphysical" character is not necessarily a sign of a religious renaissance, but rather a symptom of the search for new sources of inspiration. One could immediately retort that these sources have been exploited for a long time; one should not forget — as the fanatics of superficial modernity seem to do — that the concept of an absolute modernity is only a myth. Novelty consists in the new situations we are living through. One cannot enter twice into the same waters of the Heraclitean river of life; the metaphysics of the age of cosmic rockets and split atoms must necessarily differ from the metaphysics of Schelling or Slowacki.* Confusing metaphysics with mysticism may be used as a propaganda argument, but is pointless. The concept of progressiveness in art cannot be evaluated — as is sometimes done — in such a crude and nonscientific manner.

The spirit of the age is not synonymous with what the public likes. Today, in the same way as a century ago, those things are liked which are easy. And easy is what is familiar, and familiar — what is universal. If something is difficult, it is due either to its "content" or its "form" of expression. The public, regardless of its social origin, likes, above all, that which is easily accessible. There is nothing surprising in this, but art

* A Polish romantic poet.

cannot progress by sticking to what is already familiar. Poetry, in the entire course of its development, has always been trying to capture meanings and problems which are still obscure and dormant. Poetry tries to awaken them with a kiss, wherever they may be: in the air, in things, in human beings. The poetry of recent times tries not only to revive the imagination but, in its most radical manifestations, daringly attempts to create a new quality. Already Mallarmé has broken with the architectural encasement of the poem, retaining only the elixir, the poetic essence. It is enough to compare his method with that of Victor Hugo or consider the chasm separating images of the *Légende des Siècles* from the visions of Rimbaud's *Illuminations* to see the difference. This burning of bridges, these violent condensations and projections of thought, have made the new poetry difficult for the unprepared reader.

In Poland the process is slower, but we must not forget that already Slowacki was accused of incomprehensibility, and Norwid* is still an obscure poet to many, not to mention some contemporary trends in poetry. Nevertheless, works originally hermetic in time reach the reader; often in an indirect way, perhaps in an ersatz form. Today, surrealism reappears in Poland in a provincial edition, sometimes to the accompaniment of a guitar. The demand that poetry be immediately understandable to everyone is truly absurd. From laboratories employing complex apparatus, poetry often emerges into the outside world after a long lapse of time, just as some scientific discoveries become common property only after they have entered the blood stream of the generations. Of course, this is only an approximate, not a strict, analogy. The "knowledge" required to accept new poetic forms consists in sensitivity and imagination; it has nothing to do with scientific perception, even in the limited sense associated with the popularization of scientific and technological advances. Drawing its inspiration from solitude, poetry is also a remedy against it and — contrary to the pessimistic prophecies of, say, T. S. Eliot — can counteract the loneliness of "human atoms" in contemporary civilization.

Solitude is an essential element in poetry; marching groups and teams can give birth only to chants, songs and slogans. Since he can absorb the world with all its various idioms, a genuine poet thrives on

* The youngest of the Polish romantic poets, whose work was virtually "discovered" only at the beginning of the twentieth century.

being alone. Isolation assures him of a clear vision undulled by anyone's presence, and the fact that his room may be peopled with the voices of the present, past, and future generations offers no contradiction. How lonely Norwid was, but even he in the last, most solitary period of his life could say, "As soon as you think, you are not alone." The solitude of the poet is the uniqueness of his experience, and the particularity of his sensitivity and imagination.

Character — as Schiller claimed — develops amidst the tumult of life; talent — that is to say, the ability to see the world in a unique way — matures and grows in isolation. Environment grinds us, forces us to adjust, and — consciously or not — kills our most precious possession: that something which enables us to speak with ourselves and with God. For, although lyric poetry is always a monologue, the dialogue, the desire to communicate our experiences to others, is a constant driving force in art, its inspiration and its meaning.

The social function of poetry does not lie in the repetition of universally known truths, but in discovering new areas in a sphere which is not identical with the sphere of consciousness. Even such a well-balanced poet as Goethe, whose thought ran in the categories of great cultural and humanist traditions, confessed that he was more indebted to the unconscious than to the rational. The surrealists, supported by modern psychology, particularly by Freud, went furthest in the exploitation of the subconscious. However, not only these excursions into the little-explored regions of the human soul make the poetry of recent times so difficult to understand for a reader who is not aware of its historical development, and has neither the time nor the desire to overcome the obstacle. There is, in addition to the transformation of the meaning of poetry, the further evolution of the forms of its expression. This evolution is no less necessary here than in the field of the exact sciences and technological discoveries. Of course, these are different values, but the correlation should be noted.

The history of the creative progress of individual artists also shows that, along with their spiritual growth and the increasing complexity of their inner life, their forms of expression become more complex. Norwid's early poems were satisfying to the average reader of poetry and earned him the favorable opinion of the literary critics of the time. But as his work developed and deepened, the same critics began to voice disappointment, betraying a complete lack of understanding of what made his poetry great. To cover up their own blindness, they accused him of "obscurity."

Although Slowacki's poems about the Polish insurrection did not introduce any new values into Polish poetry, they were enthusiastically received, but as he began to move away from the clichés, an ever deeper silence of the critics enveloped him. In more recent times, Rilke was also a case in point. He started with easy, not overly ambitious lyric poems. Only his mature works — from the "poetry of things," in the two volumes of *New Poems*, to *Duino Elegies* and *Sonnets to Orpheus* — with their tremendous complexity and "difficulty" in forms of expression, showed his full stature. Rilke is, to the present day, one of the most famous poets in the world, but in Germany his lesser works, those with inferior intellectual and poetic content, enjoy the greatest popularity. Above all, it is so with *The Tale of Love and Death of Cornet Christopher Rilke*, a story written in poetic prose and based on popular lyric themes.

In his later years, Rilke renounced his youthful poetry, as did Slowacki, who, at the peak of his creativity, was ashamed of his early efforts. In the end, time is the best ally of poets. It clarifies their works and makes them accessible to an ever widening circle of readers. In this way, the important and necessary process of raising the general level of artistic sensitivity goes on. The significance of this fact is not diminished by the procession of snobs and tricksters who follow in the wake of genuine art.

Exhortations to "simplicity" and readability are as meaningless and ineffective as is the lament of lazy people so petrified in their habits that they have to complain about the tempo of technological civilization and the progress of science. I think that the solitude of poetry will deepen as time goes on, but we must not expect its demise. Those who look with misgivings at its flight into abstraction, at its "assumption into heaven," ought to remember that it is precisely in our age that heaven has ceased to be an abstract and theological concept.

— *translated by* Maria de Gorgey

(From *Miedzy Slowem a Milczeniem*, essays. Published by Panstwowy Instytut Wydawniczy, Warsaw, 1960.)

IV

Their Humor

A Happy Creature

BY MARIA DABROWSKA

(The biographical note on Maria Dabrowska appears in the section "How They See Life.")

ALTHOUGH SHE was seventy, Martha Wondrausz had to get up every morning soon after five, so that she could prepare breakfast on the hot plate for herself, her husband and their dog before getting herself ready in time to reach Warsaw by eight. She still had a job; because of her long and distinguished career she had not been fired as had most of the other elderly employees, pensioned off with cheerful farewells and showered with medals as consolation prizes.

Professor Felix Wondrausz, two years older than his wife, was still a lecturer at the university. For the time being, he was confined to the house with severe circulatory trouble, his doctor having ordered him to stop work for a month.

Martha walked to the station past many gardens, fresh and green in this month of May, and through the remains of a wood into which the suburban settlement had made its inroads. The almost forgotten branch line was still served by old-fashioned steam engines, which were noisy, smoky and dirty. Martha traveled standing in a crowd so dense that on each part of her body she felt the pressure of a part of somebody else's flesh. Suddenly she realized that the arm resting on her collarbone belonged to a woman teacher who lived not far from her. She had to laugh at the lunatic situation which compelled a friend, a kindly and pleasant person, to behave as if she wanted to crush her to death. The woman recognized Martha's laugh, and turned her head slowly toward her, trying not to hit anyone in the nose or eye.

"So it's you, Mrs. Wondrausz! I am so sorry about my elbow, but as you see — I can't move it."

"It doesn't matter," said Martha. "I'm digging my bones into somebody's bust or buttocks, I don't know which; I can only feel that it is soft."

"It's terrible that you should have to travel under these horrible conditions . . ." replied her friend. "I am so much younger, and I can hardly stand it."

"But think of the training this provides for old muscles! This is what keeps me fit," Martha assured her. "And what about contact with real life?" She rolled her eyes at the surrounding crowd. "It would be difficult to get nearer to the masses, you must admit . . ."

"And how is that delightful dog of yours?" asked the teacher. "To have such a pleasant creature in the house must be very nice."

"Darek is not really our dog, you know. Milo, my husband's great-nephew, left him in our care, or rather abandoned him. He could not bear it that Darek seemed to like us. The dog even likes Madam Gronek, you know whom I mean — the woman who cooks our meals. Milo was near despair when Darek followed her around. He was so angry that he refused to take the animal back with him to Warsaw. He wanted a dog exclusively for himself, one that would growl at everybody else and love nobody but himself."

"How is this possible?" asked the teacher. "So much is being done now in the way of social education, and yet children seem to grow increasingly more selfish . . ."

"People have always complained about this. But the dog is really delightful. I believe he is the only happy creature I know."

"I thought *you* were happy. Everybody seems so bad-tempered and worried now, but you are always cheerful . . ."

The train stopped. The throng increased. Martha tried to carry on the conversation:

"Happiness? Altruism? Social conscience? You must forgive me . . . . in such an inhuman crush? One needs some space for that — not very much, but at least two yards between one face and another."

She now felt a different arm poking into her collarbone — her teacher friend had been pushed away from her into the crowd.

At about five Martha returned home. She was pleased because she had succeeded in getting some smoked pork fillet for Felix and a scrap of meat with a bone for the dog. It was not every day that she had time to shop. There were usually queues waiting in front of already crowded shops, but that day she had found a shop which was nearly empty.

At the office she had succeeded in completing some statistical graphs. "After all," she thought, "for a long time now life has consisted of whether or not you have managed to do this or that. Work, bits of business, errands, worries, crowd in on you and knock you about just as people do. When you have done this or that — got it out of the way — it means a day without a loss, therefore a successful day."

Martha was a pessimist by nature, and like most pessimists, she rarely got angry at life. The fact that not the whole of the world lay in ruins, that not the whole of the human race had been exterminated, was already something.

Felix Wondrausz waited for her on the balcony on their first-floor flat. They now occupied two rooms of the house, slowly built over many years as a retreat for their old age; the rest, including the kitchen, was inhabited by tenants allocated by the Housing Office. Everybody said that the Wondrauszes as intellectual workers could have saved their house from forcible requisition, but they themselves never discussed the subject with anyone.

Seeing his wife turn the corner, Felix slowly walked downstairs. Darek, the fox terrier, ran in front of him and, in a succession of leaps of welcome, rushed toward the gate. He sprang wildly at Martha, as if he were not one dog but a whole bevy of dogs. He appeared to multiply in her eyes and jumped so high that he seemed to float. Martha caught him in mid-air to prevent him from licking her mouth and eyes. Darek was now at her feet but danced about madly until both the Wondrauszes had reached the top of the stairs. He wriggled, snorted, and then smiled broadly, baring such a profusion of teeth that Martha said to Felix: "Darek looks as if he had just had a set of false teeth fitted!" The ecstasy subsided into a thin whining sound, a violin song of happiness.

"And how have you been, doggy?" Martha now asked Darek, while stroking him. "A bad dog or a good dog? Darek, own up! Have you been watching the house or running wild?"

Darek made strange guttural noises, like those made by a dumb person.

"Well, what is it you want to say now? That you were bored by your old master? That it would have been nicer to have a run with Milo? Or to visit a lovely lady dog?"

Darek was in the middle of his first mating season and inclined to wander off. He was forever eying the gate for a chance to slip away.

"He seems to have a natural talent where these things are concerned," chatted Professor Wondrausz. "But otherwise he is quite untrainable. He'll never learn to retrieve."

The intractable Darek, exhausted by the orgy of welcome, was already dozing on the floor, in a patch of evening sunlight. He lay on his side, in the position of an embryo, with paws folded, his head resting on his chest. But when he heard Felix speak, he woke at once and pricked up his ears. Adopting a sphinxlike pose, he looked attentively from Martha to Felix, his enormous eyes gleaming like dark amber.

"He understands that we are talking about him," said Martha, smiling. "Mrs. Sulima tells me that she has friends who talk French to one another when they don't want to be understood by their dogs."

"Mrs. Sulima of the dogs?" asked Madam Gronek, who came in at that moment with the supper. "She looked in this morning and asked when you would be at home. She'll call again tomorrow."

Mrs. Gronek, the widow of a university porter, who had a small house on the other side of the street, cleaned the Wondrauszes' flat, made the fires, and served their evening meals, which she cooked in her own house. She liked to converse while the old people ate their food, and now the talk was mostly about the dog. Darek had become a serious competitor for former leading topics — the Geneva Conference, German revisionism, the geopolitical situation, the Soviet Union and interplanetary rockets, not to mention strontium 90 in the atmosphere and in human bones.

Tonight the conversation centered around the Sulimas. "A dog is a dog, and even the best of them have fleas." Madam Gronek stated this fact beyond question. "But how those people can put up with their flea-ridden kennels beats me."

The Sulimas had at one time been great landowners on the Russian border. They had lost everything at the outbreak of the Russian Revolution, had escaped to central Poland, and had managed somehow to survive the twenty interwar years, bringing up two sons, both of whom were subsequently killed in the Warsaw Uprising. After the

Second World War, the Sulimas started breeding pedigree dogs in a small place among the oak trees, on the far side of the village.

Mr. and Mrs. Wondrausz had not known the Sulimas or their kennel until some eighteen months before. During a Sunday visit of Felix's relatives, the Ladnowskis, their son Emil, nicknamed Milo, had set out for a walk in the forest, as he had been bored — and it is difficult to express just how bored that boy could be. He had discovered the kennel and in it an eight-week-old fox terrier puppy. He came back trembling with excitement and, pouting, declared there and then that he would die unless he was given the dog. The threat was unnecessary, because his parents complied with every whim of their only son for fear that he might grow up inhibited. More accurately speaking, it was Milo's mother who blackmailed his father with the son's possible complexes. "You wait and see what happens if you refuse him anything," she would say. "The child will have an inferiority complex for life." And the father, a sailing instructor, would capitulate when faced with this cryptic dogma. In short, the puppy, called Darek, was immediately bought, and accompanied the Ladnowskis to Warsaw.

After all this, Mrs. Sulima, like everybody else, was surprised when Milo had abandoned his pet; and when she called on the Wondrauszes, she again commented on it: "Milo probably wanted Darek to have more freedom. In a city, dogs have nowhere to run."

"Well, no," Martha corrected her, with the sober common sense characteristic of a pessimist. "Milo wanted the dog to love nobody but himself. And whenever they brought the dog here with them, it courted us."

"Milo already has the wrong attitude toward life," added Professor Wondrausz. "He cares less for the dog than for his own pleasure."

"Everybody does that" — once more Martha had to put things right. "Do you know anybody interested in self-sacrifice?"

Felix spread his arms resignedly, with an eloquent look at Mrs. Sulima, as if to say that it was useless to continue a discussion which had reached such a point. But all the same he declared, "The important thing is *what* it is that gives pleasure."

"Exactly. We have literally gone to the dogs, which is probably unpleasant, but we like it. I don't know whether it is a good or a bad thing," said Mrs. Sulima, laughing coyly. And then she stated her business: she had come as a marriage broker, to ask permission for

Darek to spend a few days at the kennels, to be mated with one, or perhaps two, of her three fox terrier bitches, Darek's own grandmother, mother and sister.

"Smooth-haired fox terriers are difficult to come by now. They are out of fashion. Even dog shows won't accept fox terriers unless they are wire-haired."

Darek was clearly shattered by the visit. Mrs. Sulima herself smelled like a hundred female dogs, and Darek greeted her with the warmest effusion. Moreover, she had with her a little bitch called Katie. Not a thoroughbred, but one that brought the kennel other benefits; a most talented creature which acted in films and was even in demand for radio sound effects, whenever barking, growling, or whining of a particularly sensitive nature was required.

As behooved an attractive lover, Darek, disregarding the mundane negotiations concerning his marriage of convenience, was paying court to the shaggy Katie. He walked gracefully around her on his long, springy legs, now stiff with emotion; he crouched on the floor, softly singing a song of bliss, or stood upright, tenderly lifting his paw, to delicately stroke Katie's shaggy face.

"Darek, darling," said Martha. "Don't flirt with her. You don't stand a chance. She is a film star — she won't be interested!"

And, in fact, the film star would from time to time lift a corner of her lip, showing one fang and growling unpleasantly.

Thus Darek, without much enthusiasm, contracted the incestuous marriages with his grandmother, mother and sister, but longingly and romantically wooed the shaggy, unapproachable Katie. He was not at all content with his unrequited love. Frustrated by the hopeless courtship, or else carried away by memories of his childhood, he started regular visits to the Sulima kennels. There were forty-five bitches there, large, medium and small, and of every breed — smooth- and long-haired dachshunds; large, standard and miniature poodles; pop-eyed Pekingese, enormous Alsatians, sheep dogs and retrievers. The kennel buildings were modest and primitively constructed, and it was easy for Darek, with his strong paws, to dig an entry through the light soil under the wire netting, as it was not secured to a cement foundation.

Mrs. Sulima, whom Martha met by chance one day, confessed that Darek had defiled some of her valuable pedigree bitches.

"He is even able to get into the boxes," said Mrs. Sulima, worried but at the same time amused. "He will have puppies with a spaniel bitch, imagine!"

"Would you believe it?" Martha said later to her husband. "Even in a kennel everything has a different name nowadays. Boxes — this sounds so much better than 'cages.' "

She scolded Darek severely:

"You should be ashamed of yourself! So this is what you really are: a libertine! At your age! What do you think you are doing? We shall have to pay alimony for you! Come to your senses!"

Darek seemed to smile, and produced his slightly hoarse, sexy bark. He pranced about, inviting her to play.

But he continued to behave as before. He was, on the whole, obedient if untrainable, but only within the limits he considered compatible with his freedom. He would go, like a good dog, for a long walk with the professor, and only on the way back would he slip away from in front of the gate, racing toward the Sulima kennels with the speed of a space missile. He would run there for a mild afternoon of games even when the bitches were brooding over their future worries of motherhood; he just liked female company. And when he had had enough of casual amusement, he escaped from the kennels again. People saw him rushing about in the neighboring villages, and sometimes he would be missing from home for forty-eight hours at a stretch. The Wondrauszes were apprehensive lest he should be bitten to death by rival dogs, or poisoned by unwholesome food — or even stolen, since he was so astonishingly beautiful. His personal charm attracted the attention not only of bitches and humans, but even of other dogs.

Darek knew that his lust for adventure was not popular, and when he returned from his wanderings, he would not rush in with his usual leaps and bounds, but rather creep in, legs bent, an expression of guilty happiness in his enormous eyes.

"A tramp of a dog," Felix would say. "I wish that boy Milo would take him back to Warsaw. There wouldn't be so many occasions there, and perhaps the creature would settle down."

Throughout his life, Felix Wondrausz had been a solemn optimist. Like Martha, he never complained and never grumbled, but, unlike her, he was quite ready to listen to other people's complaints and recriminations. He would immediately set out to prove to the grumbler that his every misfortune was of his own making. Inherent evil did not exist, he would say. What did exist was human folly, people's failure to make a better job of their lives and the world. Felix was kindly and helpful, always ready to give good advice; he did not like people to indulge in self-pity and to get depressed. His students had adored him, and he loved them too, for he could teach them what a powerful weapon a proper attitude to life was. It had seemed that the Olympian professor would survive everything, like a shining column of flame, showing those who were troubled a way through the darkness of life. As it happened, the Second World War and the nightmare of the German Occupation broke him completely, and in the postwar years, when the students began brazenly to teach *him* how to live, his state of depression deepened. Now Felix Wondrausz listened to what people had to say, mostly kept silent, or repeated the same admission over and over again:

"You see, I had founded my whole philosophy on the belief that human beings are good but stupid. I was wrong. Man is evil. And he wants evil."

The arrival of the dog had cheered Felix up. Although the training of the boisterous creature was a failure, the whole affair of Milo and Darek had reawakened the professor's old educational passions.

"I must speak to Milo," he would say. "He is not bad, just badly brought up. The Ladnowskis have no idea of the proper attitude toward life and toward people."

"Leave it alone." Martha would cut him short. "Milo is already an 'angry young man.' He has caught the sickness of the age. You won't change him by talk."

All the same, when one Sunday the Ladnowskis again came to visit them, the professor tried to engage the thirteen-year-old Milo in a noble conversation. It was hard going, for the boy was sulky, morose and very rude. His rather handsome face and fine blue eyes were marred by an unattractive, peevish and, at best, mistrustfully ironical expression. None of the adults had ever heard from Milo a pleasant, or at least a polite, word. To listen to a question asked of him seemed to fill him with indescribable tiredness and boredom.

His parents were talking about a performance of *Hamlet* to which they had taken him the night before.

"Well, what can you tell me about it?" Felix chanced it. "Did you like the play?"

"It may perhaps have been too difficult for him," Mrs. Ladnowska intervened nervously.

"I think so too!" whispered Martha, half to herself, and trembled in anticipation of a murderous look, a shrug of the shoulders or a harsh, inarticulate mutter. Milo, however, did not display any of these reactions. He said calmly, but with distaste:

"A mortuary."

"At his age" — his mother sped to the rescue (while his father whispered: "Not only at his age") — "one obviously prefers sports. Milo, tell Great-uncle how excited you were last Sunday about that football match against Hungary. You liked their goalkeeper so much, do you remember?"

"So it's football." The truth dawned on Felix. "The match was tops, was it?"

"Not bad," grunted Milo.

"Well, I can't help feeling, young man," burst out Felix, "that perhaps you lack a proper attitude toward life and people."

After a moment's silence, Milo announced:

"Well, I hate people."

Felix saw this as a golden opportunity and even lightly rubbed his hands:

"And why, my boy, why do you hate them? Has it never crossed your mind that all you have comes from people? Your parents work hard so that you can have everything you need. You are more fortunate than millions of other children of your age. Think how you are housed compared with the majority of your school friends."

"I don't need all that," declared Milo. "I would prefer to live in a tent."

"What do you mean, you don't need it?" Felix plowed on. "Your mother always says that you are fond of television, of movies. Well, you get as much of these as you can wish for, and all you have comes from people."

Some result had been unexpectedly achieved. Milo became voluble.

"Movies?" he almost shouted. "Don't make a fool of me, Great-uncle. Movies are for the over-eighteens!"

"Oh, not all movies," retorted Felix lamely, and tried to recall with difficulty when he had last been to a movie theater — probably a quarter of a century ago.

He changed the subject:

"And what about books? I hear you are doing quite well at school. You love reading and have more books than any other boy of your age. This you also owe to people . . ."

"Take thrillers . . ." Milo interrupted. "You can't get them anywhere now. They are also written by people . . . I wouldn't mind those."

"I shall lend you a first-class thriller. A wizard thriller!" Tactlessly Martha winked at the boy.

Paying no attention Felix continued the argument:

"It's from people, too, dear boy, that you have received that little dog of yours . . . Darek . . ."

"*My* dog?" snarled Milo so viciously that Martha and Felix suddenly felt like dog-thieves. The boy got up ostentatiously, mumbling, "'nk you," and ran into the garden. The grownups sat around in silence, embarrassed. A little while later they heard Darek whining in the garden.

"He is beating the dog!" exclaimed Mr. Ladnowski. "It's scandalous that a son of mine should behave in such an unsportsmanlike fashion!"

"Why do you always pick on him?" asked his wife angrily. "Why should he beat him? Don't you remember how that dog always gets under one's feet? Milo has probably trodden on his paw unintentionally. I don't know why you are all so irritable today."

"'O moment, endure, thou art so beautiful,'" quoted Martha ironically.

"Who is irritable?" wondered Felix, checking his impatience. "Parents always imagine that their children are irritating. But this is not so. As an old pedagogue I can assure you . . ."

"Of course! You know all about it, Uncle." Milo's mother was gratified. "Thirteen is the worst age. Milo can still change. He *has been* different."

"He has never been any different." Ladnowski shrugged his shoulders. "Since he was so small, he has had a heart like a block of wood. He's angry and never pleased."

"Because man is generally . . ." Felix began, but encountering Martha's warning look, he finished jovially, "But at least he has character, that young man!"

Martha concluded:

"Come on, let's go into the garden."

They all quickly agreed.

The summer passed. Felix's leave was over, the holidays came to an end. Because of the state of his health, the professor was granted the right to use the university car for his journeys to Warsaw. Martha did not have to endure the crush in the crowded trains all the time, although she used her husband's official car infrequently and without much enthusiasm, for, as she put it, she did not like to act as "a fifth wheel."

Darek, left to himself for the greater part of the day, kept close to Mrs. Gronek or wandered about in search of adventure. Mrs. Gronek scolded him vigorously, calling him a tramp and a good-for-nothing cur, but when he was away for any length of time, she went out into the road and looked out for him with fond anxiety. It was easiest to find Darek when the Wondrauszes were due back from the city. Wherever he might have been, he would hurry to his own gate and greet them with rapture, as if they represented each day a new, most happy event in his dog's life.

But one autumn morning, Darek called on the Sulimas at a time when most of the bitches had puppies. The large Alsatian bitches, which had previously ill-treated the visitor under similar circumstances, set upon him and attacked him so savagely that he breathed his last within the hour. And so he perished like Orpheus, torn asunder by angry bacchantes.

Mrs. Gronek mourned him as if he were her son. Martha and Felix could not even speak about the disaster. And how were they to break the news to Milo? The Ladnowskis were expected the next day.

"Milo seemed to care so little about Darek that perhaps he won't mind. We shall simply tell him," Martha decided.

Milo did not, in fact, ask why Darek was nowhere to be seen. His parents did. Carefully, they were all told that Darek was dead.

Milo went terribly red in the face. At first he casually put his arm on the table, but then his head slowly sank on his arm, and he began to cry. The Ladnowskis and the Wondrauszes looked at him in silent awe; no one had ever seen the boy crying with grief.

Felix felt inspired. This was his moment. A few well-chosen words about the proper attitude toward life would penetrate into a heart softened by tears.

Filled with the memories of his past great speeches, he laid his hand on the boy's arm, which shook with sobs. And in a stifled, strange voice he mumbled:

"Come, come, little rascal . . . Oh, you poor devil . . . you rascal . . . you . . ."

— *translated by* CELINA WIENIEWSKA

(From *Tworczosc,* a monthly. October 1959. Warsaw.)

Victory

(*Fragment*)

BY WOJCIECH ZUKROWSKI

WOJCIECH ZUKROWSKI was born in Krakow in 1916. His university studies were interrupted by the war. In the Polish campaign of 1939 he was an artillery officer and, though wounded, escaped from a German prisoner-of-war camp. Under the Occupation while actively engaged in the Underground as an instructor in sabotage, he worked in a quarry. At the same time, he studied philology at one of the secretly operated universities. After the liberation of Krakow, he joined the Second Polish Army, formed in Russia. His studies were completed at the University of Wroclaw. Zukrowski has traveled widely, was twice in China and Tibet, and was a war correspondent in Vietnam during the Dienbienphu operation. A travel diary, *House Without Walls,* was translated into several languages, and his two years in diplomatic service in India furnished him with material for a volume of stories, *Wanderings with My Guru.* He was also a war correspondent in Laos. Other of his books are *From the Land of Silence,* which is about the Polish war and the Underground; *Kidnap in Tuturlistan,* a fantasy for children; *With a Flamingo Quill,* a collection of whimsical stories, one of which appears here. The author lives in Warsaw.

"GET UP AT ONCE and come home," my wife said, touching me on the arm.

I got up in consternation and followed her. I listened admiringly to her scoffing at the Powers, the Bounds, and Death.

"I don't understand," she said sternly, "what bug is biting you, that you wander so far away when you know it will be difficult for you to get back. But remember I shall always find you and call you back . . . You'll never be able to hide from me."

When, late the following afternoon, I went into the garden, which she allowed me to do as a favor, I felt a shiver of apprehension. What new thing would I be confronted with now? I knew that the struggle between my wife and the Powers must be decided one way or another. I was filled with fear, for I was more and more becoming an object, and whoever possessed me would be proved the victor.

I walked along the neatly weeded paths. On the overaged and stunted trees, fruit, covered with a silvery down, was beginning to swell; bees were murmuring contentedly around the fading flowers of the gooseberry bushes. The air was filled with the scent of luxuriantly growing plants.

As I passed I stroked some flowers unknown to me with the tips of my fingers; they opened their tiny hounds' mouths at my touch, pretending they would like to bite me.

The source of my wife's strength lay in her lack of comprehension. Armored with faith in her own superiority, and reinforced in her faith by my submissiveness, she would not entertain any doubts. To tell the truth I was torn in two: I didn't know which side I preferred. I wanted her to win, but the thought that the Powers might humiliate her also had its sweetness and attraction.

"Why is our married life a constant conflict?" I thought bitterly. "We stand locked in a powerful embrace, like gladiators." Love had now revealed other features to me: lips pouting for a kiss went authoritatively rigid.

"Why can't we be like others?" I whispered regretfully, but not without the pride that comes of certainty in one's preferment. Twining my fingers in the wire netting of the fence, I gazed enviously, but contemptuously too, at my neighbors' idyl.

They were sitting over a late supper, under a willow tree, yellow with overbloomed pussies which formed a shady cavern of mobile tracery above them. The man was in his shirt sleeves, and just starting to read his paper. The woman spoon-fed her child as it turned great eyes on the rosy gleams walking over the boughs. It procrastinated with every mouthful, aware that after the last scrape of the empty plate its mother would thrust it into the darkness of sleep.

Suddenly I noticed that the twigs of the willow tree began to open out like an umbrella, and as they extended horizontally I realized that it was now easier for me to lift my feet than to keep them on the loose earth of the border. I clung more firmly with both hands to the netting and, my eyes dilated with astonishment, stared at this new trick the Powers were playing, for I divined that a new test was approaching. And it would be decisive.

I raised my head. The sky had grown infinitely empty. The clouds had dispersed, and the stars scattered, released from their orbits. The sky had an entrancing blueness, more translucent than right above the earth, but the farther I penetrated into it, the more it deepened into a sucking indigo.

I saw with horror that my neighbors also were being lifted out of their chairs and beginning to fly along the branches of the willow, the boughs extended again, like the funnel of an umbrella which the wind has blown inside out, and turned upward more and more swiftly. The stones sped up from the grass like birds. Obviously, the earth had lost its force of gravity.

I clenched my fingers convulsively around the netting of the fence. Slowly I, too, was turned over. So this was the end of the world! My heart almost burst with pride that I could observe this aberration of the elements so calmly, and even rapturously.

My neighbors had already flown off some distance; they had fallen into the sky, and were increasingly separating from each other. The distance between the child's open mouth and the mother's outstretched hand with the last spoonful of gruel increased; they were both enveloped in an azure haze. I knew that the terrible maw above us was so capacious that they might never meet again.

The birds flew down toward the earth. They beat their wings over the clods, trying to maintain their position; but, like skylarks at the height of their soaring, they hung only a moment above the flowering strawberries and then, as they grew weaker, fell back into the dark blue of the insatiable sky.

The tiles began to pull away from the adjacent roof. The clouds whirled like leaves. No! Not like leaves, for their flight was straight and unerring.

The nearby lake swelled up into a cupola, as though a monstrous eye had begun to blink among the osiers; but it was already scattering in a rainbow cloud of drops which flowed in all directions, leaving no trace.

The silence brought a piercing cold. I saw the bees still nestling on the flowers; but I could not hear any humming — it was carried away by the wind. So far I was not choking, though I was swinging my legs in the air above me with extraordinary ease, while I clung to the wire netting with fingers turning blue. I had only to let go, and I would fly like an arrow into the unbridled galaxy.

"Now if I'm late for supper," I thought spitefully, "you'll simply have to believe that I couldn't make it. . . . We shall never see each other again. . . ." I imagined my fall into infinity, with its piercing frost. The wire cut into my fingers, and I swayed gently, hanging on with my last strength.

The earth's cohesion was being dissolved, and the stakes of the fence slowly began to rise out of it. The last, the final seconds, were at hand.

Then a window was opened; my wife leaned out and shouted sternly:

"Come back to me at once."

Her voice thundered through the universe. The sky swarmed with the solidity of falling objects. They came flying in an increasing tumult: my neighbors, the birds, the stones, the tiles, sprinkled down like a handful of handbills. Now the earth was too small to accommodate them all, and they came hurtling around me like an avalanche.

I drew my legs down to my body several times and kicked up into the sky, in order to turn over. My neighbors went past me and fell in their places. First the wicker chair creaked under the man, burying itself in the ground; then the newspaper thrust itself into his hand; finally the willow covered the pair and their offspring with a gentle, golden-hued grotto of interlocking twigs.

"Neighbor," I called, "what was it like up there?"

He did not reply. He kept his eyes fixed on his newspaper. He licked up the lines of print. He refused to entertain the thought that the dream which had enveloped him had been reality. He didn't want to remember the frenzy of the elements. So I alone had seen the end of the world, without losing my *sang-froid.*

"How much longer do you intend to go on making a fool of yourself?" my wife said, as she came up to me along the path. "Come home at once."

Now I was maintaining my equilibrium only with difficulty; I was not hanging but standing on my hands on the stout, swaying wire of the fencing. She put her hand behind my trouser belt and dragged me down to the ground.

"I asked you not to go out of the garden. At the very last moment I saw you trying to climb over. Come on, supper's ready."

So she, too, didn't know that with her call she had prevented the destruction of the universe, that she had restored order to it. I followed her proudly. It was no humiliation to submit to a woman who had triumphed over all Bounds, Powers, and Death.

(From the short story "Zona" in *Wybor Opowiadan*. Published by Pax, Warsaw, 1956.)

An Unknown Fragment from Dostoevski's Life

BY STANISLAW DYGAT

STANISLAW DYGAT was born in 1914 in Warsaw. He studied architecture and philosophy in Poland. It was during the war, when interned in Switzerland, that he was inspired to write his first novel, *The Boden Lake*. Published in 1946, it was an immediate success and has been translated into many languages. His other books are *Farewell; Champs Elysées; Rainy Evenings*, short stories (two of which appear here); *The Pink Diary*, short stories; *Journey*. He contributes to Warsaw literary weeklies, mostly material in a humorous vein, and does much work in radio, films and television. He is living in Warsaw.

ONE NIGHT, as the great writer sat bent over his candlelit manuscript, there was a knock on the door. Since he did not employ a butler or any other servant, Dostoevski answered it himself: "Please, come in."

The door opened slowly. A strange light flashed into the room, followed by a man of vigorous stride. He was of medium height, bearded, and wore striped pants and a dark coat — altogether the sort one would describe as not extraordinary in any way except, of course, for the fact that he had wings, and that he was the source of the strange light which now pervaded the room. Life had taught Dostoevski not to be surprised at anything, and in fact, he did not become alarmed by his nocturnal visitor. His sensitive soul, together with his innate subtlety, led him to pretend not to notice the unusual attributes of his guest, and to treat him quite as he would any ordinary fellow in striped pants.

"Please sit down," said the author of *Crime and Punishment.* "What can I do for you?"

The man had stopped in the middle of the room in a rather silly pose of a dance master. He shook his head and appeared to be somewhat chagrined that Dostoevski was treating him like any ordinary fellow in striped pants.

"I am," he announced, "the Archangel Gabriel. I've come here on behalf of the Power of Heaven and Earth . . ."

Then, all at once, he relaxed; his manner became more natural. He even winked gaily as he said, "The Old Man wants to talk to you. He sent me to bring you to Him."

Dostoevski got up and adjusted his coat: "I am ready anytime," he said simply.

God stroked his beard and looked at Dostoevski with an embarrassment which he tried to cover with an expression of amiability and fatherly concern.

"Dostoevski, my friend," he said at last. "I wanted to tell you that all of us here are following with great interest the development of your talent . . ."

Dostoevski bowed silently.

". . . Only," continued God, ". . . how can I put it? . . . We believe that you could make better use of it. . . . There, there, don't be offended. . . . What I mean is, in describing the life which I created, you seem to concentrate, as it were, on the dark side; you seem to ignore the achievements. My dear man, you must remember that I whipped it all up in just six days, so, obviously, sometimes here and there things may not always click . . ."

It took the Heavenly Father a long time to set forth and elaborate his point. He appealed to the writer's conscience, extolled the value of an optimistic view, and observed that the reality he created also included joy, lightheartedness, and idyllic love.

When Dostoevski returned home, he gave profound thought to all that he had heard. He felt sorry for God. "Well," he thought, "he is trying to do his best for people. He needs help. Well then, why not? I'll write him a novel about idyllic love."

He sat down and wrote *The Brothers Karamazov*.

— *translated by* Wanda Jaeckel

(From *Na Piec Minut Przed Zasnieciem,* short stories. Published by Ludowa Spoldzielnia Wydawnicza, Warsaw, 1960.)

The Usher of the "Helios" Movie Theater

BY STANISLAW DYGAT

The "Helios" Theater dominated the center of a large square—the largest square in town. It was a thoroughly modern building, an unusual sight in this place. White stucco walls framed a plate-glass entrance, over which a violet-pink neon sign flickered brightly. A violet-pink light poured out from the lobby through the glass door. The lobby was lined with purple carpets, its walls decorated with marble friezes and fantastic frescoes. Jutting out from the entrance into the square was a wide terrace, ending in a stairway. On both sides of the stairway stood statues of beautiful nude girls resting on granite pedestals, their eyes fixed straight ahead over the rooftops of the gray, sad houses surrounding the square. Toward evening, when the lights were turned on, and the theater looked like a transatlantic steamer sailing over a dark ocean, a pink dusk settled above the rooftops of the gray houses. In front of the theater there hung big posters showing Indians and cowboys, slender girls, ladies and gentlemen in evening clothes, knights, trains and ships, glittering cities and Arabs riding camels, elegant ballrooms and thatched huts, snow-capped mountain peaks, waterfalls, prairies and lurid slums.

On the day that, after many years, I had finally saved enough money for a movie ticket, I got up at 6:00 A.M., although the first showing started only twelve hours later. I shaved carefully and as carefully brushed my hair. I polished my shoes for a long time; I ironed my suit. For the first time, I put on my beautiful pink shirt, the only legacy my poor departed father had been able to leave me. I found some excuse for not going to work, and spent the day wandering through the streets, thinking over my life. It somehow seemed to be quite extraordinary, not because of any remarkable or unusual happenings, but because of its mere tenacity. The clock on the church tower tolled the hours.

At five o'clock the big square began to fill with people. A crowd had already formed in front of the "Helios" Theater.

I stood in line trying to control an occasional slight shiver. The girl at the ticket window didn't even look up. She counted my change, tore off a ticket, and wrote down the number of the row and seat.

An usher stood at the entrance. He wore a violet-pink uniform, trimmed with gold buttons and gold braid. The word "Helios" had been embroidered in gold thread on his cap. He was tall and slim, with a pale, long face. His eyes were deep and dark, and somehow sad. As he took in the tickets, he would tear off the stub and let the people pass without looking up, the same as the girl at the ticket window.

But when my turn came and I handed him my ticket, he examined me carefully and did not return the stub. I started to go on past, but his hand reached out and drew me back toward him. He let several other people through, but still held on to my ticket.

"Excuse me . . ." I said, feeling a great dryness in my throat. "Excuse me . . . Is there something wrong with my ticket?"

He shook his head.

"No, no," he said in a very low, deep voice. "Everything is in perfect order."

"Then may I go through?"

He shrugged his shoulders slightly and helplessly. I noticed that his sad face had become even sadder.

"There is nothing, really, to prevent you from going in," he said. "Legally, you have every right to enter. But . . ."

I took an uncertain step forward. Gently, without any suggestion of violence, his hand stopped me again.

"You may enter," he said, "You have an absolute right to do so. I don't intend to stop you. But . . ."

Again he shrugged his shoulders, and I noticed that his face took on a still deeper shade of mourning.

People kept on going through. The usher tore their stubs off without a glance.

"May I go in now?" I asked again after a while.

He spread his arms in a helpless gesture.

"Of course, in point of fact, you may. There is nothing to stand in your way and you have a perfect right to do so. But . . ."

I took a step forward. Again gently, carefully his hand stopped me and drew me to the side.

"You may go in," he continued softly, while his face looked sadder and sadder. "You should go in, because this ticket is all right and everything is all right. I don't intend to stop you, and I don't have any right to do so . . . but . . ."

The flow into the theater continued. Smart cars discharged handsome men and beautiful women in décolleté dresses and fur wraps, with flowers in their hair. They swished past me at the entrance, leaving a trail of wondrous scent behind them.

A bell sounded. I trembled. The usher, lightly, oh, so very lightly, squeezed my arm. The lobby was now empty. The curtain at the door had been pulled. The music started. Slowly, the usher tore my ticket to tiny pieces. He didn't look at me, altogether oblivious now of my presence.

I turned around very slowly, and went out. I crossed the terrace and, stopping by the stairs, sat down under the granite pedestal of one of the beautiful nudes. I pulled my legs up, clasped my knees in my arms, rested my chin on them, and stared at the pink sunset over the rooftops of the sad, gray houses.

Inside the theater I could hear music, voices, shouts and murmurs of admiration.

From the empty lobby came the sound of the usher's rhythmic footsteps and his occasional sigh.

Night was falling; the sunset paled over the rooftops of the sad buildings. From the streets leading into the square came a cool breeze.

— *translated by* WANDA JAECKEL

(From *Na Piec Minut Przed Zasnieciem*, short stories. Published by Ludowa Spoldzielnia Wydawnicza, Warsaw, 1960.)

En Route

BY SLAWOMIR MROZEK

SLAWOMIR MROZEK was born in 1930, the son of a postal clerk. As he himself says, "I began but never finished the following studies: architecture, fine arts, and Oriental languages." He made his first attempts at writing in Krakow, but earned his livelihood as a cartoonist, doing satirical and humorous drawings; then he became a journalist and finally a professional writer. His first volume, a collection of short short stories, *The Elephant* (1957), was followed by three other books consisting of parodies, literary pastiches, and satire. He is also a playwright, and *The Police,* first produced in Warsaw in 1958, has been widely seen on television and the stage in various countries on both sides of the Atlantic. Four other plays (three of which are one-acts) have been translated into several languages and met with acclaim when produced. Mr. Mrozek lives in Warsaw.

IMMEDIATELY after passing N., we went through flat, damp meadows, amidst which a few stubble fields bristled up like the heads of recruits. Our carriage bowled along at a brisk rate, past potholes and bogs. In the distance stretched a strip of forest, no higher than the horses' ears. The road was empty, as it usually is at this time of year. It was only when we had been going for some time that I saw in front of us the silhouette of a man; I could make it out better the nearer we came toward him. It was a man with an ordinary face, in the uniform of a post office clerk. He was standing motionless by the roadside, and when we passed him he cast an indifferent glance at us. Scarcely had he disappeared from sight when ahead of us appeared another one, in similar uniform, likewise standing motionless. I studied him carefully, but soon a third loomed up, and then a fourth. They were all standing with their faces turned toward the highway; all had apathetic eyes and shabby uniforms. I was intrigued and raised myself up in the seat, the better to see the road over the driver's shoulder. Sure enough — from afar I could already see the next erect figure. After another two I was seized with an overpowering curiosity. They were standing at quite a considerable distance one from another but sufficiently close to be able to see one another, in identical postures, and taking no more notice of the carriage than do telegraph poles of passing travelers. I strained my eyes; over and over again, after each one we passed, another appeared. I was just on the point of asking the coachman what it was all about when he, pointing toward the next one with his whip, said, without turning, "They're on duty."

And again a motionless figure appeared before us, gazing indifferently in front of him.

"How do you mean?" I asked.

"Like I say, nothing out of the ordinary. They're placed there on duty. Gee up!"

The driver betrayed no desire to explain further, or perhaps he thought no explanation necessary. He urged the horses on, from time to time lashing out mechanically with his whip. The wayside blackberry bushes, shrines and lone willow trees advanced to meet us and fell back; between them every so often I would pick out the now familiar silhouette.

"On what duty?" I asked persisting.

"What duty d'you think? Government duty. It's the telegraph line."

"What!" I exclaimed. "But for a telegraph you need wires, and poles!"

The coachman looked at me, then shrugged his shoulders. "It's obvious you're a stranger here," he said. "Of course, everyone knows you need wire and poles for the *ordinary* telegraph. But this is a telegraph without wires. In the plan there was to be one with wires, but the poles were stolen, and there isn't any wire."

"No wire?"

"Nothing out of the ordinary. There just isn't any. Gee up there!"

I fell silent in astonishment, but I wasn't going to drop the subject.

"But how can that be, without wires?"

"How? Why, the first one shouts whatever the message is to the second, he to a third, the third to a fourth, and they holler like this until the telegram reaches its destination. At the moment they are not transmitting, but if anything were to come through, you would hear them for yourself."

"And a telegraph like this works?"

"Why shouldn't it work? Of course it works. Only they often twist the wording of telegrams. The worst is if one of them gets drunk. Then they add various words for fun, and it goes through like that. But, apart from that, it is better even than the ordinary telegraph with wires and poles. It is a well-known thing that live people are always more intelligent. Storms don't interfere with the service, and there is a saving in timber; as you know, our Polish forests have been terribly reduced. Only in winter the wolves interrupt things a bit. Gee up!"

"Well, but these people, are they happy in their work?" I asked in amazement.

"Why ever not? The work isn't hard; it's only that one has to know foreign words. Our postmaster has just now gone to Warsaw to sort things out. They are to be given newfangled tubes, so that they don't bawl their lungs to pieces. Get along there!"

"And supposing one of them is deaf?"

"Deaf men aren't taken on, nor people who lisp. Once through pull a chap with a stammer got in, but he was chucked out, because he blocked the line. They say that at the twentieth kilometer there is a fellow who was at drama school — he shouts the most distinctly."

I fell silent again, confused by these arguments. I no longer took any notice of the men along the roadside. The carriage bounced along the defiles, rolling toward the forest, which was getting nearer and nearer.

"All right then," I said warily, "but wouldn't you like a new telegraph with poles and wires?"

"God forbid!" the driver returned emphatically. "Besides, as things are, it's easy to get a job in our neighborhood, in the telegraph service, that is to say. And what's more, a telegraph pole man can make something on the side, for if it is particularly important to someone that his telegram shouldn't be twisted, he takes a carriage, rides to the tenth or fifteenth kilometer and tips each man on the way something. Yes, a telegraph without wires is quite a different matter from one with wires. More progressive. Gee up!"

Above the creaking of the wheels a sound, as of a feeble cry, overtook us; it was something between the noise of the wind and a distant plaintive chanting. It sounded more or less like this: *Aaaeeeaauuu-aa . . .*

The driver turned around on his box and pricked up his ears.

"They are transmitting," he said. "Let's stop, then we shall hear better."

When the monotonous rumbling of the carriage ceased, a deep silence hung over the fields. In the silence a cry was borne toward us ever more distinctly, a cry like the call of birds on the marshes. The pole man nearest to us cupped his hand and put it to his ear.

"Any moment now it will reach us," whispered the coachman. And sure enough it did. Hardly had the last *"aaa"* finished than, from behind a clump of trees which we were just passing, there re-echoed:

"Faaatherrr deeaad fuunerraal Weeednesdaaay!"

"God rest his soul," sighed the driver, and whipped up the horses. Now we were entering the forest.

— *translated by* MARCUS WHEELER

(From *Slon,* short stories. Published by "Wydawnictwo Literackie," Krakow, 1958. Copyright by Karl H. Henssel Verlag, Berlin-Wannsee.)

The Wedding at Atomice

BY SLAWOMIR MROZEK

I TELL YOU, technology has reached a high level here, a high level. . . .

The bridegroom had quite a decent little laboratory down by the wood, a couple of reactors along the high road, and a small but neat chemical synthesis plant in his own back yard. The bride's father was giving her for her dowry a complete power station, well situated, being right in the middle of the village by the church. In addition she had some half-dozen biochemistry patents which she kept in a painted chest. It was no wonder that a match was made between the young couple and that the parents of both speedily consented to the marriage. So the wedding was announced in Atomice.

I was just cold-rolling a piece of sheet iron when the bride's brother came to invite me to the wedding. He was a scientist of considerable standing, I may say, and had been a friend of mine since our college days. He passed the time of day, wiped his bare feet on the straw mat, and sat down on a stool.

Conversation was a little difficult as the jets were flying overhead constantly that year and they had built their take-off runways behind the barn. There was always one just taking off and drowning our words with its loud warbling.

"Yes, we're marrying her off," said my guest with a sigh. "Only there's to be no larking about at the wedding," he added bitterly.

"Why should there be?" I replied. "After all, this is to be a Wedding of Peace, isn't it?"

We sat for about another quarter of an hour, watching the youngsters returning from the university and old Jozwa carting fuel to the barn, then he said good-bye and went on his way.

The wedding day arrived. It was a trifle ill-timed, as they had just started transforming the natural landscape in our area. The part which had been wooded was now cultivated and, what is more, improved, while the barren section had been forested. The river had been diverted to flow in another direction. In connection with this, the road to the church now ran some way further on, while in my yard they had built a big dam which was of considerable importance in the country's economy; it was so placed that my door would not open an inch and it was scarcely possible to get out of the house.

When I arrived on the scene, the ceremony of putting on the bride's bonnet was just beginning. The bridesmaids were singing:

Look up at the ceiling when
They put your bonnet on;
In order that your children then
May have black eyes, each one.

After that they carried out an electrolysis on the bride and conducted her to the pressure chamber.

Meanwhile the guests had been arriving. They all sported peasant-style thermostats over dark-blue tennis costumes. Some of them were drunk already, and alcohol fumes came out of their space helmets. In the courtyard tipsy pilots were letting off bangs from their exhaust pipes. Dogs were barking.

But the real fun began when the church ceremony was over.

I was standing on the porch outside the cottage where the reception was being held in order to get some of the evening air into my lungs. From within proceeded sounds of lively music, now dodecaphonic, now synthetic. The sounds of chorusing and of feet stamping out time poured forth continually. The lewd forces of production boiled and seethed. A star appeared in the sky. Children were throwing stones at it.

The celebrations were still in full swing, when, shortly before eleven, the renowned dancer, singer and comedian, young Smyga from across the river, leaped into the center of the throng. He spun around a couple of times, took up his stance in front of the band, and broke into a song:

> For us and our community
> A bright future is designed,
> Through the happiness of society
> To the happiness of mankind!
> Tra-la-la, tra-la-la!

This was greatly admired by one and all. There was laughter and loud applause. But now young Pieg took up the challenge, cut a caper, twisted his cap to one side, and sang in answer:

> Our argument should we begin
> From questions of morality:
> Societies should their happiness win
> Through spiritual purity!
> Heigh-ho!

At this there was more laughter and applause. Some started teasing Smyga, exhorting him to have a go at Pieg. He made no reply. Then casually he went up to Pieg and suddenly lit him up with an atomic warhead which he had concealed under his jacket. Pieg reeled and began to be radioactive, and just managed to press a button on his coat and from a discharger, which he had concealed in his right trouser leg, launched a medium-range rocket right into the other's face. He would undoubtedly have finished Smyga off, but the final stage of his rocket failed to ignite and in consequence it went off course. Smyga retreated, staggered, and leaned against the heat barrier, but it burst and Smyga flew off into the center of the high-temperature belt, the coefficient of which was rising steadily.

"Hey, folks, what's happening?" cried the bride's father, pointing to the old-fashioned Geiger counter on the wall.

But by now there was uproar and confusion, and in the middle of the room huge blue ferns had begun to grow apace — a normal occurrence in conditions of increased radioactivity in a closed building. Now more rockets had begun to fly about and only one man, Banbula, preserved the decorum and was carving conventionally with a knife. Then a high-pitched whistling began. This was caused by the landlord, who, seeing that there was no other way of calming the guests, had dashed to the house gas tank and turned on the tap, which released war gases into the room and set off contamination. Everyone rushed for their anti-gas suits, but mine, as it happened, was not fully gasproof; moreover I was a bit sleepy by now, so I decided to pack the party and by degrees made my way home.

It was a bright night; such powerful radiation was coming from the farm where the wedding reception had been held that I was able to find my way without difficulty. I walked at a smart pace, as a radio-active shower fell every so often. The only thing that incommoded me slightly was that I could feel a sucking in my body — well, but that's quite usual after a party — and the fact that I had begun to grow extra legs, three pairs on either side, a green horn on my forehead, and a chitinous carapace on my back. Still, I managed somehow to reach my shack; I climbed in through a crack in the window frame, and having found myself a quiet spot on a ledge behind the cupboard, well away from the spiders, I fell asleep, peacefully thinking about that rowdy wedding.

— *translated by* MARCUS WHEELER

(From *Wesele w Atomicach*. Published by "Wydawnictwo Literackie," Krakow, 1959. Copyright by Karl H. Henssel Verlag, Berlin-Wannsee.)

I Kill Myself

BY JULIAN KAWALEC

(The biographical note on Julian Kawalec appears in the section "How They See Life.")

TODAY I shall destroy the Zeta bomb. I shall do it this evening, when I begin my tour of duty in the army laboratory. Today I have achieved the capacity for sacrifice; I realized that when I looked at the slender, mournful boughs of the trees; I can't say why it was just at the moment when I noticed the trees.

I am walking along an avenue in the park. I feel a keen rawness in the air. People go past me. They pay no attention to me. They don't know that I, a homely-looking man in a gray raincoat, with big ears and a mole on the cheek, am capable of a great self-sacrifice; that this evening I shall turn the key in the door of an iron safe, open it, and take out something which looks like a large goose egg. That's the Zeta bomb. The distance between the contact pin and the critical point of the bomb is three millimeters. That is the distance to which Professor Lombard set the contact pin when he solicitously laid the Zeta in its plush case. The Zeta rests like a child in swaddling clothes; today I shall destroy that steel child, for today I have achieved the capacity to make this great sacrifice of myself.

I must do it, I must free humanity from the terrible nightmare and that powerful mite. Why should a tiny steel pin have power of life and death over people? . . . So long as it doesn't touch the critical point, the sun will go on shining; when it does touch, night will fall, all men will die, and the birds will drop like meteors. By the force of its explosion the Zeta bomb exceeds the most powerful hydrogen bomb a billion times. If it were to explode, the result would not be death, for death is an equal partner with life — one can argue with it, one can quarrel and be reconciled with it. In comparison with the consequences of an explosion of Zeta, death is something anodyne. The term "death" doesn't apply to the effects of that. One must create a new word for it.

I'm walking along the park avenues, waiting for the evening. When evening comes, I shall destroy Professor Lombard's "iron child." I shall unscrew the contact pin; I shall throw the bomb into a marsh, and the pin into a river some five kilometers distant from the marsh. The Zeta and the pin will never meet again. And if they don't meet, the world will continue to exist. I shall burn the documents giving the sketches and specifications of the bomb, and tread the ashes into the ground. Professor Lombard will not live long enough to give birth to a second "iron child."

I shall destroy the Zeta bomb. I shall do it for the sake of the trees, the animals, the birds, the people, the insects. I shall do it for my own sake, and for the sake of that young man with black hair who is sitting on a bench hidden among the trees, waiting for a girl; for you, gnarled elm, and for your inhabitant the woodpecker, and for you, black worm corkscrewing through the earth.

In the midst of all these people and trees I feel an enormous and oppressive loneliness. I cannot tell anyone what I'm planning to do. I'm afraid they might stop me from destroying the bomb. But after all, great sacrifice demands great loneliness. If I talk about it, I'm sharing it with others, reducing its greatness. But the feeling of loneliness doesn't weaken my determination.

The sky withdraws from the far end of the avenue, a sign that evening will soon be coming on. I leave the park. Today I shall walk to the laboratory. I take a road which shows up white among the small houses and crisscrossed fallow land. On my left someone is singing; on my right a gentle breeze is noisily tousling withered branches. After a moment the singing and the sound of the wind both stop. All is still.

Beyond a small pine wood I come to the first control barrier. They shine a beam of light toward me. They've recognized me. The guards know the senior laboratory assistant very well; he's a quiet sort and docile, with large ears and a mole on the cheek. I pass the first control barrier; the road is as smooth as a table top; the army laboratory has good roads leading to it. In a clump of leafy trees I come to the second control barrier. They pick me out with three beams of light; as they did so a single bird woke up in a tree and began to twitter. They scrutinize me closely, though all of them know me, though they know I'm the senior laboratory assistant and initiated into all the secrets. Beyond the second control barrier the road passes underground. Now I'm walking along a lighted tunnel. The side walls of the tunnel have innumerable little windows, through which guards poke their heads. One must walk steadily and calmly along the tunnel; the best thing is to whistle.

In a small hall, brilliantly lit, I show my identity papers, then I enter a narrow corridor. A tall guard opens an iron door for me. Now I'm in the anteroom of the laboratory. I am alone. I set to work. I bend over the secret drawer which contains the keys; it is known only to Professor Lombard, the commander-in-chief, and myself.

I pick up the key. In the third room of the laboratory I disconnect the alarm signal fixed to the iron safe. I open a drawer and take the Zeta bomb out of its plush case. Zeta is cold and slippery. I could destroy it here, in the laboratory; I could thaw it out; but that would take time, and the three junior laboratory assistants will be arriving in a few minutes. I conceal the bomb and the sketches in the broad pocket of my light raincoat, which I hang over my arm. I telephone to Professor Lombard, using a one-figure number known only to me and the commander-in-chief. I tell him I've forgotten to bring important reagents from the store and I must go for them myself at once.

In a minute or two I am on my way. I am not detained at the control points. The commander of the guard has been informed that it is a question of getting important reagents swiftly.

I have passed the last control barrier. Now there are no more lights. I turn off the main road. I'm going across flat, soft ground, in the direction of an alder grove. Surely this must be a sown field. It is night. Cold. I put on my raincoat. I have it, I have the bomb; with every step I take I feel it knocking against my ribs. Now and again I put my hand into the raincoat pocket to make sure it's there. It is, it is. I touch it with my hand. It is cold, slippery. Professor Lombard polished it, smoothed it. He gave it the gleam of a monstrous distorting mirror. Under my forefinger I feel the tiny head of the contact pin. All I have to do is to slip back the safety catch, press that little head, and then only invisible, inchoate fragments will be left of everything. However, the words "visible" and "invisible" wouldn't have any meaning whatever then. But that will never happen. Quite soon now I shall throw the Zeta bomb into the marsh. I shall throw it with all my strength, so that it flies into the very middle, where the mud is thinnest, where it will sink most easily and swiftly. I shall throw the contact pin into the river. Who will ever find a pin only a little thicker than a needle?

And then? Then I must go into hiding. I must find a good hiding place, for they are sure to search for me. I dare say the whole of the police force, the special military departments and forces, and the secret service will all be called in to search for me. I can already see, already hear, the orders being issued, the instructions intercrossing; how they'll be shouting, how they'll be whispering, all to find out where I am. But the great sacrifice to which I have dedicated myself cares nothing for such things. The great sacrifice must even require such things. And yet the great sacrifice doesn't require that after I've destroyed the bomb I should voluntarily and even frivolously put myself in the hands of those who have produced it. No, I cannot give them that pleasure. I cannot do anything which would give those wicked people the least satisfaction. And so, after I've destroyed Professor Lombard's "iron child," I must conceal myself thoroughly. The people, for whom I am making this great sacrifice, will not defend me. It will be a long time before they even learn of my exploit, before they have any realization of its benefits. They will stop to consider the matter; they will discuss, doubt, suspect; they will pluck up courage and succumb to cowardice; and maybe they will be ready to come to my defense only when it's too late. So I must seek out a good hiding place. But if they come upon my tracks, if I hear their steps, the clatter of belts hung about with weapons, the rustle of uniforms, and the snorting of highly sensitive, perfectly trained dogs, shall I leave my hiding place with my hands up? Does my self-sacrifice call for putting up a valiant resistance or for valiant renunciation of resistance? For valiant resistance, for resistance. But my sacrifice connotes prudent resistance, which in certain circumstances demands that I should hide from the enemy, should deceive the enemy. So I shall not go out to meet the police with my hands up. Rather, the moment they see me I shall spring at the throat of the nearest policeman. If I had a revolver I could kill several before I died. If I had a machine gun I could mow down several dozen from my hiding place.

The ground over which I'm now walking is no longer even and soft; it is hard and crowded with little tussocks. So it must be quite close to the alder grove. I think I see a dark patch in front. Yes, that surely is the alder grove. The marsh lies just beyond it. I am coming across more and more of those little tussocks. My steps are inevitably becoming broken, and short. At times my feet slip farther down then I expect. Then my body is subjected to an involuntary jolt. Then Zeta strikes more violently against my ribs. It reminds me more insistently of its presence. I swiftly thrust my hand into my raincoat pocket. It's there, it's there. It's not so cold now as it was, it's rather warmer. Its shape also isn't so ugly. But it's a monster threatening something which cannot be called death or silence, or by any word from a modern dictionary. It's a tiny, sleeping monster.

The dark patch grows blacker. Now the alder grove is very close. All around is still.

Now I can hear the gentle murmur of the trees. I am in the alder grove. I'm walking along a narrow path. The trees surround me with a friendly air; they're whispering something to me. The Zeta bomb must be destroyed so that the alders can live. Beyond the alder grove the ground turns soft again. But it's not the softness of a sown field, it's the springy softness of India rubber. I am conscious of the marsh; I can hear it. It too has its voice. The voice of the marsh is like the heavy breathing of a dying man. I can still go on for the time being; my feet are not sinking in yet; I know I shall go on safely as far as the first clump of tall spear grass. So now only minutes are left. The ground is getting softer and softer. Now I am at the spot, by a clump of spear grass. I hurriedly thrust my hand into my raincoat pocket. The bomb is warm. I hold its warm, smooth metal a long time in my palm. Then I cautiously take Zeta out of my pocket. Now it is lying on my palm. And so, in a moment *that* will be happening. In a moment the world will be freed from multitudinous death. But the world knows nothing about it. The world is quiet, indifferent, and sluggish. Is it possible that such a great deed can be accomplished in such great silence? I put the thumb and forefinger of my right hand on the safety catch. But just as I do so I hear a loud rustling. I seize the safety catch between my fingers and release it. I'm being pursued. No, it's only the wind running over the reeds. . . . But if it were indeed a pursuit, if dogs picking up my trail began to bark at the edge of the marsh, if the first policemen were to put in an appearance . . . after all, I could threaten them with the bomb. I could shout to them: "Halt. I've got the Zeta bomb in my hand. With the safety catch released. The contact pin is one millimeter away from the critical point. If you advance a single step I shall press the pin. And don't try shooting at me, for if I fall the bomb will be given a violent jolt and it will explode. You'll perish!" But I wouldn't be the only one to perish. And not only would they perish. Millions of innocent people would perish. Such reasoning is not worthy of a man who has decided to sacrifice himself. And yet, the police will not move one step if I threaten them with the bomb. They're cowards. So nothing will happen to the world. My courage, which should accompany my sacrifice, will not suffer either, for I shall threaten the police, not because they're afraid, but because they're in the service of those who produce the bomb, those I hate. So that threat and that hatred should be included in the program of sacrifice. I cling to this thought; I consider it fine and pure, for I can hold the makers of the Zeta bomb, and their assistants, under threat, I can do as I like with them. That's a wise sacrifice. I can command them to march to a hollow between hills and leave them there, and starve them. I can send Professor Lombard there, and even the chief of staff himself. I'm grateful to that rustle in the reeds. It has brought about a judicious change in my thinking.

I shan't destroy the Zeta bomb today. Pity I didn't bring the plush box also when I brought it away, I'd have had something in which to keep it. I shall keep Zeta and devote it to the service of the good. I'm astonished that I could ever have forgotten the great significance of the bomb in this kind of service.

Blind self-sacrifice made me regard it only as the source of a great evil. Prudence, which I now associate with the desire for sacrifice, makes it possible for me to consider Zeta from various aspects. With Zeta's aid I can set the world free from Zeta. By using it as a threat, I can order the laboratories in which it was to have serial production to be destroyed. I can render Professor Lombard harmless, and all the experts on the bomb, and its guards. I can do this if I screw the contact pin to a distance of one millimeter from the critical point. The threat of its explosion will compel them to submit and be absolutely obedient to me. With Zeta in my possession I can destroy every wicked man. With Zeta I can do much, I can do almost everything. Why do I say "almost"? I'm in a position not only to achieve general reforms, but to break into the life of every man on this earth and arbitrarily change it. If I wish, the wealthiest of merchants will hand over his store to me. If I wish, Mrs. Emilia will forsake the husband she loves, will bow to me and go wandering about the world. If I wish, the daughter of the chief of staff will present herself naked to me. If I give the order, the Nestor of science will shave off his beard and climb a tree in the city park in broad daylight. I imagine the scene and laugh: the Nestor of science climbing to the top of the tree with the agility of a monkey. I already see people coming from all over the world and bowing to me and handing me all sorts of articles and titles. One gives me a sumptuous villa at the seaside; another proposes that I should accept a doctorate of all the sciences; a third humbly explains that kingship is the finest form of government and that I am highly suited to be king, for I have a fine bearing and profound intelligence. Someone tells me I have very handsome ears.

I try to cast out these thoughts. For I am to serve the good. I must set about the destruction of evil. That's why I'm keeping Zeta. In order to destroy evil I must divide the people into wicked and good.

I can do that: I shall be the supreme judge. But why the future tense? I am the supreme judge. There is no one higher than I. I touch Zeta. I stroke it. How beautiful it has become, how smooth and pleasant it is, how brilliantly it shines. I press Zeta to my heart, I kiss it. What am I saying, what am I doing? But why ask? I'm doing and performing that which ought to be done; all this is included within my enlarged, human program of sacrifice. I cannot hesitate — I should be ridiculous if I hesitated. I am Caesar, Napoleon, Alexander the Great; I am the supreme judge, I am God, I surpass God. I shout: "I am God." The trees already know; they bow down to the ground. The human beings don't know it yet. I hurry back to the city by the shortest route. To judgment. I shall judge. All human beings are wicked; they must all be destroyed. I alone am good. I ALONE AM GOOD, FOR I POSSESS ZETA.

— *translated by* HARRY STEVENS

(From *Blizny,* short sories. Published by "Wydawnictwo Literackie," Krakow, 1960.)

Thirteenth Voyage

BY STANISLAW LEM

STANISLAW LEM was born in 1922. He received a medical degree from Krakow University and also studied philosophy. Under the German Occupation he worked as a mechanic. His first novel was published in 1954. He specializes in science fiction tinged with satire. His chief works are *The Astronauts, The Cloud of Magellan, Eden,* and *Solaris,* novels; *The Sezam* and *Star Diaries,* short stories (one of which appears here); *Dialogues,* a collection of essays in the manner of Bishop Berkeley — Hylas and Filonous converse upon subjects ranging from philosophy to cybernetics. Mr. Lem is a much-translated author, and his novel *The Astronauts* was made into a film in East Germany. He lives in Krakow.

IT IS with mixed feelings that I sit down to describe this expedition, which brought me more than I could ever have expected. My aim when I set forth from the Earth was to reach a planet in the constellation Goat, which planet was famous for having produced one of the most eminent personalities in the cosmos, Master Oh. This man, who has been called Benefactor of the Cosmos, has devoted his life to the task of bringing happiness to the various tribes of the galaxies, and in unceasing labor has created a science for the fulfillment of desires, which is also known as the General Theory of Prosthesis. This theory gave birth to his own definition of his activities; as you know, he calls himself a Prosthetist.

My first introduction to Master Oh's activities was in Europia. Through the ages this planet had been troubled with discord, hatred, and mutual backbiting among its inhabitants. But when I arrived there I was struck by the general courtesy the inhabitants, contrary to rumor, showed to one another in this planetary society. Of course, I did my best to discover what had been the cause of such an edifying transformation.

One day, as I was walking along the streets of the capital in the company of a local acquaintance, in certain shop windows I noticed life-sized heads set up on stands, also large dolls which were perfect representations of Europeanites. When I asked my companion about those dummies, he explained that they were lightning conductors of unfriendly feelings. If a man feels a dislike or prejudice against someone he goes to this sort of shop and orders a faithful likeness of the person concerned. Then, shutting himself away in his home, he wreaks his will on it. The more affluent individuals can afford a complete doll; the poorer ones have to content themselves with maltreating just the heads.

I had never come across this flower of social techniques before; it is called the Prosthesis of Freedom Activity, and it set me looking for more detailed information concerning its creator, who turned out to be Master Oh.

During later visits to other globes, I came across further traces of his salutary activities. For instance, I learned that on the planet Ardeluria lived a certain eminent astronomer who maintained that the planet revolved on its axis. This theory was contrary to the Ardelurians' beliefs, for they thought the planet was immobile at the center of the universe. The sacerdotal college summoned the astronomer to face judgment, and demanded that he abjure his heretical teaching. When he refused, he was condemned to be purged of his offense by being burned at the stake. Master Oh learned of this verdict, and traveled to Ardeluria. He discussed the matter with the priests and the scientists, but both parties held firmly to their position. After spending a night in meditation, the sage thought of a clever device. This was a planetary brake. With its aid the planet's rotation was halted. The astronomer in his death cell, through observing the sky, became convinced of the change and readily acceded to the dogma of Ardelurian immobility. This was the genesis of the Prosthesis of Objective Truth.

When free from his social activities, Master Oh occupied himself with research of a different kind: for example, he established a method of discovering from a great distance planets inhabited by intelligent beings. This method was called "Key a posteriori"; like all ideas of genius, it was incredibly simple. The appearance of a new starlet where previously there has been no stars testifies to the fact that a planet is just falling to pieces, because its inhabitants have achieved a high degree of civilization and know how to liberate atomic energy. Master Oh did his best to prevent such incidents by teaching the inhabitants of such planets as had exhausted their reserves of natural fuels to raise electric eels. This method was adopted on a number of planets under the name of Prosthesis of Progress.

As time passed I grew more and more anxious to get to know Master Oh. However, I realized that before I could meet him I had to work honestly and diligently to raise myself to his intellectual level. Stimulated by this thought, I decided to devote the whole period of the flight, reckoned to take some nine years, to self-education in the realm of philosophy. So I set off from the Earth in a rocket filled from the hatch to the tip with library shelves.

For two hundred and eighty days I investigated Anaxagoras, Plato and Plotinus, Origen and Tertullian, went through Johannes Scotus Erigena and Bishop Hincmar of Reims; I read Ratramnus of Corbei and Servatus Lupus from cover to cover, and Augustine too. Then I tackled St. Thomas, the Bishops Synesius and Nemesius, and the pseudo-Areopagite, St. Bernard, and Suárez. When I reached St. Victor I had to make a break, for I have a habit of rolling little balls of bread while reading, and the rocket was filled with them. I vomited them all out into the empyrean, closed the hatch, and returned to my studies. But I quickly realized that certain themes were repeated again and again, the only difference being in their interpretation. That which certain of them, plainly speaking, set on its feet, others stood on its head; and so there was quite a lot I could ignore.

So I traveled through the mystics and scholastics, and made some acquaintance with infinitism, the perfection of the Creator, prelaw harmony, and monads, endlessly astonished at the amount each of the sages had to say about the human soul.

As I was studying the truly exuberant description of prelaw harmony my reading was disturbed by quite a serious adventure. By this time I was already in the void areas of magnetic storms, which magnetize iron objects with inconceivable strength. And that is what happened to the iron tips on my boots; stuck to the steel floor, I could not move a step toward the cupboard containing food. I was threatened with death by starvation; but I remembered just in time that I had a primer for cosmonauts in my breast pocket. In it I read that in such circumstances the thing to do was to get out of one's boots. After this I returned to my books.

I had just turned to the next shelf, which was filled with *Critique of*

Pure Reason, when an energetic knocking came to my ears. I raised my head in amazement, for I was not expecting any guests from the void. The knocking was repeated more insistently, and at the same time I heard a muffled voice:

"Open up! We're the Piscitia."

I undid the screw of the hatch as quickly as possible, and three creatures in divers' suits sprinkled with milky dust entered the rocket.

"Aha! We've caught him red-handed," one of them exclaimed, while the second asked:

"Where's your water?"

Before I had time to answer, a third said something to the others, which appeased them somewhat.

"Where've you come from?" the first asked.

"From the Earth. But who are you?"

"The Free Piscitia of Pinta," he snarled, and handed me a questionnaire to fill in.

I had hardly glanced at it and then back at the divers' suits of these creatures, who at every step made a gurgling noise, when I realized that through an oversight I had flown into the proximity of the two twin planets: Pinta and Panta, which the textbooks advise should be given as wide a berth as possible. While I was filling in the questionnaire the creatures in divers' suits systematically listed all the articles in the rocket. When they discovered a can containing sardines in oil they gave a cry of triumph, after which they sealed up the rocket and took it in tow. I noticed that the divers' suits they were wearing each ended in a broad, flat excrescence, as though the Pinta creatures had fish tails instead of feet. Soon afterward we began to descend onto the planet. It was entirely covered with water, but the water was shallow, and the roofs of buildings emerged from it. When the Piscitia removed their divers' suits on the airdrome I saw that they were quite similar to human beings, except that their limbs were horribly distorted. I was put into something that resembled a boat, except that it had big holes in the bottom and was filled with water to the brim. Thus sunk in water, we slowly floated toward the town center. I asked whether it would be possible to stop up these holes and bail out the water; my companions made no reply, but feverishly noted down my remarks.

The inhabitants of the planet were wading along the streets with their heads under water, poking them above the surface every other moment to draw a breath. Through the glass walls of the handsome houses I could see them: the rooms were approximately half full of water. When our vehicle stopped at a crossing not far from a building with the notice, "Main Irrigation Office," through the open windows I caught the sound of the employees gurgling. The squares were adorned with arrowlike statues of fishes decorated with wreaths of algae. When our boat stopped again for a moment, I gathered from the conversation of passers-by that a spy had just been unmasked.

Then we floated along a broad avenue decorated with varicolored inscriptions: "Hurrah for aquatic freedom!" "Fin to fin, we shall conquer the dry land!" At last the boat arrived outside a skyscraper. Its front was adorned with festoons, and above the entrance was an emerald-colored tablet, "The Free Aquatic Piscitia." An elevator which looked rather like a small aquarium took us up to the sixteenth floor. I was led into an office, filled to above the level of the desk with water, and ordered to wait. The whole room was lined with beautiful emerald scales.

I mentally rehearsed answers to the questions: where had I come from and where was I planning to go to. But nobody asked me these. The investigator, a stocky little Piscitia man, entered the office, measured me with a stern look, then rose on his toes, and asked me, his lips poked above the surface of the water:

"When did you commence your criminal activities? How much have you been paid for them? Who are your confederates?"

I replied that, as I lived, I was no spy; I explained the circumstances which had brought me to the planet. However, when I declared I had come to Pinta by accident, my questioner burst into laughter. Then he turned to the study of the protocols, occasionally asking me questions. This took him a very long time, for each time he had to get up to draw breath.

He gently tried to persuade me to confess everything. When I went on replying I was innocent, he pointed to the can of sardines.

"Then what does that mean?"

"Nothing," I answered, somewhat taken aback.

"We shall see! Take this *provocateur* away," he shouted.

The room in which I was now locked was dry. I noted this with genuine pleasure, for the penetrating dampness was already having serious effects on me. Besides myself there were seven Pintians in the small room; they gave me a friendly welcome, and because I was a foreigner they made room for me. From them I learned that according to law the sardines found in the rocket were an affront to the highest Pinta ideals, because of what my new acquaintances called the "criminal allusion." I asked what allusion, but they were unable, or rather unwilling (it seemed to me), to say. I also learned that places of confinement like the one in which we were accommodated were the only waterless spots anywhere on the planet. I asked whether they had lived in water all through their history, and they replied that at one time Pinta had had quite a lot of dry land, and few seas, and that there had been a large number of loathsome dry spots on it.

The present ruler of the planet is the Great Piscon Ermezinius. During the three months I spent in the dry cell I was examined by eighteen different commissions. They ordered me to breathe on a mirror and ascertained the shape of the mist I left on it; they counted the number of drops that streamed off me after plunging me into water, and they tried to fit me with a tail. I also had to tell experts my dreams, which they at once classified and referred to the appropriate paragraphs of the criminal code. By autumn the pleadings on my case filled eighty large volumes, while the evidence was packed in three cupboards. In the end I confessed everything they charged me with. Because of certain mitigating circumstances, namely my ignorance of the blessings of submarine life, as well as the approaching birthday of the Great Piscon, I was given a moderate sentence of two years' forced carving of fish statues, with suspension in water for six months, after which I was set free on parole.

I resolved to make myself as comfortable as possible during my stay on Pinta, and as I couldn't find a room in a hotel I put up in one corner of a house owned by an old woman who occupied herself training snails—namely, teaching them to arrange themselves in definite patterns on national holidays.

The very first evening after leaving the dry cell I went to hear a performance by the city choir. It was a great disappointment, for the choir sang under water, gurgling.

At a certain moment I noticed that a Piscitia man on duty took out an individual who, after the auditorium was plunged in darkness, had been breathing through a cane reed. The dignitaries occupying the seats in the waterlogged boxes incessantly showered water over themselves. I could not free myself from the queer feeling that they found it all rather uncomfortable. I questioned my landlady, but she only asked how high I would like the water level to be in my room. When I answered that I would be glad not to see any water at all except in a bath she pursed her lips, and left me.

Well, a certain young and agreeable Pintian, an editor at the popular journal *Fishy Voice,* also rented a room from my landlady. In the newspapers, I frequently came across references to baldurs and badubins, and I gathered that these were some kin of living beings, but I couldn't make out what they had in common with the Pintians. Those I questioned on the matter usually dived under the water, deafening me with their gurgling. And so, one day, I tried to ask the editor about it, but he looked grim. Over supper he admitted to me that something serious had happened to him. By an oversight, in a leading article he had written that water was wet. And now he was expecting the worst. I tried to reassure him; I also asked whether according to the Pintians water was dry. He replied that everything had to be regarded from the fish's-eye view. Water wasn't wet for fishes, *ergo* water wasn't wet. Two days later the editor disappeared.

When I paid my first visit to the theater, I found it difficult to follow the performance because a constant whispering was going on. I assumed it must be my neighbors whispering. At last I shifted to another seat, but there too I heard the same whispering. When any reference to the Great Piscon was made on the stage, a quiet voice would murmur: "Your members are filled with a happy trembling." And, indeed, I noticed that all the hall would begin to tremble gently. Later I realized that in all public places special whispero-phones were installed, whose task it was to suggest the correct reactions to everybody present. In my anxiety to get to know the Pintians' customs and qualities better I acquired a large number of books — novels as well as school primers and scientific works. I still have some of them, for instance: *The Little Badubin, On the Horrors of Draught, How Fishy It Is under Water, Gurgling in Pairs,* and so on. In the university library a work on Persuasive Evolution was recommended to me, but I didn't learn much even from this beyond detailed descriptions of baldurs and badubins.

When I tried to draw my landlady out, she shut herself away in the kitchen with her snails; so I went back to the bookshop and asked where I could see at least one of these badubins. My question caused the shop assistant to dive under water, and some young Pintians who happened to be in the shop took me off to the Piscitia as a *provocateur*. I was flung into the dry cell, and found three of my former companions still there. Only from them did I discover that neither baldurs nor badubins yet existed on Pinta. They were noble forms, perfect in their fishiness, into which in due course the Pintians would be transformed in harmony with the science of persuasive evolution. I asked when this would come about. At this they all began to tremble and tried to dive under, which of course they couldn't do because there was no water. The oldest of them, a creature with badly misshapen limbs, said:

"Now listen, foreigner; things like that aren't said with impunity among us Pintians. If the Piscitia were to hear of your questions, your sentence would be increased, and rightly so."

I sank into a mournful meditation, from which I was aroused by the exclamations of my fellow sufferers. They were discussing the crimes they had committed. One was in the dry cell because, as he had fallen asleep on a couch over which water was pouring and had begun to choke, he jumped to his feet shouting: "This is enough to kill me." Another had carried his child about on his shoulders instead of teaching him how to live under water from infancy. And the third, the oldest, the one I have already mentioned, had been unfortunate enough to gurgle, in a manner which the experts pronounced insulting, during a lecture on three hundred aquatic heroes who had perished in setting up a record for living under water.

It was not long before I was summoned before the Piscitia. There I was informed that this second crime of mine made it necessary to sentence me to a total of three years' forced carving. Next day, in the company of thirty-seven Pintians, I sailed, sunk in water up to my chin, in a boat like the one I have already described, to the carving camps. They were a long way outside the city. Our work consisted in carving statues of fish belonging to the cod family. Within my own knowledge we carved some 140,000 of these. We floated to work each morning, singing songs as we went; the one I remember best began with the words: "Hail, liberty! Oh, liberty, add strength to our carving." When work was finished, we returned to our barracks; but every day before supper, which we had to eat under water, a lecturer arrived to give us an educational talk on subaquatic freedom. And anyone who wished could join the Club of Contemplators of Finniness. At the end of the lecture we were asked whether any of us had lost our enthusiasm for carving. No one else said they had, so I didn't either.

One day our leaders seemed unusually agitated, and over dinner we learned that the Great Piscon Ermezinius would be floating past our place of work that same day. So from noon onward we swam to attention, awaiting the arrival of the exalted personage. Rain was falling, it was horribly cold, and we were all shivering. The whispero-phones, afloat on buoys, broadcasted that we were trembling with enthusiasm. The retinue of the Great Piscon, which filled seventy boats, took almost till nightfall to sail past us. As I was fairly close I had an opportunity to see Piscon himself; to my astonishment he didn't resemble a fish at all. To look at, he was quite an ordinary, but quite ancient Pintian, with horribly misshapen limbs. Eight officials attired in scarlet and gold scales supported the ruler's arms when he raised his head above water to take a breath. As he did so he coughed so fearfully that I felt sorry for him.

About a week later I first felt the nasty aching sensation in my hands; my companions explained that it was incipient rheumatism, which is Pinta's greatest plague. But no one is allowed to call it a disease; it was said to be a manifestation of the organism's heathen refusal to become a fish. Only now did I realize why the Pintians had such twisted limbs.

For some five months my life continued like this. Toward the end of that time I made friends with an elderly Pintian, a university professor, who was doing forced carving because in one of his lectures he had said that water was of course indispensable to life, but in a different way from that universally practiced by Pintians. In the course of our conversations, carried on mainly at night, the professor told me the history of Pinta. Once the planet had been plagued by hot winds, and the scientists deduced that there was a danger of it being transformed into unrelieved desert. And so a great irrigation scheme was drawn up. The appropriate institutions and central administration were set up in order to put it into effect. But after a network of canals and reservoirs had been constructed, the bureaucrats didn't wish to be laid off, and so the offices went on functioning, flooding Pinta more and more with water. The professor said things came to such a pass that the element which should have been mastered simply mastered them. Yet no one was prepared to admit it, and the next, inevitable step was to declare that everything was exactly as it ought to be.

One day extraordinary news began to circulate among us causing great excitement. It was said that an epoch-making change was coming, and some even ventured to mutter that the Great Piscon himself would very shortly introduce areas of residential dryness, and possibly even general dryness. The authorities set to work at once to combat defeatism. None the less the rumor persisted, more and more fantastic; with my own ears I heard someone murmur that the Great Piscon Ermezinius had been seen with a towel.

One night we heard the sounds of noisy merrymaking coming from the management's building. Swimming outside, I saw the director and the lecturer pouring water out of the windows in large buckets, singing aloud as they worked. The lecturer arrived with the break of dawn; he was seated in a boat thoroughly calked, and he told us that everything that had happened had been a misunderstanding; now really free ways of life were being worked out, and in the meantime gurgling had been abolished because it was detrimental to health, and quite unnecessary. To sum it all up, he said he had always been against water and had realized better than most that no good would come of it. We didn't go to work for two days. Then they took us to the statues which were ready for use; we knocked off their fins and fixed on legs instead. The lecturer busied himself teaching us a new song: "The Soul Rejoices When Everything's Dry"; and it was the general opinion that any day now pumps would be sent down to pump away the water.

However, after the second verse the lecturer was summoned to town, and didn't come back. Next morning the director swam up to us with his head hardly showing above the water, and handed out waterproof newspapers to us. They reported that gurgling had been abolished once for all as detrimental to health, but this by no means signified a return to pernicious dry land. On the contrary. It was decreed that all over the planet breathing was to take place exclusively under water, this being the ultimate stage of fishiness. But, having regard for the public good, this was being introduced by degrees. In other words, each day every citizen had to remain under water a little longer than on the previous day. To make this easier for them, the general level of the water was being raised to eleven depths (their measure of length).

And in fact, late in the afternoon the water level was raised so much that we had to sleep standing up. As the whispero-phones had been flooded over, they were fixed rather higher, and a new lecturer set about organizing exercises in underwater breathing. After several days, by the gracious command of Ermezinius complying with the citizens' respectful wish, the water level was raised by a further half depth. Now we all began to walk about on tiptoe. Soon all the shorter Pintians disappeared. As all were unsuccessful in breathing entirely under water they developed the practice of taking a slight jump above the surface in order to get a breath. In a month or so everybody was quite efficient at this. The press reported on the enormous progress in underwater breathing all over the country, and a large number of individuals were brought along to the forced-carving works because they had gone on gurgling in the old fashion.

All this caused me so much worry that at last I decided to get away from the forced-carving camp. One day, at the end of the work, I concealed myself under the plinth of a new statue (I have forgotten to mention that we had knocked the legs off the fishes and had restored their tails), and when the place was deserted I swam off to the city.

I tired myself out, but I managed to reach the airdrome. Four Piscitia men were guarding my rocket. Fortunately, someone not far away began to gurgle, and they rushed in that direction. So I tore away the seals, jumped inside, and started up as quickly as I could. Within fifteen minutes the planet was already twinkling below me like a little star, that star on which I had had to suffer so much. I lay down on the bed, luxuriating in its dryness; unfortunately, my pleasant rest didn't last long. I was aroused from sleep by an energetic knocking on the hatch. Only half awake, I cried out, "Hurrah for Pinta freedom." That shout was to prove costly, for a patrol of Panta Angelitia had caught up with the rocket. My explanations that they hadn't heard me properly, that I had shouted, not "Pinta" but "Panta freedom," were useless. The rocket was sealed up and taken in tow. To make things worse, in the larder I had a second can of sardines, and had opened it before retiring to rest. When they saw the open can the Angelitia men shuddered; then, with cries of triumph, they drew up a report. Soon afterward we landed on the planet. When I was put into the waiting vehicle, I heaved a sigh of relief, for, as far as I could see, the planet was completely without water. My escorts removed their space suits, and I realized that these creatures, too, were amazingly like human beings, only they all looked so much alike they might have been twins; and every one was smiling.

Though dusk was falling, the city was so brightly lit it might have been noonday. I noticed that if any of the passers-by glanced at me they shook their heads in consternation, while one Panta female even fainted at the sight of me, which was all the more strange because she didn't stop smiling.

After some time I developed the impression that the inhabitants of this planet wear a kind of mask. Our journey ended before a building on which I read the inscription: "The Free Angelitia of Panta." I spent the night alone in a small room, listening to the noises of a great city. Next day I was taken to the office of the investigating judge, where the charge was read out to me. I was accused of the crime of angelophagy at the instigation of Pinta, and the further crime of personal differentiation. The evidence against me consisted of two items: the open can of sardines, and a mirror, in which the judge allowed me to look at myself.

He was an Angelitia man of the fourth rank, in a snow-white uniform, with diamond flashes across his chest; he explained that the crimes I had committed put me in danger of identification for life, and he added that the court would allow me four days in which to prepare my defense. The authorities would provide me with a defense lawyer.

Having already had some experience with court procedure in these regions of the galaxy, I wished above all else to find out what sort of punishment threatened me. According to my wish, I was taken to a small hall of amber color, where my defense lawyer already waited. He was an Angelitia man of the second rank.

"Foreigner," he said, "you must understand that we have discovered the source of all the cares, sufferings and misfortunes to which creatures assembled in societies are heirs. This source is the individual, the private personality. The society, the community, is eternal, subject to permanent and inviolable laws, just as the powerful suns and stars are subject to them. But the individual is characterized by irresolution, haphazard behavior, and above all transiency. And so we have completely liquidated individualism for the sake of society. Only collectivity exists on our planet; you will not find any individuals here."

"But surely," I said, "what you are saying is only a figure of speech, for after all you are an individual."

"Hardly at all," he answered, with a fixed smile. "Surely you must have noticed that you cannot distinguish our faces? In this way we have achieved the highest degree of social interchangeability."

"I don't understand."

"I'll explain. In every society you will find a definite number of functions, or in other words, statuses. There are professional statuses, such as rulers, gardeners, technicians, doctors; there are also family statuses: fathers, brothers, sisters, and so on. Now a Pantian functions in any one status only for twenty-four hours. At midnight there is a single combined operation all over the country; it's just as if, speaking figuratively, we all took a single step; and thus the person who yesterday was a gardener today becomes an engineer; yesterday's building worker becomes a judge, the ruler a teacher, and so on. The same thing occurs with families. Every family is made up of relations, such as father, mother, children. But only the functions remain invariable, while the persons performing the functions change every twenty-four hours. And so, do you see, the collective remains unchanged. The number of parents and children, of doctors and nurses, and so on, all through the spheres of life, remains always constant. The mighty organism of our state has endured inviolable and invariable, more enduring than rock, throughout the ages; and this is due to the fact that we have put an end, once for all, to the ephemeral element of individual existence. That is why I said that we are all perfectly interchangeable. You'll be convinced of this quite soon, for after midnight, if you send for me, I shall come to you in a new capacity . . ."

"But how can each of you perform the functions of all the professions?" I asked. "Is it possible for you to be not only a gardener, a judge, or defense lawyer, but a father or mother at will?"

"There are many professions," my smiling companion answered, "which I am not able to practice well. But bear in mind that the performance of any particular function lasts only a day. In a society of the old type the great majority of individuals perform their professional functions badly, and yet that doesn't stop the social machinery from functioning. Someone who is a poor gardener will ruin your garden, a bad ruler will reduce the country to ruin, because they both have time in which to achieve so much. And besides, in an ordinary society, in addition to professional inefficiency, you have the impact of the negative and even ruinous individual striving. Envy, pride, egotism, laziness, the lust for power, all exert a consuming influence on public life. In our state this evil influence doesn't exist. In fact in Panta no one strives to make a career, and no one is governed by personal interest, because there is no such thing as personal interest in our society. It is no good my taking any step in the hope that it will bring me reward tomorrow, because tomorrow I shall be someone else, and today I don't know who I'll be tomorrow.

"The change in status takes place at midnight, by means of a general lottery, over which no living being has any influence. Now do you begin to realize the profound wisdom of our system?"

"But what about feelings?" I asked. "Can you love a different person every day? And what happens in regard to fatherhood and motherhood?"

"Formerly," my companion answered, "there was a complication; we found that sometimes an individual temporarily in the status of fatherhood would give birth to a child; for it does sometimes happen that a woman takes over that status the very day she gives birth. However, the difficulty was eliminated when it was laid down by law that fathers also can give birth to children. As for feelings, we have satisfied two apparently mutually exclusive hungers inherent in every intelligent being: the hunger for permanence and the hunger for change. Feelings of affection, respect, and love in the old days were eaten up with constant unrest, the fear of losing the beloved being. We have overcome that fear. In every deed, no matter what shocks, illnesses, catastrophes, every one of us always has a father, a mother, a wife, and children. And more. Anything invariable turns to boredom after a while, whether it is good or bad. And yet we want to have permanency; we want to defend life against troubles and tragedies. We want to exist, yet not to pass; to change, yet to endure; to be all, while risking nothing. These contradictions seem irreconcilable, but we have reconciled them. We have obliterated even the antagonism between the higher and lower social strata, for everyone may become the supreme ruler one day; and no kind of life, no field of activity, is closed to anyone.

"Now I can tell you what the sentence hanging over you is: it means elimination from the general lottery, and transfer to a lonely, individual existence. Identification is the act of crushing a person under the burden of lifelong individuality. But you must hurry if you wish to ask me further questions, for midnight is approaching. I shall have to leave you soon."

"How about death?" I asked.

His brow furrowed, his lips smiling, my defense lawyer scrutinized me as if trying to understand the word. At last he said:

"Death? That concept is obsolete. In Panta nobody dies . . ."

"But that's rubbish," I exclaimed. "Every living being must die, and that goes for you too."

"Me? Whom do you mean by that?" he broke in with a smile.

There was a moment's silence.

"You — you yourself."

"But who am I? I myself. A name? A forename? I haven't either. A face? Thanks to biological measures carried out in our planet centuries ago, my face is exactly like everybody else's. Status? At midnight that changes. So what is left? Consider what you mean by death. It is a loss, tragic because irrevocable. But the one who dies — whom does he lose? Himself? No, for the dead no longer exist, and a being who doesn't exist cannot lose anything. Death can affect only the living, it means the loss of someone close to us.

"But we never lose anyone close to us. I have already told you that, haven't I? In Panta every family is eternal. Among us death would be a cancellation of status. And our laws do not allow any such cancellation. But now I must go. Good-bye, foreign visitor."

"Wait," I cried, seeing that he was getting up. "But differences do exist among you — they must exist. You must have old people who . . ."

"No. We don't keep any record of the statuses any individual has occupied. Nor do we keep any record of the astronomical years. None of us knows how long he lives."

With these words he departed. I was left alone. A moment or two later the door opened and my defense lawyer appeared again. He was wearing the same snow-white uniform with the gold flashes of an Angelitia man of the second rank, and the same smile.

"I am at your service, accused arrival from another star," he said.

"Oh, so there is one invariable thing in Panta, and that's the status

"You are mistaken. That only affects foreigners. We cannot allow

of the accused," I exclaimed.

anyone to try to disrupt our state from within by hiding behind his status."

"Are you an expert on law?" I asked.

"The codices are expert in it. And in any case your trial won't take place till the day after tomorrow. The status will defend you."

"I renounce defense."

"Do you wish to undertake your own defense?"

"No. I wish to remain condemned."

"You're being frivolous," the white-robed man said with a smile. "Remember that you won't be an individual among individuals, but in a wilderness greater than the interplanetary void . . ."

"Have you ever heard of Master Oh?" I asked.

"Yes. It was he who created our state. He created through it his greatest work: 'The Prosthesis of Eternity.'"

When I was brought to trial three days later I was sentenced to lifelong identification.

— *translated by* Harry Stevens

(From *Dzienniki Gwiazdowe.* Published by Panstwowe Wydadnictwo "Iskry," Warsaw, 1958.)

Untrimmed Thoughts

by Stanislaw Lec

Stanislaw Jerzy Lec was born in Lwow, Poland, in 1909. His poems first appeared in 1929, and his first satirical work was done in 1933 with the Warsaw Cabaret Theater Cyrulik. From 1941 to 1943, Lec was in a German concentration camp, from which he escaped to join the Polish Underground army. Since the end of the war in 1945, he has published a number of books, both poetry and satire. In 1956, his aphorisms were first published in Polish periodicals. Later, they appeared in book form. The German edition of this book has had great success. An American edition, titled *Unkempt Thoughts,* will be published by St Martin's Press in 1962.

Those who cannot rise above man debase him.

* *
*

Evil, too, only wants to make us happy.

* *
*

If you are ashamed to give in, well, take over.

* *
*

Woe to the idol whose head gets between the applauding hands of his fans!

* *
*

Let's not underrate prejudice as a means of fighting it.

* *
*

Even man, when touching up the world picture, does not go unpunished.

* *
*

At last they have come to an understanding: they reached the undisputed conclusion that they are enemies.

* *
*

He called me a "rotten liberal." I slapped his face. He saw his mistake and apologized.

* *
*

Some backgrounds do not tolerate anything against them.

* *
*

It is a terrible thing to swim against the current in a dirty river.

* *
*

Some think they are descended from apes who sat on the tree of knowledge.

* *
*

They tortured him. They were searching his brain for their own thoughts.

* *
*

— gleaned from various Warsaw periodicals and translated by MARIA KUNCEWICZ